LARVAE OF INSECTS

LEPIDOPTERA AND HYMENOPTERA

Part I

LARVAE OF INSECTS

An Introduction to Nearctic Species

Alvah Peterson
Ohio State University

Part I

Lepidoptera and
Plant Infesting Hymenoptera

Columbus, Ohio
1962

Lithographed in U.S.A. by

E D W A R D S   B R O T H E R S ,   I N C .

Ann Arbor, Michigan

TABLE OF CONTENTS OF PART I

- - - - -

INTRODUCTION

What is that larva? This question has been kept in mind continuously in the preparation of the following publication. This book (2 parts) is prepared to serve as a guide and aid for students endeavoring to learn facts essential for determination of insect larvae. If the two parts in their present form prove to be of some value to professional entomologists and others, so much the better.

No one appreciates better than the author the incomplete nature of this publication. Facts speak for themselves. If there are 71,709 plus species of insects in the United States (see Table 1) that pass through a larval stage in their development the small number represented in this publication is a mere fraction of the total. Possibly in the future when the author has had access to more named specimens for study, particularly most larvae of economic significance, (those not marked with an asterisk in the lists of common and important species and others) a more complete revision may be produced. It is the hope of the author that this publication may stimulate entomologists to make comprehensive studies of the immature stages of various genera, families, orders or special groups. Eventually after more extensive studies have been made of smaller groups someone may compile for us a very satisfactory book on larvae of insects.

Determination of an unknown larva is usually not as difficult as one may imagine. Many common species can be determined quickly and accurately if the diagnostic characters are known. To determine an unknown larva it is usually essential to have at hand the following information. First, it is distinctly helpful and in many cases essential to know the family to which the species belongs. In large measure the information presented in this publication is constructed about the family. In ascertaining the family of an unknown specimen one must observe the outstanding morphological characteristics. With careful study and some patience this publication should be of some value in determining the family of an unknown larva. Probably the next fact most essential in the determination of a larva, especially if the species is a crop pest, is information on its food and feeding habits. In addition to the above, any information available on such points as seasonal appearance, distribution, species pecularity, color variations and other facts may be very useful. Armed with some or all of the above facts, one may examine the figures and descriptions of the species of a given family and reach a tentative conclusion, provided the species is included in this volume. To confirm any determination reached one may then consult further descriptions of the structure, life and habits frequently available in the extensive taxonomic and economic entomological literature, for the most part cited in the bibliographies.

Illustrations and their descriptions, keys, discussions, descriptions of families, family names, lists of common, important and unusual species, references to important literature and a glossary comprise most of the contents of this book. Of these, the illustrations and their descriptions may prove to be the most valuable in determining the species of an unknown larva. The author is distinctly visual minded, consequently much factual matter is presented in the form of drawings rather than in lengthy detailed descriptions.

The word larva in this publication is restricted to the active feeding stage existing between the egg and pupal stages of insects that undergo complete metamorphosis. Orders represented are Lepidoptera and Hymenoptera in part I and Coleoptera, Diptera, Siphonaptera, Neuroptera, Trichoptera and Mecoptera in part II. All larvae figured, with few exceptions have been drawn by the author from named or reared specimens. Particular emphasis has been placed on larvae of economic importance. Unfortunately there are quite a number of pests and other fairly common larvae, especially among the Lepidoptera, which the author has not been able to obtain. Descriptions of these are omitted. It is hoped that entomologists may send in well preserved, named specimens so that they may be figured in some future revision of this volume. Lists of larvae needed for study are available and will be gladly furnished upon request.

For several years the author has presented courses on the identification of immature stages (chiefly larvae) of insects. For these courses keys to families and other groups have been prepared. These have been used and criticized by numerous beginning students. This criticism has been most helpful in producing simplified and more perfect keys. In this publication the morphological characters used in the family keys are stressed because in many cases the same characters are useful in separating genera and species.

Where special characters are employed these are figured or discussed in each order. Most of the keys and figures deal with mature or nearly mature larvae. Early instars of some species differ decidedly from late instar larvae. For the most part the early instars have not been included.

During 1912-1916, when the author was a graduate student at the University of Illinois, he became deeply interested in identification of immature stages of insects under Dr. A. D. MacGillivray's supervision. About 1916, Dr. A. D. MacGillivray started to work on a book covering the subject of immature stages of insects. The author assisted in this project by preparing figures of nymphs and larvae. Dr. McGillivray's premature death brought this study to an end. It is only of late years that the author has had an opportunity to continue this study. During the past ten years it has been possible for him to assemble a comprehensive collection of immature insects and devote all of his restricted research time toward becoming acquainted with many species, genera and families of larvae. Needless to say only the surface of this most fascinating subject has been scratched. The following pages record some of the facts about larvae learned and assembled to date.

This introductory publication is in lithoprinted form in order that errors and the incomplete presentations of several portions may be revised readily. It is to be hoped that in the not too distant future the subject matter in its entirety may be sufficiently satisfactory for a more permanent type of publication

PREFACE

For several years the author has been preparing drawings, keys and other phases of a manuscript for a book on larvae of insects. This study is still in progress; however, the portion covering the introduction to orders, larvae of Lepidoptera and plant infesting Hymenoptera is complete. Since the author's research time is limited it may be from one to several years before the drawings, keys and manuscript on larvae of Coleoptera, Diptera, Mecoptera, Neuroptera, Trichoptera and Siphonaptera are ready for publication. Consequently it seems wise to present this study in two parts. Part I covers all introductory matter, keys and figures of nymphs (naiads), larvae and pupae, larvae of Lepidoptera, and larvae of plant infesting Hymenoptera. For more details see Table of Contents or Index.

ACKNOWLEDGMENTS

For more than ten years the author has been collecting insect larvae toward a comprehensive collection. He has received numerous species from entomologists and other interested persons located in various sections of North America. No attempt will be made to list the many contributors. The author extends his sincere thanks to all who have provided larvae for this study. The following have shown special interest in this project by collecting and providing numerous well preserved and named specimens; J. N. Knull, L. D. Anderson, H. H. Ross and J. S. Houser (deceased). He is especially indebted to J. N. Knull, not only for assistance in collecting and identifying material, but for cooperative and competent help in innumerable ways. H. H. Ross also rendered much help, particularly in the identification of sawfly and caddice fly larvae. He is greatly indebted for help in determining unknown larvae and for contributions and the loan of material, especially larvae of Coleoptera, to C. F. W. Muesebeck and his coworkers, Carl Heinrich, H. W. Capps, W. H. Anderson, C. T. Greene and others associated with the U. S. D. A. Bureau of Entomology and Plant Quarantine. He also wishes to thank Mrs. Dorothy J. Knull for her critical reading of portions of the manuscript, Mrs. R. W. Knopf for her efficient stenographic service and his wife, Helen H. Peterson for her editorial assistance.

THE IMPORTANCE OF LARVAL RECOGNITION

Why should a student preparing himself for a professional entomologist's career learn to recognize insect larvae? The following information provides a partial answer to that question.

A recent census of insects from Washington, D. C. shows that there are 83,780 recognized species in U. S. A. and 662,298 for the world. (See Table 1.) An analysis of the figures given for the various orders reveals that 85 per cent belong to orders that possess larval stages in their development. Practically all of our insect pests possessing larvae belong to the Lepidoptera, Coleoptera, Diptera, Hymenoptera and Siphonaptera. An analysis of the more common insect pests, especially those that attack plants of value to man, shows that approximately 60 per cent of the species are destructive as larvae. This is particularly true among pests of deciduous fruits, corn, cotton, shade trees, shrubs, and other plants growing in the temperate zone of North America.

Another significant point is the fact that the food and habitat of a given larva attacking plants, animals and their products, except for some of the Coleoptera, is usually very different from that of the adult. Since adults of many insect pests among the Endopterygota are not as a rule associated with the destructive larval stage, frequently an entomologist will find it necessary to determine the species in the larval stage. For example, farmers, fruit and vegetable growers, floriculturists, cattle men and others may bring or send in larvae of the codling moth, oriental fruit moth, apple maggot, cabbage looper, greenhouse leaf tyer, wire worms, white grubs, cutworms, cattle grubs, screw worms and many other species for determination. Many larvae also come in for determination that are beneficial species or of no economic importance. Under field conditions an economic entomologist will see the larvae of many insect pests much more often than the adults of the same species.

Larval recognition played an important role in the armed forces, especially in connection with insects that transmit human diseases. This was particularly true in the field of malariology. Recognition by competent entomologists of Anopheles larvae capable of transmitting malaria helped to bring about a marked increase in the respect for entomology.

Larval recognition is also very essential in the enforcement of quarantine regulations especially at ports of entry into this country. Many foreign plants or plant and animal products enter this country every year. Some potential pests appear in plants or products as larvae. These must be recognized by competent entomologists in order that important exotic pests or other potential pests may be prevented from gaining a foothold in the United States. It is obvious that in the past a number of our pests must have been introduced in the larval stage.

The above statements suggest some principal reasons why larval recognition is important. In addition to the acquisition of knowledge on how to recognize various larvae a well planned course in this field will broaden and deepen the student's knowledge and interest in insects. It should also give the student a rigid training on accurate detailed observation so greatly needed in entomology. Many will also learn to appreciate more fully the significance of old entomological slogans "Keep your eyes focused on the insect" or "Be sure your are right, then look again."

EQUIPMENT AND INSTRUCTION

To study and determine the species of an insect larva it is necessary to have well preserved material, high grade optical equipment, and ample light. Instructions on how to prepare satisfactory specimens have been presented elsewhere.

To observe the detailed structure of most larvae it is necessary to have access to a satisfactory binocular microscope. This instrument should be equipped with objectives and oculars which will give a wide range of magnification (10 to 100 diameters) of minute detailed parts. High magnification in many cases is needed in order to determine the exact structure of some diagnostic characters on many larvae, especially species measuring less than 10 mm. Most objects magnified more than 15 to 25 diameters are seen best under a spot light of considerable intensity. The beam of light should be cool, at least not so warm that it is

unbearable on the hand. Armed with a high grade binocular microscope equipped with magnifications ranging from 10 to 100 diameters and a strong cool spot light one can make the observations needed to determine most species. Occasionally it is necessary to magnify objects more than 100 diameters. In such instances a high power microscope is usually satisfactory if the object to be observed is prepared properly.

In the introductory course in larval taxonomy the following sequence has been followed at the Ohio State University. At the outset the student is asked to identify to orders 100 to 150 immature stages (nymphs, naiads, larvae, puparia and pupae), representing all the more common orders of insects. Upon completing this task he is then expected to identify to families 40 to 75 species of larvae of each of four orders, Coleoptera, Lepidoptera, Diptera, and

Hymenoptera. The families represented include more common and important groups and some unusual ones. Among the specimens provided many are species of economic importance. After the families of a given order are determined the student is asked to identify the common and economic forms to species. On or in each vial containing an unknown specimen information on the food and environment of the species is usually furnished. Near the end of the course, if time is available, other orders or groups of special interest to the student are studied in more detail. The above experience with immature insects gives the student a fair introduction to larval recognition. In most cases he is prepared to take up special groups and pursue studies on these in a more advanced course or as a special problem.

To conduct courses and problems on immature stages of insects requires continuous and extensive collecting for several years by the instructor or someone who knows where to go and how to get the many and varied species needed for study. Larvae are kept in alcohol in cork or rubber stoppered vials held in small wooden trays with celluloid fronts. A specimen is removed by the student and placed in a Syracuse watch glass in alcohol and oriented into position between broken pieces of glass of varying thickness. On an average one or two specimens may serve five students. When it is necessary to dissect out mandibles and other detailed parts these are removed, cleaned and placed in a tiny glass shell vial, 4 x 10 mm., completely filled with alcohol and stoppered with a tiny cork or cellucotton. If the vial containing the object to be observed is completely submerged in alcohol, one can usually see the diagnostic character without removing the dissected part from the tiny vial. The tiny vial containing the dissected part is kept in the larger vial with the unknown specimen. If ample material is available it is advisable to let the student do his own dissecting.

Students are encouraged to make collections of their own. Equipment and instructions for collecting, preparation and preservation of material are provided. Some of the most enthusiastic collectors have been insecticide entomologists. A number of these students have assembled excellent comprehensive and special collections of immature stages of insects.

COLLECTING, KILLING, DISSECTING AND PRESERVING LARVAE

Collecting Larvae. A great deal could be told about various collecting experiences. This discussion is very general, emphasizing a few essential facts about collecting terrestrial and aquatic larvae.

So far as equipment for collecting terrestrial species is concerned the author finds the following useful; a sturdy, flat-bottomed, leather bag with a large opening at the top (a Boston bag) equipped with a few common gadgets, namely, a small sturdy trowel, a large screw driver, a small hand ax, two or more forceps with strings tied to them which can be placed about ones neck, several small mailing tubes, tin pill boxes, empty vials and one or two round or square flat bottomed tin cans each containing 10 or more 6 drahm homeopathic vials filled with a killing solution or 95 per cent ethyl alcohol, extra corks, pencils, and a note book. If aquatic collecting is to be done one will need in addition to much of the above equipment a substantial aquatic dip net, several sturdy hand sieves, two or more large flat-bottomed enameled trays, a white enameled dipper, pipettes, one or more large metal buckets, glass jars and other containers. Other special equipment used by limnologists is useful, but in most cases not essential

Where and how to collect larvae depends largely upon the species sought. Insect larvae live in all kinds of situations, consequently many species can be found most anywhere one may look. In general more species and a greater diversification of forms are found in moist to wet situations than in dry places.

Many larvae, especially caterpillars and sawfly larvae, feed externally on the leaves, buds, flowers and other parts of living plants. As a rule these are easy to collect, many can be captured by sweeping or beating plant parts.

Many and more diversified forms of larvae live within plants, some producing galls. Leaf miners of the four major orders occur in leaves of many kinds of plants. Other species are borers within stems, twigs, shoots, buds, flower heads, fruit, trunks, crowns, and roots of living plants. Plants that are dying or dead, especially trees that have fallen, yield many interesting species under the bark or deeply embedded in the wood. To collect these requires careful work and much patience. In the dormant season hibernating larvae can be found in the dead stems, flower heads and seeds of many annual and perennial species of weeds and cultivated plants. In addition to the above suggestions one will find interesting larvae on or within fungi of all kinds, moss and lichens or under stones, boards and logs.

Leaf and ground covering (duff) if scratched, cultivated, sifted or placed in heated funnels will yield some unusual beetle larvae and other species. Soil inhabiting species are found by digging, following a plow or by sifting soil. If one is able to withstand offensive odors, larvae of a number of families of the Coleoptera and Diptera especially, may be found within or under dead and decaying vegetables, fruits, animals and faecal matter. Stored food and animal by-products, especially grains, cereals, nuts, cheese, meats, wool, hides, feathers, etc., often yield larvae of economic importance. Larvae of predacious species are usually found where the hosts live that they prey upon.

In aquatic collecting possibly the most interesting and diversified species live in moving water attached to submerged stones, vegetation or debris. Other species are found on, under or within the living and dead vegetation along the shore line or in shallow or deep water. Other larvae are free swimming, usually found most abundant in shallow water. Some species live on the bottom in the mud, gravel or sand in fairly deep or shallow water. Usually, if a stream or pond is a permanent body of water, larvae of a given species can be found in the same place year after year. This is not true of many terrestrial species.

Killing Larvae. Proper killing and preservation of insect larvae, especially soft bodied forms, is highly important especially if unknown specimens are to be studied and determined readily. It is exceedingly difficult or impossible to observe detailed morphological characteristics on shriveled, distorted or darkened specimens.

All known methods for killing and preservation, except inflation, destroy or change the colors of most brightly colored species especially if greens, yellows and some reds predominate. This loss or change of color is regrettable, but not serious provided larvae normally light in color do not turn brown or black. Some killing and preserving methods produce shrinkage of tissue, especially 95 per cent ethyl alcohol by itself. Less shrinkage and better results for most larvae are produced if isopropyl alcohol (rubbing alcohol) is used. Alcohols alone should be avoided for most insects. Some of the exceptions are aquatic species especially nymphs of Odonata and Ephemeroptera. With these species 95 per cent ethyl alcohol as a killing and preserving agent produces the best specimens. It is distinctly advantageous to provide specimens for study which have retained their normal shape. Some methods bring about inflation of tissues. For many forms this is not undesirable provided the inflation is not excessive. Some inflation of tissue will make mouth parts, crochets, glands and other structures more conspicuous and easier to observe than the same structures in a normal resting larva. Personally the author prefers to study specimens which are completely distended even though some soft areas may be slightly enlarged.

Chemicals without heat. For several years the author and some of his students have been interested in finding a mixture of chemicals which will kill and produce larvae that closely resemble natural living specimens, at least so far as form is concerned. Many combinations of xylene, ketones, oils, alcohols, acids, dioxane and other chemicals have been tried. Some of these combinations have produced interesting and satisfactory results for many species of larvae under field and laboratory conditions. If a larva is to be killed in any of the following chemical mixtures it should be placed in a bottle with a horizontal diameter greater than the length of the larva or if the larva is inserted into a long narrow vial the container should be placed in a horizontal position until the specimen is completely distended and fixed. Six drahm homeopathic vials are satisfactory killing tubes for most larvae. With most of the killing solutions it has been noted that many larvae placed in the various mixtures at room or outdoor temperatures at time of death are distinctly distorted, however, as the solution penetrates the exoskeleton the larva gradually straightens and the entire specimen becomes slightly inflated so that the mouth parts, glands, crochets and other parts are distended and readily visible. In some cases the anal portion of the alimentary canal may protrude slightly. If the exoskeleton is soft or easily penetrated certain materials enter quickly, inflate rapidly and may burst the body covering at some weak point while a larva with a more highly sclerotized exoskeleton shows less inflation and no bursting occurs. The marked difference in the perviousness of the exoskeleton of various insects indicates that one killing agent at a given strength satisfactory for all immature insects may never be found, however, a satisfactory general formula may be discovered which can be altered slightly for different kinds of larvae. For published results to date see Jour. Econ. Ent. 1942, 35:788; 1943, 36:115 or the eighth edition (1955) "Manual of Entomological Techniques" by Alvah Peterson.

So far in the tests the following four combinations with alterations have been found to be quite satisfactory for some or many larvae. To date the author's mixture; K.A.A.D. (4) has proven to be most satisfactory. The figures indicate the volume of each product in the respective mixtures.

1. X.A. mixture; xylene-1 part and 95 per cent ethyl alcohol-1 part.
2. X.A.A.D. mixture; xylene-4 parts, commercial refined isopropyl alcohol-6 parts parts, glacial acetic acid-5 parts, and dioxane - 4 parts.
3. Ketone mixture; unsaturated 14 carbon ketone* (2-methyl - 7 - ethyl undecen - 5 one - 4) - 2 parts, glacial acetic acid - 1 part and refined methyl alcohol-4 parts.
4. K.A.A.D. mixture; kerosene-1 part, 95 per cent ethyl or commercial refined isopropyl alcohol-7 to 10 parts, glacial acetic acid-2 parts and dioxane-1 part.

1. X.A. Mixture. Several years ago when C. B. Huffaker was a graduate student at Ohio State University, he learned that a 50-50 mixture of xylene and 95 per cent ethyl alcohol was a satisfactory killing agent for larvae of the southern armyworm, Prodenia eridania (Cram.). This solution distended segments and crochets and produced larvae that were turgid. Further tests with the X.A. mixture were conducted by L.D. Anderson at Norfolk, Virginia, on numerous larvae collected in that state. The author has seen many of these specimens, especially larvae of the Lepidoptera and Coleoptera and in general it can be said that most specimens were quite satisfactory. The X.A. mixture is unsatisfactory for many soft bodied insects including most Diptera. Larvae killed in the X.A. mixture become somewhat transparent if permitted to remain in this solution for an indefinite period. Most species should be removed and transferred to preserving alcohol after 24 hours. The above mixture becomes cloudy and may take on a green or muddy color after a few specimens have been killed in it. This change apparently has no appreciable effect on the results provided the solution is agitated previous to its use.

2. X.A.A.D. Mixture. During 1941, R. L. Blickle, while a graduate student at the University of New Hampshire, learned that an X.A.A.D. mixture consisting of xylene - 4 parts; isopropyl alcohol - 6 parts; glacial acetic acid - 5 parts and dioxane - 4 parts, was very satisfactory for many insect larvae. The author has seen the larvae killed in this mixture and the

results are very good for a number of species of Coleoptera and Lepidoptera. Some species of Lepidoptera fail to completely distend their crochets unless they are kept in the killing mixture for a number of hours. This mixture also may explode thin walled larvae of Diptera. It also tends to produce some transparency and a pulling away of internal structures from the exoskeleton, especially if the specimens are kept in the killing solution too long.

3. Ketone Mixture. Early in 1941 J. M. Hutzel at Ohio State University, conducted killing tests on house fly maggots and full grown larvae of the southern armyworm. He learned that a ketone mixture consisting of 14 - carbon ketone - 2 parts, glacial acetic acid - 1 part, and methyl alcohol - 4 parts, produced a clear amber solution which, when used as a killing agen for the above insects, produced very satisfactory results. This mixture was given an extensive trial during 1941 and it was learned that most larvae of Coleoptera, Lepidoptera, nonaquatic Diptera, Hymenoptera, especially the Symphyta and other immature forms placed in this solution alive under field conditions were killed rapidly and the resulting specimens were opaque, turgid and completely distended. This mixture, however, is unsatisfactory for nymphs of the Ephemeroptera, Odonata and other aquatic species because it produces inflated baloonlike gills or the gills of some species, especially the Zygoptera, break off easily.

Most larvae were kept in the ketone mixture for one or more hours, usually no longer than 24 hours, before they were transferred to 75+ per cent alcohol. Many terrestrial species were kept in this killing solution for more than one year without deterioration. After a number of larvae have been killed in a given amount of the killing mixture the solution becomes cloudy and separates, producing an oily layer on top. This messy solution will still produce satisfactory specimens provided it is agitated somewhat before additional living larvae are introduced.

The ketone mixture can be made with 95 per cent ethyl alcohol if methyl alcohol is not available and satisfactory specimens will be obtained. The chief objection to the use of ethyl alcohol is the fact that the mixture on standing becomes very dark (coffeelike) in color which makes it difficult to observe larvae placed in the solution.

For many larvae the above mixture is probably the best killing agent discovered to date, however, it is not free of objectionable points. At the present time the ketone employed is not

*From Carbide and Carbon Chemicals Co., New York City, N. Y.

a commercial product readily available, consequently its cost is high when obtainable. Furthermore, the mixture produces a tenacious and to many individuals a very unpleasant odor. So far as known its vapor is nontoxic to man.

4. K.A.A.D. Mixture. Early in 1942, with the help of Sue D. Sparks, the author made a number of tests with various chemicals, especially mixtures of oils and alcohols. It was learned that a K.A.A.D. mixture (kerosene - 1 part, 95 per cent ethyl alcohol - 7 to 10 parts, glacial acetic acid - 2 parts and dioxane - 1 part) proved to be an all-around satisfactory killing agent for many larvae. Also in 1942 Clyde F. Smith of Raleigh, North Carolina, independent of our investigations, reported satisfactory findings with a K.A. mixture; kerosene - 1 part and ethyl alcohol - 10 parts. Many larvae of Lepidoptera and Coleoptera killed in a K.A. solution without acetic acid or dioxan are distended nicely but some species will darken or turn black, especially light colored wood-boring larvae. Experience shows that the addition of acetic or hydrochloric acid to alcohol or to killing mixtures in general will prevent light colored larvae, especially maggots and scarabaeids, from turning dark or black. For this reason 2 parts of glacial acetic acid are included in the K.A.A.D. mixture. For many larvae 1 part of glacial acetic acid is satisfactory. Hydrochloric acid is unsatisfactory in the presence of kerosene. Dioxane is added to the mixture to help make the solution miscible or water clear. Some kerosenes exist which are not completely miscible even though dioxane is added. In such cases a uniform mixture usually takes place if isopropyl alcohol is used instead of ethyl alcohol. Some tests indicate that dioxane improves the fixation quality of the mixture for a limited number of species, however, it may be omitted for most larvae if the kerosene is miscible in ethyl alcohol and acetic acid.

The K.A.A.D. mixture made with ethyl alcohol penetrates rapidly and is apt to explode soft bodied larvae, especially maggots, larvae of aquatic Diptera and leaf miners. The explosive quality of the mixture can be prevented almost completely by reducing decidedly the amount of kerosene employed or by using refined, commercial, isopropyl alcohol in place of 95 per cent ethyl alcohol. When isopropyl alcohol is employed the larvae are killed less rapidly and inflation is much slower. This means that large terrestrial specimens must be kept in the solution longer before they are transferred to 95 per cent ethyl alcohol for best results.

Many larvae killed in a K.A.A.D. mixture loss their bright colors, expecially the greens.

Also they are apt to become somewhat clear if kept in the solution too long. Thirty minutes to four hours in the K.A.A.D. mixture for many species appears to be the most satisfactory period of time for killing. When the larvae are transferred from the killing solution to 95 per cent alcohol for preservation a thin film of oil may exist about the body. Usually the film will disappear within a few minutes to hours. Some larvae may not be very turgid, especially if kept in the K.A.A.D. mixture too long. If these are preserved in 75+ per cent alcohol they are apt to collapse. This can be prevented by preserving them in 95 per cent alcohol. The author preserves all larvae killed in a K.A.A.D. in 95 per cent ethyl alcohol. In general the K.A.A.D. mixture has proven to be satisfactory for very many larvae of Lepidoptera, Coleoptera, Hymenoptera, Diptera, Siphonaptera, adult Arachnida, etc., but somewhat unsatisfactory for most nymphs of Ephemeroptera, Zygoptera and heavily sclerotized larvae of Coleoptera, especially some of the Elateridae and Tenebrionidae.

The four killing mixtures listed vary considerably in their results with given species of insects, however, the results with many species are very similar. For a general killing solution the author usually employs the K.A.A.D. mixture reducing the amount of kerosene when soft bodied larvae are killed. This combination is cheaper than the ketone mixture, more readily available and produces no objectionable odor.

Heat. When living larvae are brought into the laboratory and the species is unusual or rare, the author may kill it in hot water. Some entomologists use hot Kahle's solution. The living larva is dropped into the hot solution ($180°\pm$F.) and permitted to remain until the solution cools. If the larva fails to distend satisfactorily as soon as it is dead it should be grasped lightly with forceps and shaken or stretched. Some larvae, especially certain scarabaeids and maggots, may turn dark after they are placed in preserving alcohol unless they are boiled for a short time. After the water cools transfer the larva to Kahle's solution (95 per cent ethyl alcohol - 15 parts, formalin (40%) - 6 parts, glacial acetic acid - 2 parts and distilled water - 30 parts) at room temperature for 24 to 48 hours for further fixation. Large larvae should be pin punctured at one or more places for rapid penetration of the fixing agent. Most larvae killed in hot water are preserved best in 75+ per cent ethyl alcohol. To prevent collapse of larvae possesing thin exoskeletons the specimens should be passed through 25 to 50 per cent alcohol. Fixation in Kahle's solution may be omitted for many species of larvae with good results.

Dissecting Larvae. Some attention has been paid to the condition of the internal structures of several species of caterpillars killed in some of the above chemical mixtures. In 1941 it was first noted that the internal structures of preserved larvae of aquatic Lepidoptera were in excellent condition for gross dissection two weeks after they had been killed in ketone mixture. After this experience several species of terrestrial caterpillars were killed in ketone mixture and upon dissection one to several days later the internal structures were intact and not too brittle for general gross dissection. During the summer of 1942 large larvae of catalpa shpinx were killed in the ketone and K.A.A.D. mixtures respectively. Some of each were dissected within 48 hours and others were held for one year and much longer in 75+ per cent alcohol. In all cases the internal parts were in fair to excellent shape when opened for gross dissection. Larvae killed in K.A.A.D. mixture proved to be best. Clyde F. Smith reports that most satisfactory specimens for dissection are obtained with kerosene-alcohol mixture if the kerosene content approximates 20 per cent. A few tests have been made on the histological condition of insect tissues killed in a K.A.A.D. solution by C. V. Reichart. He learned that some insect tissues were well preserved and fixed by this mixture.

The above killing agents, especially those containing kerosene, have proven to be very useful in biological control investigations. Host larvae in the field are killed in a K.A.A.D. solution and then transferred to 95 per cent alcohol. Days, weeks, or months later they may be opened to determine the status of the internal parasites.

Preserving Larvae. The most common and generally satisfactory preservative for larvae is ethyl alcohol. Most larvae preserved in 75+ per cent alcohol (made by diluting 95 per cent ethyl alcohol with distilled water) will remain firm and retain their normal size and structure for many years in this solution. Percentages of alcohol lower than 75 are apt to produce soft flabby material while percentages above 80 per cent may produce rigid brittle specimens, especially those killed by heat. It has been noted that all larvae killed in a K.A.A.D. mixture and preserved in 95 per cent alcohol are pliable and very satisfactory after prolonged preservation.

Some investigators employ preservatives containing alcohol, formaldehyde and acetic acid in varying amounts. The following are three of the numerous combinations employed: (1) 95 per cent ethyl alcohol - 100 parts, distilled water - 100 parts, formaldehyde - 13 parts and glacial acetic acid - 5 parts; or (2) 95 per cent ethyl alcohol - 55 parts, distilled water 35 parts, formaldehyde 5 parts and glacial acetic acid 5 parts; or (3) Kahle's mixture (for formula see discussion on heat in hot water killing). These are satisfactory preservatives for many larvae especially for specimens killed by heat. The chief objection to their use is the annoying effect formaldehyde fumes may have on the nose and eyes of an observer when viewing specimens in these solutions under a strong light with a binocular microscope.

One of the serious difficulties associated with the maintenance of a wet collection is the evaporation of the preservative employed. Alcohol in vials will evaporate rapidly if not stoppered properly and other precautions taken. Alcohol will evaporate with considerable rapidity if placed in small vials stoppered with regulation size corks. It is necessary to examine all alcoholic material in cork stoppered vials at least once a year. At the present time the author keeps most larvae in 95 per cent ethyl alcohol in 4 drahm homeopathic vials stoppered with a good grade of over-size corks (No. 5) or rubber stoppers (No. 0). When cork is employed the small end of the cork should be the same size or a wee bit smaller than the opening of the vial, then after the cork is pushed into the vial it does not extend below the neck, consequently only a small portion of the cork is exposed to or is in contact with the alcohol. This prevents excessive early shrivelling of the cork and also makes it possible to push the cork further into the vial when needed. The vial is filled with alcohol almost to the neck. A four drahm vial seems to be too large for many larvae yet experience has shown that the additional alcohol in a vial of this size is good insurance against complete evaporation in vials with faulty corks, especially if the collection is examined but once a year. Smaller homeopathic vials or shell vials stoppered with medium or under size corks or Bakelite screw cap vials are less satisfactory or distinctly inferior to 4 drahm homeopathic vials stoppered with over size corks.

A number of tests have been conducted with sealing materials when cork is used. The cork and the top of a vial may be dipped in hot paraffin of high melting point or dry corks may be impregnated with vaseline by submerging them in hot melted vaseline until they are thoroughly saturated. The excess vaseline is permitted to drain off and then the corks are wiped with a dry rag. Professor W. M. Barrows' spider collection at Ohio State University is kept in alcohol filled vials stoppered with vaseline treated corks. Some of these vials have not been refilled for many years. Objections to this method are the difficulties associated with the preparation of the corks (boiling in vaseline) and the fact that treated corks are apt to be somewhat greasy. In the wet collection at the Illinois Natural History Survey, Urbana, Illinois, red rubber stoppers are used in place of ordinary corks. They have been very satisfactory. Rubber stoppers cost more than ordinary corks and also experience shows that all rubber stoppers are not equally satisfactory.

For a more permanent type of preservation some entomologists place the larvae in small shell vials filled with alcohol and stoppered with cotton. A goodly number of these vials are then placed in an inverted position in a low glass jar. They are then covered with alcohol and the jar is sealed with a rubber gasket between the cover and the glass top. This method is somewhat inconvenient if one needs to make frequent use of specimens in a given vial.

At Ohio State University most vials are kept upright in single or double trays made of white pine or poplar and celluloid. A single tray has a wood bottom board (13" x 1-1/4"), two upright wood ends (3 1/2" x 1-1/8" x 1/2"), and a thin wide back board (12" x 2" x 1/4"). The front of the tray is partially covered with a fairly stiff celluloid strip (1-1/4" wide) tacked to the two end boards. The strip of celluloid is placed near enough to the bottom to prevent vials from rolling out in case they are upset in the tray. The inside width of the tray should be equal to or slightly larger than the diameter of the vial employed. The double row trays are made of wood on the bottom and ends. They possess a thin detachable center board which slides up and down in grooves located on the inner surface of the end boards. Thin narrow inset pieces of wood are used on the two outside surfaces of each tray to retain the vials. By removing the center board larger bottles may be used in the tray.

INFLATING, DEGREASING AND RESTORING LARVAE

Inflating Larvae. The most satisfactory and commonly used method for preserving the natural colors of larvae, especially delicately colored caterpillars, is to inflate and dry the specimens. This method, however, does not preserve colors (usually greens) due to colored blood or food within the body seen through the semi-transparent exoskeleton. If these colors are to be saved they have to be duplicated by injecting colored melted paraffin. To obtain the color desired in the paraffin, colored wax crayons (children's crayola) are incorporated into the melted paraffin.

Most caterpillars and other larvae, one-half inch long or longer, can be inflated and dried. Active, nearly full grown larvae produce better specimens than prepupae. The larva should be starved for 24 hours or longer before it is inflated. Starvation rids the intestine, especially the fore-gut, of newly consumed food, which if retained may produce a dark streak. Kill the larva in a cyanide bottle. As soon as it appears to be lifeless place it on a piece of absorbent paper. Apply pressure by fingers or a round glass tube near head end until the intestine starts to protrude from the anus. Puncture the protruded portion and the liquid contents will ooze out. Continue to apply pressure until the body is completely flattened and no more fluid appears. When specimen is completely deflated insert tip end of a small, clean glass, inflating tube into anal opening and apply the clamp. Before the tube is inserted it should be coated with an oil or vaseline so that it will not stick to dried specimen. Apply air slowly until larva is completely distended.

Place the inflated larva in or over a small metal oven heated by a tiny flame (an alcohol lamp). Maintain air pressure until larva is completely dry. A larva is dry if the head does not move when touched. The length of time required for drying, usually 10 to 60 minutes, varies with size of the larva. Large saturnids require much more time than small tortricids. Avoid excessive heat for it will scorch setae and destroy some colors.

Carefully remove the dried inflated specimen from the tube. It may be mounted by household cement on a dry leaf artificially colored green and reinforced with stiff paper on the lower surface and held in position by one or more pins. Some workers insert soft wood, cork, or reed plugs into the anal opening and pass a pin perpendicularly through the plug. Others glue the inflated larva to the top side of a stiff, twisted, green wire fastened at right angles to the upper part of a pin. Inflated specimens are exceedingly delicate and must be handled with care.

J. N. Knull of Ohio State University has produced many beautiful specimens by the above method. For other descriptions on inflating larvae and figures of equipment see Harrison,

A. S., and R. L. Usinger, 1934. Bul. Brooklyn Ent. Soc. 29:168; Plumb, G. H. 1936, U.S.D.A. Bur. Ent. and P. Q. mimeographed series ET-75; Raizenne, H. 1946, Canadian Dept. of Agr. Ottawa, Canada, Processed Publication No. 32; and Peterson, A. 1955, "Manual of Entomological Techniques," eighth edition, Edwards Brothers, Ann Arbor, Michigan.

Degreasing Larvae. Valentine prepares dried specimens of larvae by degreasing with ethyl ether. Larvae are killed in an ethyl acetate killing bottle. The author has used Valentin's method and also has had good success with alcohol preserved larvae that have been killed in hot water or in a kerosene-alcohol-acetic acid mixture. The killed or preserved larvae are placed in ether. As long as there is any fatty tissue in the larvae the ether will turn yellow. Several changes of ether are necessary, especially if large larvae are degreased. The time required will be one to several days.

After all fatty tissue is dissolved, the larvae are removed one at a time and placed on a piece of absorbent paper under an electric light bulb in a goose-neck desk lamp. The heat from the lamp evaporates the ether rapidly and inflates the larva somewhat. Too rapid evaporation may burst the specimen. The specimen should not be removed from the heat until all of the ether has evaporated. If removed from under the lamp too soon it will shrivel. A shriveled specimen can be restored, if it is returned immediately to the heat under the lamp. When the larva is completely dry, which may require 5 to 30 or more minutes, and all the ether has evaporated the larva will be firm and bone dry. It will resemble an inflated specimen. In the above process some colors are apt to be lost or changed.

Other investigators degrease and dehydrate larvae in a different manner. H. S. Barber kills larvae in 80 per cent alcohol in which benzol, carbon bisulfide, or some other fat solvent has been added at the rate of one part of solvent to ten parts of alcohol. The average specimen remains in the fluid for 24 hours, larger specimens require 72 hours. They are then transferred to 95 per cent alcohol for 24 to 72 hours and then dehydrated in absolute alcohol containing a piece of stone lime. Finally they are transferred to xylol and dried on a plaster block. Large specimens are punctured to facilitate dehydration.

R. L. Poat suggests that one boil larvae in water 30 to 60 seconds and then run them through 40%, 60%, 90%, 95%, and absolute alcohol for 24 hours each. Finally place them in xylol, then pin and dry the larvae. These larvae may be stained by introducing oil pigments soluble in xylol. The stain should be quite concentrated.

Restoring Larvae. A shriveled, distorted, dried larva can be restored to normal size and shape by careful use of potassium hydroxide. Place the specimen in a 3 to 5 per cent solution of potassium hydroxide at room temperature. Watch the specimen closely. As soon as it resumes its normal size, which may take a few minutes to several hours, and before the internal tissues disintegrate, transfer the larva to water for a few minutes and then place it in a weak acid solution for a short period to neutralize the potassium hydroxide present. A five or ten per cent solution of acetic acid is satisfactory. If the larva, after this treatment, remains straight and is rigid when picked up by forceps in the mid-region, usually it can be transferred directly to 75+ per cent alcohol without any collapse of the body taking place. To avoid shrivelling pass the specimen through several grades of alcohol, at least 25 and 50 per cent before preserving it in 75+ per cent alcohol. The author has used the above method extensively and has restored valuable specimens of all sizes and kinds.

Recently H. J. Van Cleave and Jean A. Ross in Science, 1947, Vol. 105, page 318, reported on the use of a 0.5 per cent solution of trisodium phosphate for restoring dried invertebrate specimens including some insects. To date the author has tested a few species with this method and the results appear to be satisfactory.

Table 1.

CENSUS OF INSECT SPECIES INHABITING THE UNITED STATES AND THE WORLD.

Note. The following figures are provided (1946) by the U.S.D.A. Bureau of Entomology and Plant Quarantine and are believed to be approximately correct. It does not include subspecies and varieties except in the case of the ants contained within the Hymenoptera.

Larvae Endopterygota			Nymphs (including naiads) Apterygota* and Exopterygota		
Orders	U.S.A.	World	Orders	U.S.A.	World
Coleoptera	26,276	263,884	Anoplura	35	270
Diptera	15,760	80,048	*Collembola	289	1,425
Hymenoptera	17,408	106,582	Corrodentia	96	993
Lepidoptera	10,768	109,055	Dermaptera	15	1,068
Mecoptera	66	333	Embioptera	7	141
Neuroptera	330	4,576	Ephemeroptera	544	1,401
Siphonaptera	319	1,055	Hemiptera	8,186	51,419
Trichoptera	782	4,192	(Incl. Homoptera)		
			Isoptera	59	1,629
			Mallophaga	308	2,665
			Odonata	406	4,707
			Orthoptera	1,172	21,969
			Plecoptera	288	1,389
			*Protura	28	64
			*Thysanura	42	382
			Thysanoptera	594	3,033
			Zoraptera	2	18
Totals	71,709	569,725		12,071	92,573

The grand total of all insect species in the U.S.A. is 83,780 and for the world 662,298. Approximately 85 per cent of all species in the U.S.A. and also for the world possess a true larval stage.

The terms nymph(s) (including naiad), larv(ae) and pupa(ae) used in this publication with a few exceptions, are defined as follows.

Nymphs. All immature stages (instars) of Apterygota and Exopterygota occuring between hatching of the egg and emergence of adult are called nymphs. This includes all naiads, a term commonly used by many entomologists for nymphs of Odonata, Ephemeroptera and Plecoptera. Approximately 15 per cent of all insect species belong to Apterygota and Exopterygota.

Nymphs of most species resemble the general structure of adults. Greatest divergence from this rule occurs among naiads. Among Exopterygota wings of all winged species develop within external cases (wing pads or buds) readily visible on the thorax, especially in late nymphal instars. Nymphs usually possess compound eyes but no ocelli. Mouth parts and legs are similar in structure to those of adults. Most nymphs, except naiads, live in the same habitat as adults and consume similar food. A full grown nymph transforms directly into an adult (a preimago among Ephemeroptera). Usually no prolonged inactive period occurs previous to adult emergence. Among Thysanoptera some workers have used the terms propupa and pupa for the two nonfeeding instars previous to adult emergence.

Larvae. The term larva refers to the active, growing, food consuming instars occurring between the hatching of the egg and the pupal stage of all Endopterygota. Approximately 85 per cent of all insect species possess true larvae. Various types of larvae have been given names which are defined in the glossary. Some of these are: apoid, campodeiform, caterpillar, cerambyciform, coarctate, elateriform, eruciform, grub, lepismoid, looper, maggot, muscidiform, oligopod, planidiform, platyform, polypod, protopod, scarabedoid, scarabaeiform, teleaform, thysanuriform, triungulin and vermiform.

Larvae of most species bear little or no resemblance to adults. Many are wormlike and may have a body length 1-1/2 to several times greater than that of adults. Wings of the future adult start their development within the thorax of the larva, consequently there is no evidence of external wing pads, so typical of many Exopterygota. Larvae never possess true compound eyes but may have one to several ocelli on each side of the head. Structure of mouth parts and the way they function may differ decidedly in larvae and adults. Special organs, characteristic of larvae only, namely prolegs, armature and glands may be present. Habitat and food of larva and adult may be very different. When growth is completed all larvae of the Endopterygota transform into pupae. Before this change occurs full grown larvae of most species seek a suitable spot where they may attach their caudal end to some object (Pieridae), or they may spin a cocoon (Saturnidae), or build a pupal cell (Scarabaeidae) or contract and harden their exoskeleton into a protective covering (Muscidae) and produce a puparium.

Pupae. When a larva is ready to change into a pupa its full grown length usually contracts to three fourths to one-half. This contracted inactive larva, called prepupa, consumes no food. Internally a pupa develops. Before the pupa emerges from the last larval instar the wings evert from their larval sacs for the first time and may be found outside the body of pupa beneath prepupal ectoskeleton. When development of pupa is complete it sheds the prepupal exoskeleton except among species belonging to families of Cyclorrhapha and others where the pupa occurs within a puparium.

The last larval exuvium, when shed, usually is found adjacent to the pupa and near its caudal end. This is particularly true of pupae located within cocoons or pupal cells. The exuvium may serve as a connecting link between larvae and adult stages. For taxonomists interested in the identification of larvae the exuvium is very helpful in determination of species.

Three types of pupae are recognized by most entomologists, namely, exarate, obtect and coarctate. Correctly speaking there are only two types, exarate and obtect. The coarctate type is not a true pupa. It is the last larval exuvium (puparium) which serves as a protective covering for a delicate, soft, exarate type of pupa located within.

Exarate pupae possess free appendages. All the wings, legs, antennae and mouth parts are independent and not attached to each other or to the body except at their points of origin. Most pupae of insects are exarate including some of the primitive Lepidoptera and most Diptera. Obtect pupae possess wings, legs, antennae and mouth parts which are firmly fastened down to the body and to each other and serve as a part of pupal covering. Except for the antennae and one pair of wings only portions of each appendage may be visible on the exterior of pupa. Most pupae of Lepidoptera and some Nemocera are obtect. For names assigned to the various changes that occur in the pupae see glossary under pupa.

When the adult completes it development and is ready to emerge, the pupa may push its way out of the cocoon or pupal cell and then the pupal covering splits along the dorsomeson and the adult emerges. Among Cyclorrhapha of the Diptera the adult breaks the delicate pupal covering about its body when it pushes its way out of the cephalic end of puparium.

KEYS TO THE ORDERS OF IMMATURE STAGES OF NEARCTIC INSECTS
(Exclusive of Eggs and Pronymphs)

A few keys to orders for immature stages are available in the entomological literature. The most satisfactory keys are limited to specific groups, particularly aquatic species. Those that attempt to cover all species are too general and abbreviated and will identify correctly only the more common forms of insects. The author presents a key which includes all nymphs (naiads), larvae and pupae of all orders except the Zoraptera and Strepsiptera. This key has undergone several revisions since it was published in 1939 and is subject to further changes when new forms are found which cannot be traced quickly and accurately to the correct order.

The order names used in the keys are similar (except Protura) to those found in "An Introduction to Entomology" by J. H. Comstock, Comstock Publ. Co., Ithaca, N. Y. For other published keys see S. W. Frost 1942, C. L. Metcalf and W. P. Flint 1939, O. Park, W. C. Allee and V. E. Shelford 1939, A. Peterson 1939, H. B. Ward and G. C. Whipple 1918.

Numbers on the left margin within parenthesis are useful in retracing major steps taken in the keys.

NYMPHS (NAIADS), LARVAE, PUPAE AND PUPARIA,
APTERYGOTA AND PTERYGOTA

1. —— Segmented thoracic appendages or a distinct head capsule with several functional (usually) mouth parts (or both) present 3

1a. Neither segmented thoracic appendages nor a well developed head capsule with several functional mouth parts present 2

2. —— Sclerotized mouth parts (at least mandibles usually present) do not resemble closely generalized opposable biting type of mouth parts typified by most larvae of Lepidoptera and Coleoptera; mouth parts may be reduced to nearly opposable, sharp pointed mandibles or parallel decurved mouth hooks which are apt to be deeply embedded in the cephalic end or absent; body covering usually weakly sclerotized and light in color (mostly shades of white or yellow); most segments concentric or flattened; if spiracles are present only on a thoracic segment (usually prothorax) or on a caudal segment (usually last) or at both ends the body is apt to be straight or peglike with the head end pointed; if spiracles occur on most segments the body is apt to be c-shaped or cyphosomatic with mid-abdominal segments thicker than those at ends (grubs); if spiracles are absent body may be straight, spindle-shaped or c-shaped. . . . . (Endopterygota), L,-Larvae

2a. Sclerotized mouth parts invisible on exterior; the external covering is the last (or late) larval exuvium (puparium) and contains within an exarate pupa or a larva (usually a hibernating form); compared with active larva external structure of the puparium is approximately the same except all segments are in a fixed position, total length is shorter usually more barrel-like, body covering is harder and tougher, cephalic and caudal spiracles (when present) are remnants or scars and general color (shades of yellow, red, brown or black) is usually much darker . . . . (Endopterygota), P,-Puparia

3,(1). — Mummylike * with all segmented appendages of future adult concealed individually in more or less fixed cases partially or completely visible; mouth parts and other appendages among pupae of the Neuroptera may show distant dentation, segmentation and sclerotized areas; legs (folded), wings (usually present and overlap), antennae, mouth parts and ovipositor (if present) are usually held close to body in a fixed position, their cases may be fused to each other and to body covering: wing cases, in many species as long as folded

*Mummylike larvae of the Meloidae-Coleoptera possessing stublike mouth parts and legs may trace to this subdivision, see Meloidae, part 2.

legs, arise from the dorsal or lateral aspects of thorax and project caudad and in many cases ventrad so that they cover a portion of ventral aspect of abdomen; head may or may not be distinct; position of compound eyes usually visible . . . . (Endopterygota), P,-Pupae

3a.   Not mummylike ; all appendages free; legs, if present, usually movable, not in a fixed and folded position; wing cases, if present, located entirely on dorsal or lateral aspects, never covering ventral aspect; head usually well defined with external (some exceptions) free and movable mouth parts; thoracic segments usually distinct; legs and wing pads may be absent 4

4. —— Wing rudiments (pads) absent on external surface 5

4a.   Wing rudiments (pads) present on external surface of the thorax, they arise from the dorsal or laterodorsal aspects of the mesothorax and metathorax (one pair may be absent) and may project dorsad, caudad or laterad but never sufficiently ventrad and mesad to cover the ventral aspect of body, as in many pupae; abdomen short rarely more than twice the length of the head and thorax combined; compound eyes usually present; ocelli absent; body covering usually thickened and pigmented, especially thoracic sclerites of sternum and pleura; thoracic segments differ in shape especially prothorax; thoracic legs usually present and with full number of parts; tarsi usually possessing more than one segment; shape of body and type of mouth parts usually similar to adult; mouth parts chewing, piercing and sucking or rasping and sucking types; two or three to many segmented cerci may occur at caudal end . . . . (Exopterygota), N,-Nymphs

5. —— Except for absence of wings rudiments (pads) description much the same for Exopterygota as in 4a; acariform or pear-shaped nymphs may possess needlelike piercing and sucking mouth parts. Among Apterygota body covering soft and uniformly sclerotized; segmentation usually inconspicuous and chewing mouth parts retracted among Collembola, Campodeidae, Japygidae, etc.; three pairs of thoracic legs present; two or three cerci, forceps, or a furcula and a collophora may be present on the abdomen . . . .
. . . .(Exopterygota and Apterygota), N,-Nymphs

5a.   Abdomen usually two to four or more times as long as head and thorax combined; compound eyes absent; ocelli, if present, one to many pairs occur on sides of head adjacent to the mandibles and antennae; body covering frequently weakly sclerotized and sclerites of sternum and pleura usually indistinct (many Coleoptera and Neuroptera are exceptions); all segments of the thorax more or less similar in shape (not size); thoracic legs usually short, rudimentary or absent; true tarsi, when present, usually one segmented; shape of body (frequently eruciform, vermiform, scarabaeiform, cyphosomatic, campodaeiform, etc.) usually unlike that of adult; type of mouth parts may be very different from that of adult . . . . (Endopterygota), L,-Larvae

N. - KEY TO ORDERS OF NYMPHS AND NAIADS
APTERYGOTA AND EXOPTERYGOTA

N1. —— Mouth parts adapted for piercing and sucking or for rasping and sucking; piercing and sucking types show a distinct troughlike labium without palpi, enclosing needlelike mandibles and maxilae (see N 15a) or labium is wanting and the short piercing stylets are retracted within head-capsule along the meson (see N 14a); rasping and sucking type shows a distinct short cone-shaped structure (consisting of clypeus, labrum, maxillae with maxillary palpi, mandible and labium with inconspicuous labial palpi) located between head-capsule and thorax on the ventral aspect (see N 15) 14

N1a. Mouth parts adapted for chewing; labium, when present, is usually exposed and not troughlike or cone-shaped; palpi of labium and maxillae rarely absent; mouth parts may be concealed in the head (see N 5a, N 7, N 9a, and N 10a) 2

N2. —— No tracheal gills present; terrestrial species 5

N2a. External tracheal gills usually present (Anisoptera - Odonata, O7, and some Plecoptera without external gills); aquatic species, called naiads 3

N3. —— Labium of normal type not modified into a scoop or hinged 4

N3a. Labium, when extended, usually four or more times as long as broad, scooplike in structure and when folded (hinged between submentum and mentum) serves as a mask that covers mandibles and maxillae; platelike gills or spinelike structures may occur at caudal end of abdomen; figs. O7 and O8 . . . . (naiads), Odonata

N4. —— Tracheal gills, plate, feather or tassellike, located on lateral margins of abdominal tergites only; three taillike many segmented cerci (in some families only two), fringed with rather long setae, occur at caudal end; each tarsus possesses one claw; fig. O6, A-D . . . . (naiads), Ephemeroptera

N4a. Tracheal gills, fingerlike, single or bunched, usually located on the ventral aspect of the thoracic segments, in some cases they occur on the jaws, also on cephalic or caudal segments of the abdomen, gills may be absent among the Nemouridae and Capniidae; two distinct taillike segmented cerci, usually without long fringes of setae, occur at caudal end of abdomen, each tarsus possesses two claws; fig. O6, E-H . . . . (naiads), Plecoptera

N5,(2). — Antennae present, may be inconspicuous or concealed 6

N5a. Antennae absent; prothoracic legs used as tactile organs; head pointed; f.g.l. very small . . . . Protura

N6. —— Antennae with more than six segments 8

N6a. Antennae with six or less segments 7

N7. —— Antennae 4 to 6 segments; mouth parts concealed in head; abdomen six segmented, if visible, and usually possesses a furcula and collophore; nonparasitic; f.g.l. under 6 mm. . . . . Collembola

N7a. Antennae not more than 5-segmented and usually located within or arise from lateral depressions on the head; body strongly depressed (flattened); head larger and broader than prothorax; ectoparasitic on birds and other vertebrates . . . . Mallophaga

N8. —— No prominent forceplike structures at caudal end 10

N8a. Prominent forceplike structures at caudal end 9

N9. —— Chewing mouth parts conspicuous; head usually broader than long; wing rudiments may exist; tarsi two or three segmented; color near brown or black; fig. O2, A. . Dermaptera

N9a. Chewing mouth parts concealed, only tip ends of parts may be visible on exterior; head usually not broader than long; no wing rudiments; tarsi one segmented; color near white; fig. O2, B . . . . Thysanura

N10. —— Chewing mouth parts conspicuous; wing rudiments may exist; if paired cerci exist and possess more than ten segments prothoracic legs are fitted for grasping or digging or metathoracic legs are fitted for jumping or head is opisthognathous; ventral styli rarely present 11

N10a. Chewing mouth parts usually concealed, only tip ends of parts may be visible on exterior; no wing rudiments ever exist; small ventral styli may be present on abdomen, usually on segments 1 to 7; two long multiarticulate (more than 10 segments) cerci always present and a median caudal filament may be present at caudal end; body may be covered with scales or fine setae; color usually near white . . . . Thysanura

N11. —— Tarsi two or more segmented with proximal tarsal segment (metatarsus) of the prothoracic leg not as large as the tibia and only differing in structure from the metatarsus of the mesothoracic and metathoracic in species where the prothoracic legs are fitted for digging or grasping 12

N11a. Tarsi three segmented with the proximal tarsal segment (metatarsus) of the prothoracic leg usually as long or longer than the tibia and also strongly dilated (bearing openings to silk glands on ventral surface); metatarsal segment of the mesothoracic and metathoracic legs normal size and shape; cerci prominent and two segmented; antennae with nine or more segments; fig. O2, C . . . . Embioptera

N12. —— Prothorax usually subequal to mesothorax or metathorax or larger; if prothorax is much smaller then cerci are present, the tarsi are four or five segmented and the legs may be greatly elongated (Phasmidae) 13

N12a. Prothorax usually shorter and narrower than mesothorax and metathorax; cerci wanting; tarsi usually two segmented and labial palpi one segmented; resemble plant lice in shape; fig. O1, F. . . . . Corrodentia

N13. —— Long axis of head and mouth parts usually vertical (hypognathus); in one family (Blattidae) the mouth parts project caudad (opisthognathus) and in another family (Phasmidae) cephaloventrad (somewhat prognathus); among the Phasmidae the prothorax is much smaller than the mesothorax or metathorax and the legs are greatly elongated; mouth parts for all species of a generalized chewing type; antennae many segmented, long and usually located on the cephalic portion of the head capsule near the compound eyes; short cerci may be present; f.g.l. usually over 10 mm; fig. O1, A-E. . . Orthoptera *mantis*

N13a. Long axis of head and mouth parts usually project cephalad (prognathous or cephaloventrad, somewhat hypognathous); head longer than broad; antennae usually located near mandibles; compound eyes may be absent; legs of moderate length and tarsi frequently four segmented (may be inconspicuous); color usually a dirty white; exoskeleton usually soft; shape antlike (called white ants); length usually under 10 mm.; live in sapwood, dead wood and soil; fig. O1, G . . . . Isoptera

N14,(1)— Mouthparts external, usually showing a distinct troughlike labium with piercing stylets or a conelike structure made up of several parts; wing rudiments usually present; acariform or pear-shaped wingless species possess long needlelike mandibles and maxillae which may be withdrawn into body; tarsi, when present, not scansorial type. 15

N14a. Mouth parts internal, short piercing stylets withdrawn into head parallel with meson (visible in cleared specimens) with no external labium; wing rudiments absent; tarsi usually scansorial type; ectoparasites of vertebrates especially mammals . . . Anoplura

N15. —— Mouth parts in form of cone (consisting of clypeus, labrum, maxillae with maxillary palpi, one functional mandible and labium with inconspicuous labial palpi) located between the ventrocaudal margin of the head and the prothorax; mouth parts asymmetrical in that only one functional mandible exists which may project a short distance from tip of mouth-cone; tarsi small, apparently one segmented, clawless and possess single, protrusile pads; body usually cylindrical, generally less than five millimeters long and pointed at caudal end; wing pads may occur in the so-called propupal and pupal stages; In these stages the antennae are usually represented by short blunt cases which arise from the cephalic margin or by elongated cases that surround the cephalic and lateral (or ventral) portions of the head; fig. O2, D-F. . . . . Thysanoptera

N15a. Mandibles and maxillae (needlelike) usually enclosed within a troughlike tubular labium which usually projects caudad between the thoracic legs; labium may be absent; if labium is cone-shaped maxillary palpi and labial palpi are absent 16

N16. —— Mouth parts, consisting of a segmented labium enclosing needlelike mandibles and maxillae, arise from cephalic portion of ventral aspect of head-capsule; in some aquatic species mouth parts appear to arise from caudal portion of head-capsule; among these the legs usually show some kind of adaptation for aquatic locomotion and prothoracic legs may be modified for grasping; figs. O3 and O4. . . . . Hemiptera

N16a.   Mouth parts, consisting of a labium (may be absent) and needlelike mandibles and maxillae, arise distinctly from caudal portion of head-capsule((opisthognathous) or on the meson between thoracic legs; no aquatic species; fig. O5 . . . . Homoptera

L. - KEY TO THE ORDERS OF LARVAE OF ENDOPTERYGOTA

L1. —— Thoracic legs absent, prothorax may possess a single or bifurcate appendage or false leg sometimes called a proleg 15

L1a. Thoracic legs present on two or more segments, legs may be reduced to paired fleshy or cone shaped protuberances or to two or more segmented clawless structures called pedal lobes, in some species the legs possess three or more segments and claws yet they are minute and inconspicuous 2

L2. —— Ventral prolegs absent on abdominal segments one to eight, in rare cases prolegs occur on what appears to be the eighth segment (Lymexylidae, Hylecoetus), also a few species of Hydrophilidae possess ventral prolegs on several abdominal segments 5

L2a. Ventral prolegs present on two or more abdominal segments, may be inconspicuous peglike structures 3

L3. —— Antennae usually located on head capsule above membranous area between base of mandible and epicranium; prolegs without crochets; no protruding spinneret or adfrontal areas 4

L3a. Antennae located in membranous areas at base of mandibles; adfrontal areas usually distinct; an inconspicuous protruding spinneret usually present on labium; paired prolegs with crochets absent on second abdominal segment, usually present on abdominal segments three to six and last, however they may be absent on segments, three, four or five; a series of hooks (crochets) usually present on all prolegs; if crochets are present prolegs are said to occur; ocelli usually six pairs with four of each set arranged in a semicircle; spiracles usually present on prothorax and abdominal segments one to eight . . . . most, Lepidoptera

L4. —— Ocelli absent or one ocellus on each side of the head; fleshy prolegs without crochets usually located on segments two to eight and last, sometimes on segments two to seven or two to six and last; no suctorial disk at caudal end; four to eight crenulations (plicae) per segment usually present on dorsal aspect of abdominal segments one to eight; plant feeding species chiefly . . . . Hymenoptera

L4a. Ocelli, seven or more, closely grouped on each side of head; prolegs, sometimes inconspicuous pointed peglike structures, present on abdominal segments one to eight or three to eight; anal segment frequently flared, disklike and fitted for suction; several branched scoli bearing feathered setae may occur on each thoracic and most abdominal segments; antennae usually two segmented and labial palpi one segmented . . . . (Panorpa) Mecoptera

L5,(2). —— Head and mouth parts directed cephalad (prognathous); distance from dorsocaudal margin of head (cephalodorsal margin of the neck) to cephalic margin (tip end) of labrum, if present, equal to or slightly greater than distance from ventrocaudal margin of head (cephaloventral margin of the neck) to distal margin (tip end) of labium; dorsal surface of the head along the meson flat, concave or slightly convex; head usually cylindrical or depressed 10

L5a. Head and mouth parts directed ventrad (hypognathous) or cephalo-ventrad; distance along meson from dorso-caudal margin of head (cephalo dorsal margin of the neck) to ventral margin (tip end) of labrum, if present, much greater than distance from ventrocaudal margin of head (cephalo ventral margin of the neck) to distal margin (tip end) of labium; dorsal (and partly cephalic) surface of head along meson distinctly convex; head usually rounded boxlike structure 6

L6. —— Legs on all (at least two) thoracic segments (includes species possessing rudimentary legs on metathorax) usually similar in size (sub-equal), structure and position; not as described in 7 or 7a 8

L6a. Metathoracic legs and usually mesothoracic distinctly larger and longer than those on prothorax 7

L7. —— Legs on metathorax and mesothorax project laterad more decidedly than legs on the prothorax; several simple eyes in a close cluster usually present on sides of head; body c-shaped; f.g.l. under 5 mm., nonaquatic . . . . (Boreus) Mecoptera

19

L7a.   All legs project cephalad; antennae usually absent; simple eyes wanting, single or several in a close cluster; pair of hooks, usually on anal prolegs at caudal end; distinct dorsal hump frequently present on the dorsal aspect of first abdominal segment; tracheal gills may be scattered over the surface of abdominal segments; most species live within cases in water . . . . **Trichoptera**

L8,(6). — Protruding spinneret on labium; antennae arise from membranous area at base of mandibles; adfrontal areas and several simple eyes may be present; many species have heads (usually incomplete) deeply embedded in prothorax; if sluglike in form thoracic legs are inconspicuous, ventral surface is flat and scoli, spines or numerous setae may occur on the dorsal aspect . . . . **Lepidoptera**

L8a.   Not the combination of characters given under 8; protruding spinneret and adfrontal areas always absent, also the antennae arise from the epicranium adjacent to or dorsad of the mandibles 9

L9. —— Thoracic legs segmented or fleshy protuberances without claws, if segmented they are straight or curved and frequently sharp pointed (bearing claws) never distinctly elbowed at several points; one pair of simple eyes present or absent; antennae frequently seven segmented and always arise from the epicranium; labial palpi usually three segmented; shape usually eruciform; dorsal surface crenulations of abdominal segments, if present usually four or more per segment; one or frequently two pairs of spiracles on thorax (usually on prothorax and mesothorax) and on most abdominal segments, one to eight; spines and setae generally absent on thorax and abdomen; segmented subanal cerci or a median caudal spine frequently present; no (nonparasitic) aquatic species. . . . . **Hymenoptera**

L9a.   Thoracic legs of most species segmented, possessing one claw and usually elbowed at two or more joints or they may be clawless and reduced to one or two segments; simple eyes absent or one to six pairs on sides of head near mouth parts; labial palpi rarely more than two segments; head rarely embedded in prothorax or concealed by thoracic segments from dorsal view (Psephenidae); proleg(s), without distinct hooks, may occur on the last or what appears to be the next to the last abdominal segment (Lymexylidae-Hylecoetus); shape variable, frequently mid-abdominal segments enlarged or body is c-shaped; crenulations on dorsum of abdominal segments, if present, usually less than four per segment; many setae or spines may occur on thorax and abdomen; one pair of thoracic spiracles on mesothorax (occasionally on prothorax) and eight abdominal spiracles on segments one to eight, rarely absent; aquatic species may possess gills on one or more abdominal segments or the last segment(s) may be elongated . . . . **Coleoptera**

L10,(5).— Thoracic legs with one claw, stout spines about or on base of claw may creat impression that two claws exist 13

L10a.   Thoracic legs with two distinct (usually movable) claws 11

L11. —— A distinct labrum and usually a clypeus <u>absent</u> or invisible from dorsal aspect (may be concealed below the cephalic margin of the head). 12

L11a.   A distinct labrum and clypeus <u>present</u>; biting mouth parts conspicuous and independent, especially the mandibles; labial palpi possess three or more segments; species may possess prolegs with hooks on caudal segment or a long, median, setiferous tail (tenth segment); gills (sometimes segmented), spiracles and fleshy filaments may occur on most abdominal segments . . . . **Neuroptera**

L12. —— Mandibles and maxillae on each side united to form a blood sucking organ; maxillary palpi absent; labial palpi usually absent; nonaquatic predators . . . . **Neuroptera**

L12a.   Mandibles and maxillae are separate structures and chewing type; each mandible may possess an internal blood duct or groove along its entire mesal surface; maxillary palpi and two (rarely three) segmented labial palpi always present; among terrestrial and some aquatic species urogomphi (cerci) may occur on the ninth segment or dorsal spurs on the fifth segment; among aquatic species the caudal segment(s) may be elongated and tubelike or (and) gills may be present . . . . **Coleoptera**

L13,(10).—Mouth parts needlclike, several times longer than the head and project cephalad along the meson; seven pairs of respiratory filaments on abdominal segments; live on fresh water sponges; f.g.l. under 3 mm. . . . . **Sisyridae, Neuroptera**

L13a.   Mouth parts normal chewing type with distinct opposable mandibles 14

L14. —— Antennae and frequently maxillae absent or very inconspicuous; mandibles small or of average size; simple eyes wanting, single, several in a close cluster or represented by pigment spots; thoracic legs five segmented, trochanter frequently subdivided; tarsal claws single, sometimes with spurs on or about base of claw creating the impression that two claws occur on some of the legs especially those on the mesothorax; distinct hooks, usually located on prolegs, occur at caudal end of abdomen; functional spiracles absent; gills, usually fingerlike or branched, may be present on the thoracic and abdominal segments; aquatic, many live in cases . . . . Trichoptera

L14a. Antennae, mandibles and maxillae usually present and of average size; simple eyes absent or several (rarely one) may be present; head frequently depressed; thoracic legs generally with less than five segments, usually elbowed at two or more joints and may possess stout spines at base of claws; anal prolegs, if present, without hooks; paired urogomphi may occur at caudal end; spiracles usually present on mesothorax (rarely on prothorax) and on eight abdominal segments among terrestrial species; body shape variable including c-shape; aquatic species may possess rudimentary spiracles, gills may occur on several abdominal segments or only on the last segment; caudal end may be pointed or tubelike . . . . Coleoptera

L15,(1). —Larva posseses a distinct, partial or completely sclerotized head, usually pigmented which may be deeply embedded in prothorax 17

L15a. Larva without a distinct, sclerotized or pigmented head 16

L16. —— Mouth parts may be reduced to a pair of opposable (or nearly so) sharp pointed mandibles or to paired sclerotized or pigmented plates or lines fused with the cephalic segment or to mere fleshy sensoria; larvae frequently c-shaped, light in color and more or less pointed at both ends with greatest diameter in mid-region; inconspicuous spiracles usually present on one, two or three thoracic segments and on five to eight abdominal segments; many are parasites of insects or live within plant tissue or in cells or nests constructed by adults . . . . Hymenoptera

L16a. Mouth parts usually one to two (parallel not opposable) median, sclerotized, dark-colored, decurved hook(s) usually embedded in the cephalic segment or the mouth parts may be reduced to an external opening; the shape of the larva may be orthosomatic, spindlelike, c-shaped, acariform or peglike with the caudal end blunt and the cephalic end pointed; abdomen usually with seven to nine segments, if ten segments occur a so-called median "breast bone" may be present on the ventral aspect of the thorax; pairs of spiracles may occur on the prothorax (usually) and on the surface of, or deeply within a spiracular cavity on the caudal or dorsal aspect of the last or next to last abdominal segment; among aquatic or moisture loving species pairs of prolegs, with or without hooks, or two or more fleshy pseudopods per segment may occur on some or all abdominal segments; also spiracles are usually absent and gills may occur on the caudal end or (and) the caudal segment(s) may be elongated and serve as a breathing tube. . . . . Diptera

L17,(15) —Head capsule complete, distinct, sclerotized and frequently pigmented, rarely embedded in prothorax 21

L17a. Head capsule incomplete, caudal or lateral portions absent, membranous or weakly sclerotized, also may be deeply embedded in prothorax 18

L18. —— Mouth parts of normal biting type with opposable mandibles and maxillae; all mouth parts, labrum and antennae usually distinct 20

L18a. Mouth parts greatly reduced and modified so that only opposable mandibles or parallel mouth hooks may exist or sclerotized mouth parts may be entirely absent; labrum and antennae usually wanting 19

L19. —— Mouth parts parallel or highly modified, frequently reduced in size and structure or apparently absent; sclerotized portions of the head may be elongated, flattened, irregular or reduced in area, also may be retracted into prothorax; mandibles, if present, usually pointed or decurved and move up and down, also they are usually located between and parallel with the larger maxillae and adjacent to the elongated median labrum-epipharynx; body shape usually straight, frequently spindlelike; spiracles absent or may occur on the prothorax or on a caudal segment or on most abdominal segments except the last. . . . . Diptera

L19a. Mouth parts may be reduced to a pair of opposable (or nearly so) sharp pointed mandibles or to paired sclerotized or pigmented plates or lines fused with the cephalic segment or to mere fleshy sensoria and a mouth opening; larvae frequently c-shaped, light in color, usually more or less pointed at both ends especially the cephalic end with mid-region of greatest diameter; inconspicuous spiracles usually present on one, two or three thoracic segments and five to eight abdominal segments; larvae are para-sites of arthropods, live within plant tissue or within cells or nests constructed by adults . . . . Hymenoptera

L20,(18).—Labrum a single free lobe located between or covering proximal portions of the mandi-bles; some species show an enlarged thorax especially the prothorax; spiracles usual-ly present on mesothorax and on eight abdominal segments; ambulatorial warts may oc-cur on abdomen; many species live in wood . . . . Coleoptera

L20a. Labrum and sometimes clypeus somewhat subdivided laterad into three parts with groups of setae or spines usually present on the two lateral portions; head usually deeply retracted within prothorax; large spiracles and gill-like structures may be present at caudal end; larval habitat frequently aquatic or semiaquatic . . . . . Diptera

L21,(17).—Head capsule directed distinctly cephalad, prognathous (for more details read L5). . 25

L21a. Head capsule directed ventrad, hypognathous, or somewhat cephaloventrad (for more details read L5a); if unsatisfactory try L25 to L28 22

L22. —— Abdominal segments usually with one or more distinct cephalocaudal (longitudinal) folds or depressions on the lateral and ventrolateral aspects; body somewhat c-shaped; mouth parts chewing type, well developed and sclerotized, especially the mandibles; simple eyes absent or more than one pair usually present; one pair of spiracles on pro-thorax or mesothorax and usually eight pairs of fairly conspicuous spiracles on ab-dominal segments one to eight; last segment of abdomen may possess a sclerotized dorsal plate with spines; most species live within or on plants or plant products . . . . Coleoptera

L22a. Abdominal segments usually without distinct cephalocaudal (longitudinal) folds, depres-sions or sutures on the lateral or lateroventral aspects; if folds or depressions appear to exist then two or three spiracles may occur on thorax or the caudal spiracles are distinctly larger than the remaining abdominal spiracles 23

L23. —— Adfrontal areas and protruding spinnerets absent; ventral prolegs with crochets or hooks usually absent 24

L23a. Adfrontal areas and protruding spinnerets, present; ventral prolegs with crochets us-ually present; antennae, if present, arise from membranous areas at base of mandi-bles; one or more (usually six) pairs of simple eyes may occur on a rounded or de-pressed head-capsule, shape may be somewhat cyphosomatic . . . . Lepidoptera

L24. —— Chewing mouth parts (at least opposable mandibles) usually present but not heavily sclerotized; one pair of simple eyes or eye spots may occur; thoracic and abdominal segments usually light colored and not heavily sclerotized; larvae may be pointed at one or both ends and c-shaped; inconspicuous spiracles usually present on one, two or three thoracic segments and on most abdominal segments; larvae live within plant tis-sue, are parasites or insects or live in mud, wax, or paperlike cells constructed by the adults . . . . Hymenoptera

L24a. Mouth parts of chewing type, possessing opposable mandibles with or without mouth brushes or they are so modified in shape that they show a median projection and parallel parts (mandibles and maxillae); body may be long and slender or c-shaped; among ter-restrial forms spiracles may be present on prothorax or mesothorax and at caudal end on one of the last three segments; if spiracles occur on several abdominal segments the caudal pair is much larger than others; aquatic or moisture loving species usually possess the following: opposable biting mouth parts frequently with mouth brushes, a false leg on prothorax and prolegs occasionally on some of the abdominal segments, gills and (or) an elongated breathing tube and frequently few or many setae (brushes or tufts) at caudal end of the abdomen . . . . Diptera

L25,(21).—Head capsule usually cylindrical, round (boxlike) or depressed type 26

L25a Head capsule variable in shape (cone or bell-shape, peglike, very irregular or united with the prothorax), if united five or more conspicuous median ventral suckers exist on the ventral aspect; the head may be deeply embedded in prothorax or exserted, if ex-serted, it may be two or more times longer than broad, distinctly pointed and heavily sclerotized; among nonaquatic species the mouth parts are usually parallel and move up and down or they may be highly modified or rudimentary; among some aquatic or semiaquatic species the mouth parts may be mandiblate with opposable mandibles and mouthbrushes; prolegs, single or paired, may exist on the prothorax or on the last abdominal segment or both; among some species two to six pseudopods or prolegs per segment occur on several abdominal segments; spiracles may be absent or inconspicuous at the caudal end; gills may occur on one or more segments; also the last abdominal segment may be elongated or a distinct respiratory tube may exist and a few or many long setae may be present . . . . Diptera

L26. —— Abdomen with a pair of short subanal processes at caudal end of last (tenth) segment; body elongated, distinctly slender and straight or slightly curved; head usually light in color; antennae and biting mouth parts present; spiracles, if present, inconspicuous; several long setae present on each thoracic and abdominal segment; length less than 10 mm. . . . . Siphonaptera

L26a. Not the combination of characters under 26 27

L27. —— Protruding spinneret on labium; antennae arise from membranous area at base of mandibles; mouth parts mandibulate, opposable mandibles may be well developed and exserted with distal margins somewhat serrated; head and body usually depressed; ventral prolegs, if present, possess crochets; adfrontal areas and ocelli inconspicuous or absent; most species are leaf, fruit or bark miners . . . . Lepidoptera

L27a. No spinneret on labium; antennae, if present, usually arising from epicranium, not from membrane between the mandible and the head capsule 28

L28. —— Mouth parts usually distinctly mandibulate with opposable mandibles; if mouth parts are highly modified and the head is depressed and broad then the cephalic margin of the head may appear to be serrated; abdomen with nine or ten segments frequently highly pigmented and sclerotized; spiracles usually present on mesothorax and eight abdominal segments; body may be straight, depressed or even somewhat c-shaped . . . . Coleoptera

L28a. Mouth parts mandibulate and opposable or mouth hooks may be parallel; abdomen usually with eight or nine segments (among some species each abdominal segment may show two or three subdivisions, called annulets); frequently long and slender; spiracles usually occur on prothorax or mesothorax and on one of the last three caudal segments; when spiracles occur on most abdominal segments and thorax, those on thorax and at caudal end of abdomen are usually larger than the remainder; rows of scattered knobs, spinelike structures or fleshy protuberances may occur on abdomen and thorax; among aquatic or moisture loving species mouth brushes may be present; spiracles are usually absent or inconspicuous; gill-like structures and (or) an elongated breathing tube may occur at caudal end; false (proleg) legs may occur on the prothorax or on a few abdominal segments; a few or many long setae (brushes, tufts, etc.) may be found near caudal end; caudal segments may be elongated . . . . Diptera

P - KEY TO THE ORDERS OF PUPAE AND PUPARIA OF THE ENDOPTERYGOTA,
(Pupae of male Coccidae and the so-called propupae and pupae of Thysanoptera also included)

P1. —— Appendages (enclosed in cases) completely or partially visible on exterior, they may be free or fused to the body wall 2

P1a. No appendages (enclosed in cases) visible on exterior; the ectal surface is a larval exuvium called a puparium, it consists of sclerotized, concentric rings or is smooth and leathery and contains an exarate pupa with one pair of wings or a hibernating larva; scars or remnants of thoracic and caudal spiracles usually visible; many puparia have a barrellike shape with blunt ends; coarctate type; fig. O12 . . . . Diptera

P2. —— All appendages free and rarely fused together or to the body wall at any point; the appendages are usually in a fixed position; exarate type 4

P2a. All appendages fused (completely or nearly so) with each other and to the body wall on the lateral and ventral aspects of the thorax; obtect type 3

P3. —— One pair of wings present (see P5a), head and thorax usually combined into one large area; among aquatic species a pair of distinct respiratory organs (gills, tubes or projecting structures) occur on the cephalodorsal region of the combined head and thorax; fig. O11 . . . . Diptera

P3a. Two prominent pairs of wings present and closely wrapped about the lateral and ventral aspects of the thorax, the outer pair (mesothoracic) conceals the greater portion of the inner pair (metathoracic), among a few species the wings are rudimentary or absent; spiracles usually present on the mesothorax and on some of the abdominal segments, respiratory organs, other than spiracles, absent on the cephalodordal region; paired galeae of the maxillae usually elongated and adjacent to the ventromeson; antennae usually adjacent to the ventral margins of the wings; functional or prominent mandibles absent except among the Micropterygoidea; usually found within a cocoon, or an earthen cell or suspended from some object by a cremaster and silken threads; fig. O10. . . . . Lepidoptera

P4,(2). — Body distinctly compressed; length under 3 millimeters; prothorax (pronotum) conspicuous; wings absent; antennae minute; compound eyes absent; mandibles long and slender; fig. O14 . . . . Siphonaptera

P4a. Body rounded or depressed, never strongly compressed; antennae and wing rudiments usually prominent 5

P5. —— Two distinct pairs of wings present. Among Curculionidae only one pair may be present, fig. O9, E-F. If wings are absent the mouth parts are distinctly mandibulate and a distinct constriction exists near the cephalic end of the abdomen or the mouth parts are in the form of a cone attached to the caudoventral aspect of the head and fitted for rasping and sucking 7

P5a. One pair of wings present. If a very small second pair exists (halteres) then pupae usually possess one or two spiracular tubes on the thorax 6

P6. —— Mouth parts present, usually not mandibulate; head and thorax usually distinct; ovipositors, cerci and a median anal projection usually absent; pupa may be enclosed within a puparium; exarate type: fig. O11. . . . . Diptera

P6a. Mouth parts absent; front legs project forward beneath head; length usually less than 3 mm.; pupae usually enclosed in molted skins or under a waxy covering . . . . male Coccidae, Homoptera

P7. —— Mouth parts mandibulate type possessing opposable mandibles, also may possess structures used for licking or lapping 9

P7a. Mouth parts of sucking type; mandibles parallel, long and needlelike or mouth parts in the form of a cone attached to the caudo-ventral aspect of the head 8

P8. —— Mandibles long and slender structures parallel with the meson and fitted for sucking on fresh water sponges; aquatic . . . . Sisyridae, Neuroptera

P8a. All mouth parts in the form of a cone located on the meson and attached to the caudoventral aspect of the head; antennae short stublike structures (propupa) or elongated cases covering the cephalic and lateral (or ventral) portion of the head (pupae); may be active but takes no food; length usually under 5 mm., terrestrial; fig. O2, E-F. . . . . Thysanoptera

P9.   —— Mouth parts for chewing and licking; opposable mandibles present, also a median (single or bifurcate) lobe consisting of parts of the maxillae and labium may be very prominent; distal segments or tip ends of the twelve or more segmented antennae which are longer than the head are frequently adjacent to and parallel with the meson; compound eyes usually distinct; mesothoracic wings (cases) larger and with more veins than metathoracic wings (cases), also not elytralike; dorsal aspect of mesothorax usually prominent and larger than the prothorax; a distinct constriction usually present between thorax and abdomen; paired ovipositors frequently visible on ventral aspect of female pupae; fig. O13 . . . . Hymenoptera

P9a.   Mouth parts mandibulate only. No prominent median (single or bifurcate) mouth appendage between the mandibles or paired ovipositors present 10

P10.   —— Antennae usually eleven segmented, shorter than the head and far removed from the meson, if elongated they are much longer than the body of the pupa and possess several stout segments; the cases enclosing the mouth parts are more or less smooth and conceal the detailed structure of the adult appendages; labial palpi are one or two segmented, rarely three segmented; wings (cases) of the mesothorax elytralike and with few veins; prothorax (pronotum) usually distinct; if the head projects forward or ventrad like a beak, inconspicuous chewing mouth parts occur at the cephalic end and elbowed antennae arise from the mid-lateral portion of the beak; fig. O9. . . . . Coleoptera

P10a.   Antennae long always with twelve or more segments; wing cases similar in structure (not size), not elytralike 11

P11.   —— Head capsule elongated with prominent mandibulate mouth parts on the cephalic end of the projected head; antennae with sixteen or more segments arise from the epicranium near the compound eyes . . . . Mecoptera

P11a.   Head capsule round or depressed, not distinctly elongated 12

P12.   —— Mandibles usually large, stout, frequently distinctly dentate and do not distinctly overlap or cross each other; the maxillae and labium may show distinct segmentation and sclerotized areas; usually the maxillary palpi, if present, are five segmented and the labial palpi, usually present, are three segmented; prothorax (pronotum) prominent; fig. O14, A-B, ... Neuroptera

P12a.   Mandibles short, stout, curved and nearly cylindrical, they usually project somewhat cephalad and cross each other; prothorax small; fingerlike or filamentous gills frequently present on thorax and abdomen; usually aquatic and located in silken cases covered with sand stones or trash. (Pupae of the Micropterygidae and Eriocraniidae of the Lepidoptera possessing functional mandibles may trace to this group, however, they are nonaquatic and not over five millimeters long); fig. O14, C-D . . . . Trichoptera

A CONDENSED KEY TO
ORDERS FOR LARVAE OF HOLOMETABOLOUS (ENDOPTERYGOTA) INSECTS.

This key, with slight changes, is a contribution from the Division of Insect Identification, Bureau of Entomology and Plant Quarantine, U. S. D. A. Washington, D. C. It is designed for the identification of larvae in the last feeding instar or, in the Lepidoptera, in all instars.

1. —— With only two pairs of spiracles, on prothorax and abdominal segment VIII or IX; legs absent; mandibles usually in the form of decurved hooks, and not opposable, i.e., not movable in the horizontal plane . . . . (part) Diptera

1a. Usually with more than two pairs of spiracles, less commonly with only one pair; legs present or absent; mandibles usually opposable or, rarely, modified for sucking . . . 2

2. —— Thoracic legs present, usually sclerotized and segmented, though sometimes (Hymenoptera, Coleoptera) fleshy and not distinctly segmented 3

2a. Thoracic legs absent 12

3. —— Antennae situated in articulating membrane at base of mandible, no sclerotized ridge or area between antenna and mandible (except Hepialidae); with distinct, protruded spinneret on labium; eyes, if present, never of closely combined elements having the appearance of compound eyes; prolegs, when present, with crochets (at least on some of the prolegs); thoracic legs with one claw, and fewer than five segments; no sucking disk at end of abdomen . . . . (most), Lepidoptera

3a. Antennae usually situated on epicranium (rarely absent or invisible), if in articulating membrane, at base of mandible, thoracic legs often with two claws or the spinneret is absent; eyes sometimes of closely combined elements having the appearance of compound eyes; prolegs, when present, without crochets; thoracic legs sometimes five-segmented; sucking disk sometimes present at end of abdomen 4

4. —— Without spinneret on labium 5

4a. With spinneret on labium 11

5. —— Maxillary palpus absent; maxilla modified as a simple appendage which is part of a sucking tube when in apposition with mandible; (mouth parts of a sucking type; no prolegs present on middle abdominal segments; terrestrial and with tarsi bearing two claws except in Sisyridae, which are aquatic and possess abdominal gills and one tarsal claw). . . . . Neuroptera

5a. Maxillary palpus present; maxilla not modified as above; (mouth parts usually of a distinctly chewing type). 6

6. —— Labrum present and free; labial palpus three-segmented, sclerotized; thoracic legs five-segmented, each terminated by two tarsal claws; no prolegs present on middle abdominal segments; (post-cephalic ring usually present anterior to prosternum; sometimes aquatic, if so, abdomen bears lateral filaments and is terminated by either a median filament or paired grasping hooks). 7

6a. Combination of characters not as above;(tarsus with a single claw except in some Coleoptera) 8

7. —— Terrestrial insects, without lateral filaments . . . . (Raphidiodea), Neuroptera

7a. Aquatic insects, with conspicuous long lateral filaments . . . (Megaloptera), Neuroptera

8. —— Labrum present and free; thoracic legs five-segmented and terminated by one tarsal claw (a prominent spur often at base of single claw); no prolegs present on middle abdominal segments; (almost always aquatic; gills frequently present; abdomen almost always terminated by paired grasping hooks) . . . . (part), Trichoptera

8a. Combination of characters not as above; (thoracic legs less than five-segmented except in some Coleoptera) 9

9. —— Labrum present and free; thoracic legs three-segmented and terminated by one tarsal claw; eyes sometimes of more than 12 elements resembling a compound eye; abdominal segments I to IX bearing small prolegs, sometimes vestigial on segments I and II; (apex of abdomen often with ventrocaudal surface in the form of a sucking disk composed of anus combined with an eversible anal fork) . . . (Panorpidae and Bittacidae), Mecoptera

26

9a.   Combination of characters not as above; eyes never of more than 12 elements or re-
       sembling a compound eye 10
10. —— Prothoracic legs small, directed ventrally; mesothoracic and metathoracic legs much
       larger, extending ventrolaterally in striking contrast to prothoracic pair; prolegs ab-
       sent on middle abdominal segments; thoracic legs three-segmented and with one tarsal
       claw; labrum present and free; general form curved, scarbaeiform . . . .
       . . . . (Boreidae), Mecoptera
10a.   Combination of characters not as above . . . . (part), Coleoptera
11,(4a).___Thoracic legs long, with five segments exclusive of the claw, trochanter sometimes di-
       vided also; prolegs absent on middle abdominal segments; pronotum with distince scler-
       otized plate; abdomen usually with terminal grasping hooks; gills often present; (labial
       palpus typically with two segments) . . . . (part), Trichoptera
11a.   Legs short with at most four segments exclusive of the claw; prolegs usually present
       on middle abdominal segments; pronotum rarely with sclerotized plate; abdomen with-
       out terminal grasping hooks; gills absent; (labial palpus typically with three segments).
       . . . .(Symphyta), Hymenoptera
12,(2a).— With protruding or conical spinneret on labium, or if undeveloped (early and flat stage
       miners) antennae adjacent to mandibles, without a sclerotized area or ridge between an-
       tenna and mandible . . . . (part), Lepidoptera
12a.   Without protruding spinneret on labium (in Hymenoptera the silk is ejected through a slit
       or pore); antennae not adjacent to mandibles, either separated by a sclerotized ridge or
       comparatively remote from mandibles 13
13. —— Abdomen usually with 8 or 9 distinct segments or segmentation indistinct, if with 10 seg-
       ments (Cecidomyidae) larva without a distinct head capsule and usually with a sclerotized
       "breast-bone" on second thoracic segment; with a complete or incomplete head capsule;
       (sometimes with only one pair of spiracles) . . . .(part), Diptera
13a.   Abdomen usually with 10 distinct segments, rarely with fewer than 10 or with 11 (Siphon-
       aptera), but head capsule always distinct. 14
14. —— Abdomen with 11 distinct segments and a pair of subanal processes . . . . . Siphonaptera
14a.   Abdomen with less than 11 distinct segments and without subanal processes 15
15. —— Maxillary palpus with two or more segments (except Platypodidae, with one segment, but
       pleura of abdominal segments subdivided); thorax with one pair of spiracles . . . .
       . . . . (part), Coleoptera
15a.   Maxillary palpus unsegmented, frequently reduced to a sensorium; thorax with one or two
       pairs of spiracles . . . . (Apocrita and Orussidae), Hymenoptera

Note: This key has not been subjected to students for criticism. It may need revision.

EXPLANATION OF FIGURES O1-O14, L1-L58 and H1 to H12

Except for a few figures, namely some on plates O6 and L1 to L8 all of the drawings were made by the author from preserved specimens. Almost all larvae or their parts are drawn to a given size. The actual length of each specimen figured is stated near each drawing. Drawings of entire larvae are omitted for many species. In general only those portions which show diagnostic characteristics are included.

So far as possible the species figured of a given family are grouped together and the families, especially among the Lepidoptera, for the most part are arranged alphabetically. The figures representing nymphs, naiads, pupae and puparia were chosen at random from common insects. Among plates L1 to L58, including all larvae of the Lepidoptera, plates L1 to L8 show the essential external characteristics of caterpillars and figures L9 to L58 show characteristic structures of many common and important species. Among Hymenoptera Figure H1 shows the characteristic structures found on most Symphyta. Figures H1 to H5 are chiefly drawings of right and left mandibles while figures H6 to H11 are drawings of larvae of Symphyta and figure H12 larvae of Apocrita.

For each species figured the following sequence in the explanation is presented the scientific name, common name (if such exists), full grown length, color and shape of living specimens, distinctive morphological characteristics food habits and in many cases citations to literature which describe the larval stages. For explanation of abbreviations used on figures see page 278.

NYMPHS
EXPLANATION OF FIGURES O1, A-G
ORTHOPTERA, CORRODENTIA AND ISOPTERA

Figures A and B. Orthoptera, Locustidae. An early instar nymph of a short-horned grasshopper showing the characteristic position of the wing pads (buds). Among grasshopper nymphs the metathoracic wing pads cover or partially conceal the mesothoracic pair. In the adult the reverse position exists.

Figure A. Dorsal view of nymph.

Figure B. Lateral view of the thorax showing the wing pads.

Figures C and D. Orthoptera, Gryllidae, Gryllotalpa hexadactyla Perty. mole cricket nymph.

Figure C. Dorsal view of a wingless, early instar nymph.

Figure D. Lateral view of the left, prothoracic, fossorial leg of a late instar nymph.

Figure E. Orthoptera, Blattidae. Lateral view of a cockroach nymph.

Figure F. Corrodentia. Dorsal view of a psocid nymph infesting plum foliage.

Figure G. Isoptera. Dorsal view of a late instar termite nymph possessing wing pads.

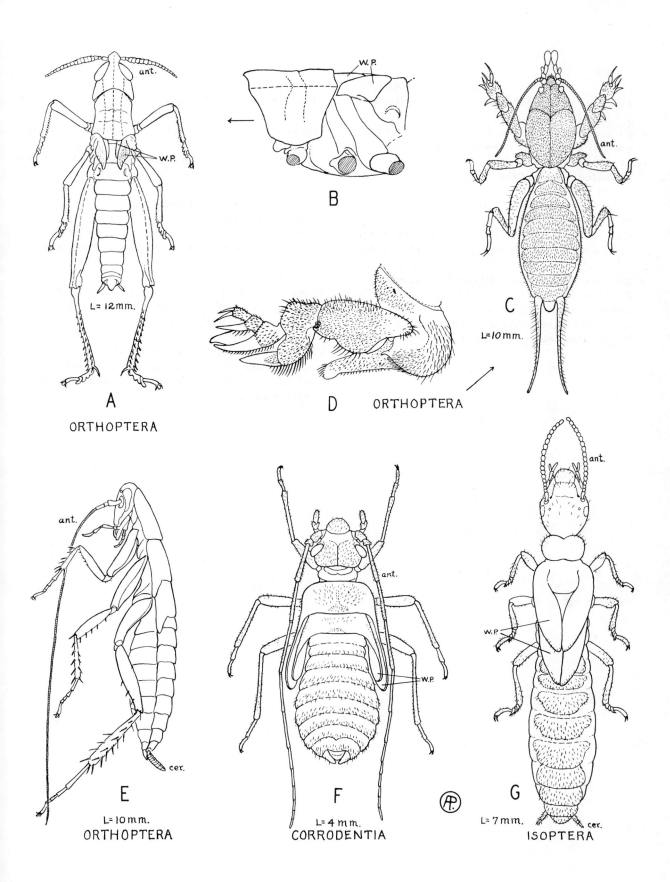

A
ORTHOPTERA
L=12mm.

B

C
ORTHOPTERA
L=10mm.

D ORTHOPTERA

E
L=10mm.
ORTHOPTERA

F
L=4mm.
CORRODENTIA

G
L=7mm.
ISOPTERA

NYMPHS
EXPLANATION OF FIGURES 02, A-F
DERMAPTERA, THYSANURA; EMBIOPTERA AND THYSANOPTERA

Figure A. Dermaptera, Forficulina. Dorsal view of a wingless earwig nymph found in greenhouses. Note the pincerlike claws, modified cerci, at the caudal end.

Figure B. Thysanura, Japygidae. Ventral view of a Japyx nymph. In addition to the forcep-like cerci at the caudal end paired abdominal styli are present on most of the segments.

Figure C. Embioptera, Gynembia tarsalia Ross found in California on grass slopes and hillsides in areas where wet winters and dry summers exist. Dorsal view showing the enlarged first tarsal segment of the prothoracic legs.

Figures D-F. Thysanoptera, Tubulifera, Acanthothrips, sp. Dorsal view of the three last nymphal instars of a common thrips found under loose bark of deciduous trees.

Figure D. The last feeding nymphal instar, frequently called a larva, color red or orange when alive. The lateral view of the head shows the cone-shaped mouth parts and their position.

Figure E. The first nonfeeding nymphal instar, sometimes called a propupa. Note the short antennae and wing pads.

Figure F. The last nonfeeding nymphal instar, sometimes called a pupa. Note the antennae, which surround the head, and the well developed wing pads.

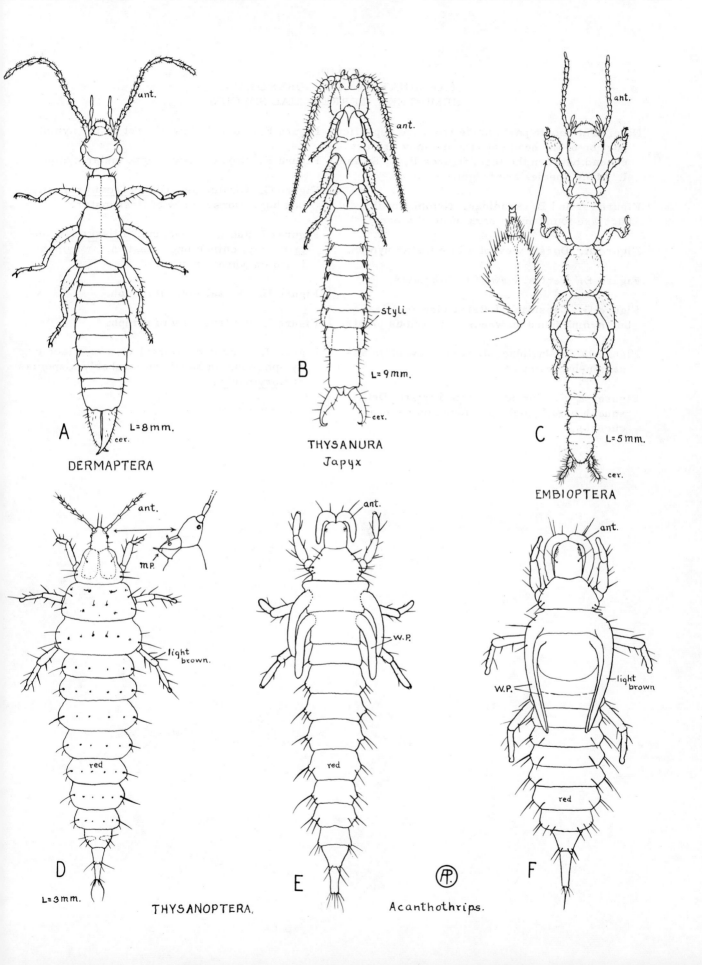

A

DERMAPTERA

ant.

cer.

L=8 mm.

B

THYSANURA

Japyx

ant.

styli

L=9 mm.

cer.

C

EMBIOPTERA

ant.

L=5 mm.

cer.

D

THYSANOPTERA.

ant.

m.p.

light brown.

red

L=3 mm.

E

Acanthothrips.

ant.

W.P.

red

F

ant.

W.P.

light brown

red

NYMPHS
EXPLANATION OF FIGURES O3, A-J
HEMIPTERA, TERRESTRIAL SPECIES

Note. The mouth parts arise from the cephalic portion of the head capsule and may project caudad between the legs, figures B, C, E, and I. Many species are brightly colored.

Figures A and B. Aradidae. Nymphs of flat bugs are found under bark of dead trees.

Figure A. Dorsal view of a late instar nymph.

Figure B. Ventral view of mouth parts.

Figure C. Capsidae. Lateral view of a leaf bug nymph found on weeds and various plants.

Figure D. Reduviidae. Lateral view of an assassin-bug nymph.

Figures E-F. Coreidae. Anasa tristis DeG., squash bug. Nymphs are found on several cucurbs.

Figure E. Dorsal view of first instar nymph.

Figure F. Dorsal view of late instar nymph.

Figure G. Cimicidae. Cimex lectularius L., bed bug. Dorsal view of first instar.

Figures H and I. Lygaeidae. Blissus leucopterus Say, chinch bug. Last instar nymphs found on wheat or corn.

Figure H. Dorsal view of nymph.

Figure I. Ventral view of nymph.

Figure J. Tingidae. Dorsal view of a lace bug nymph found on hawthorn, probably a species of Corythucha.

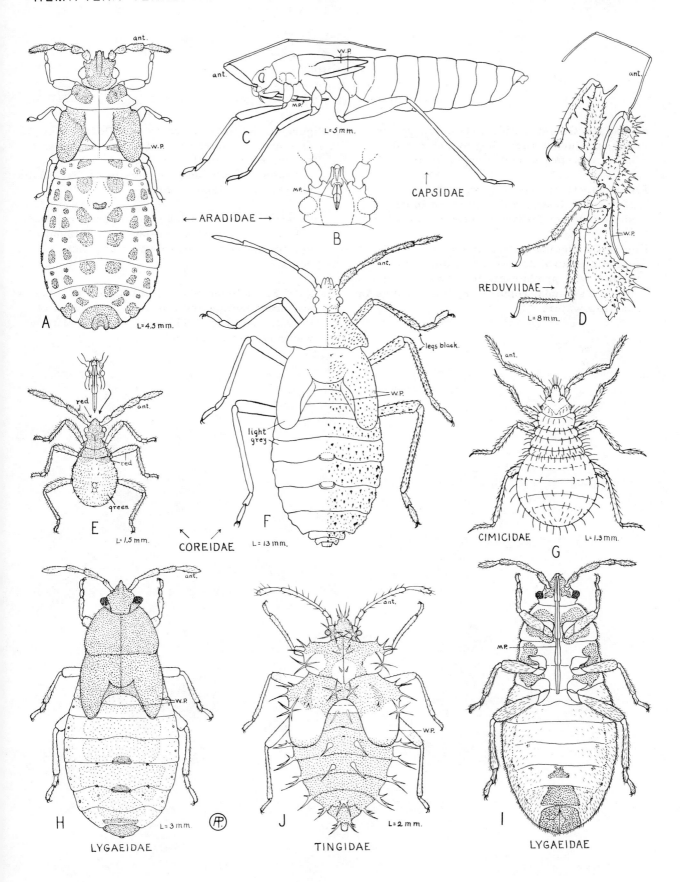

ant.

w.P.

A   L=4.5 mm.

W.P.

ant.

C   L=5mm.

M.P.

M.P.

B

← ARADIDAE →

↑
CAPSIDAE

ant.

W.P.

REDUVIIDAE →

L=8 mm.   D

red

ant.

red

green

E   L=1.5 mm.

ant.

legs black.

W.P.

light grey

COREIDAE   F   L=13 mm.

ant.

CIMICIDAE   L=1.3 mm.

G

ant.

W.P.

H   L=3 mm.   (P)

LYGAEIDAE

ant.

W.P.

J   L=2 mm.

TINGIDAE

M.P.

I

LYGAEIDAE

NYMPHS
EXPLANATION OF FIGURES O4, A-F
HEMIPTERA, AQUATIC SPECIES

Figure A. Gelastocoridae, Gelastocoris sp. Dorsal view of a toad bug nymph found in shallow water of muddy streams or ponds.

Figure B. Corixidae, Corixa sp. Dorsal view of a water-boatman nymph found in deep and shallow water feeding chiefly on plant life.

Figure C. Nepidae, Nepa apiculata Uhl. Dorsal view of an oval depressed, water scorpion nymph with prothoracic legs fitted for grasping and a caudal respiratory tube. Lives in shallow water.

Figure D. Nepidae, Ranatra sp. Dorsal view of an elongated, narrow, grayish brown water scorpion with prothoracic legs fitted for grasping and a caudal respiratory tube. Lives in shallow or deep water.

Figure E. Belostomatidae, Belostoma sp. Dorsal view of a giant water-bug nymph found chiefly in quiet, shallow water of ponds and pools.

Figure F. Notonectidae. Dorsal view of a back-swimmer nymph and a near-ventral view of the head and legs. They are found in shallow water of ponds and pools.

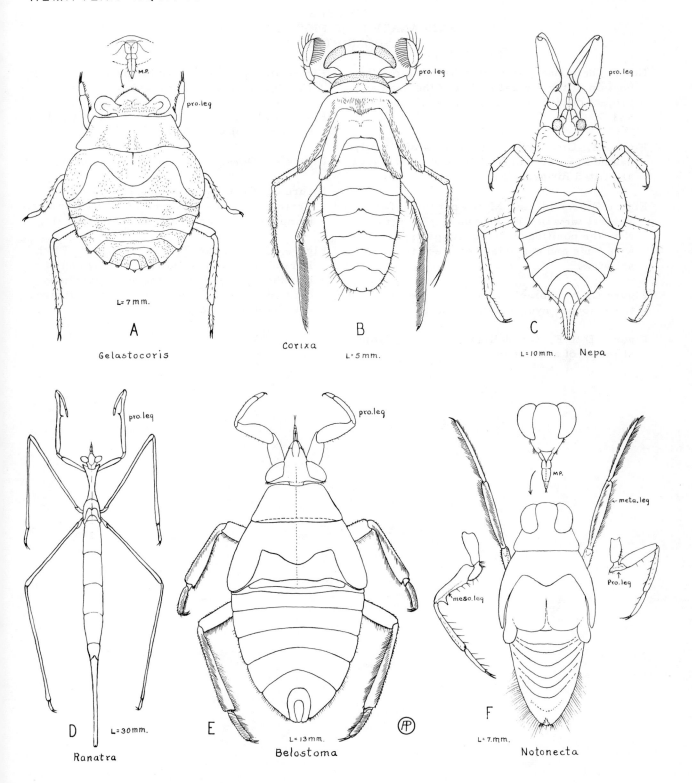

A Gelastocoris L=7mm.

B Corixa L=5mm.

C Nepa L=10mm.

D Ranatra L=30mm.

E Belostoma L=13mm.

F Notonecta L=7mm.

NYMPHS
EXPLANATION OF FIGURES O5, A-H
HOMOPTERA

Note. The mouth parts arise from the caudal portion of the ventral aspect of the head and project caudad between the legs, figures A-D and G.

Figure A. Cicadidae. Lateral view of a newly hatched cicada nymph. The prothoracic legs are fitted for grasping.

Figure B. Aphididae. Myzus persicae, Seely. Ventral view of a green peach aphid nymph. Note the position of the mouth parts, also the wing buds and cornicles best seen from a dorsal view.

Figure C. Membracidae. Lateral view of a tree- hopper nymph found on oak.

Figures D to F. Cicadellidae. The last nymphal instar of a leafhopper.

Figure D. Lateral view of the head and thorax showing the position of the mouth parts.

Figure E. Dorsal and lateral views of the distal portion of a prothoracic leg.

Figure F. Dorsal view showing wing buds.

Figure G. Coccidae, Lepidosaphes ulmi L. Ventral view of a newly hatched, first instar, nymph or crawler of an oyster shell scale.

Figure H. Psyllidae, Trioza tripunctate Fitch. Dorsal view of a partially grown nymph of a blackberry psyllid with the wax secretions omitted. For more details and other figures see Peterson, 1923.

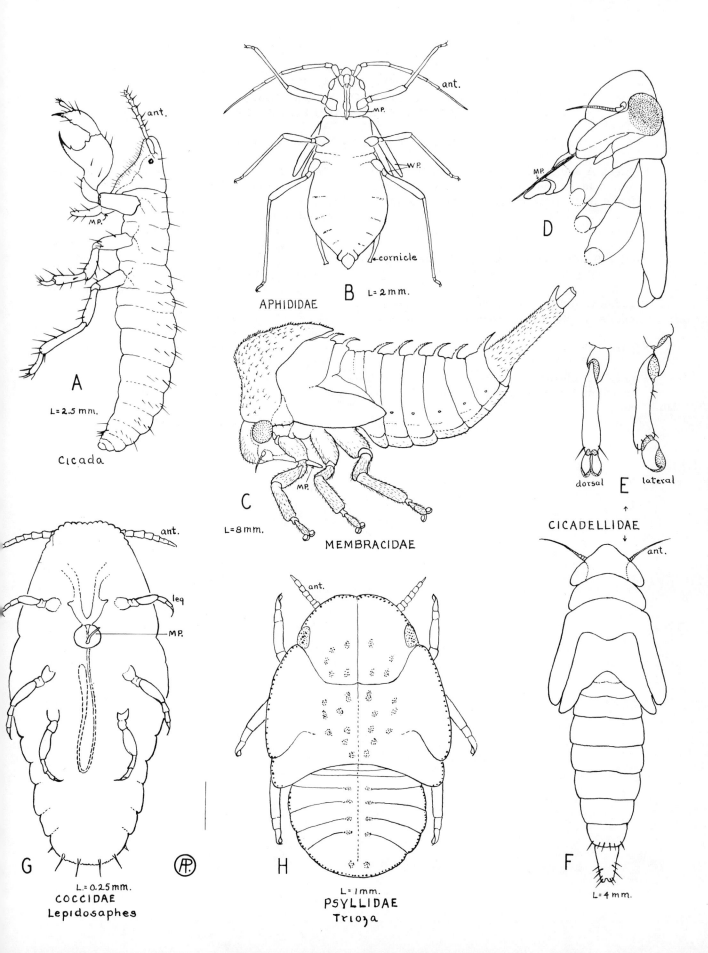

A
L=2.5mm.
Cicada

APHIDIDAE   B   L=2mm.
MP.
ant.
W.P.
cornicle

D
MP.

C
L=8mm.
MP.
MEMBRACIDAE

dorsal   E   lateral
CICADELLIDAE

G
ant.
leg
MP.
L=0.25mm.
COCCIDAE
Lepidosaphes

H
ant.
L=1mm.
PSYLLIDAE
Trioza

F
ant.
L=4mm.

NYMPHS (NAIADS)
EXPLANATION OF FIGURES 06, A-I
EPHEMEROPTERA AND PLECOPTERA

Mayfly and Stonefly Nymphs (naiads).

Figures A and B. Ephemeroptera, <u>Hexagenia</u> sp. A large mud burrowing mayfly nymph found in shallow ponds and stream pools.

Figure A. Dorsal view of a late instar nymph.

Figure B. One enlarged, bifid, tassellike, abdominal gill.

Figures C and D. Ephemeroptera, <u>Chirotonetes</u> sp. A mayfly nymph found in moving water.

Figure C. Lateral view of a late instar nymph.

Figure D. Mesal surface of an enlarged abdominal lamella showing the position of a gill tuft.

Figure E. Plecoptera. Dorsal view of a typical stonefly nymph. From Frison, 1935.

Figures F to I. Plecoptera, <u>Perla</u> sp. A common stonefly nymph found on rocks in swiftly moving water.

Figure F. Ventral view of the head, prothorax and mesothorax showing the position of the tracheal gills.

Figure G. Ventral view of the caudal end showing the two groups of tracheal gills located between the proximal ends of the cerci.

Figure H. An enlarged labium.

Figure I. An enlarged maxilla.

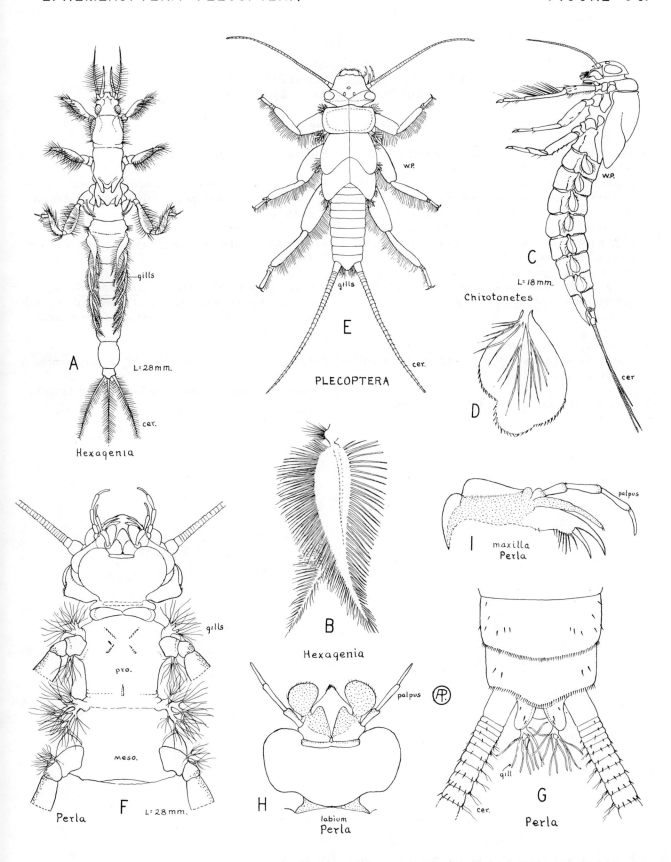

Hexagenia

L=28mm.

gills

cer.

A

PLECOPTERA

gills

cer.

E

Chirotonetes

L=18mm.

W.P.

cer

C

D

B

Hexagenia

Perla

gills

pro.

meso.

F

L=28mm.

palpus

labium

Perla

H

palpus

maxilla

Perla

I

gill

cer.

Perla

G

Dragon-fly Nymphs (naiads)

Note. With very few exceptions nymphs of the Odonata live in water. Many species are found in shallow parts of pools, pond or lakes containing mud bottoms and some vegetation. Other species live near the shore lines of streams. A few occur on rocks in swiftly moving water. The hinged lower lip, which can be extended, is the most striking character of all nymphs of the Odonata. No external gills occur at the caudal end among the nymphs (naiads) of the Anisoptera, dragonflies.

Figures A and B. Gomphidae, Hagenius sp. A distinctly depressed nymph possessing parallel wing pads (buds).

Figure A. Dorsal view of full grown nymph.

Figure B. An enlarged antenna.

Figure C. Gomphidae, Ophiogomphus sp. Dorsal view of nymph possessing divergent wing pads (buds).

Figure D. Gomphidae, Lanthus sp. An enlarged antenna.

Figures E to F. Corduliinae, Epicordulia sp. A nymph possessing parallel wing pads (buds) and dorsal hooks on the meson of the caudal abdominal segments.

Figure E. Dorsal view of a late instar nymph.

Figure F. Lateral view of a late instar nymph.

*Figures taken from Wright and Peterson, 1944, (Plate 1).

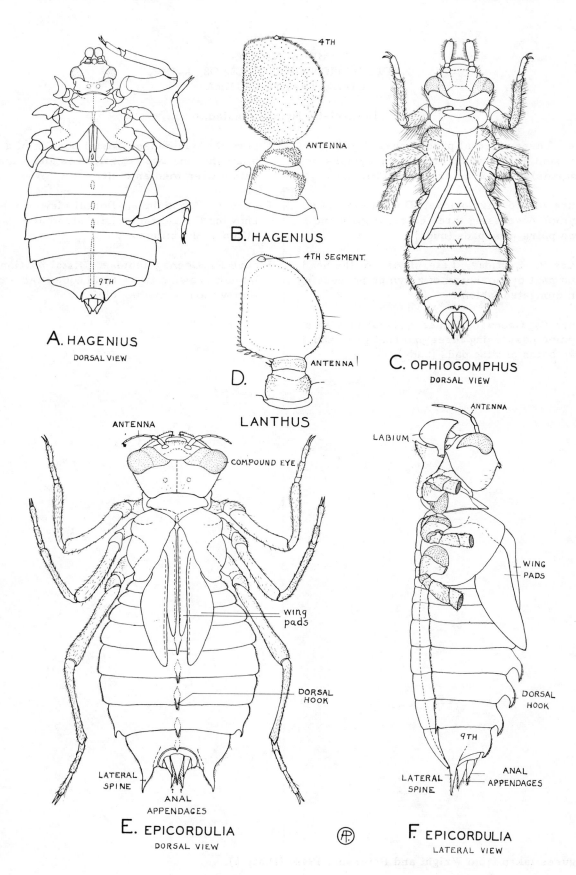

B. HAGENIUS

4TH

ANTENNA

A. HAGENIUS
DORSAL VIEW

4TH SEGMENT

D.
ANTENNA
LANTHUS

C. OPHIOGOMPHUS
DORSAL VIEW

ANTENNA

COMPOUND EYE

wing
pads

DORSAL
HOOK

LATERAL
SPINE

ANAL
APPENDAGES

E. EPICORDULIA
DORSAL VIEW

ANTENNA

LABIUM

WING
PADS

DORSAL
HOOK

9TH

LATERAL
SPINE

ANAL
APPENDAGES

F. EPICORDULIA
LATERAL VIEW

9TH

EXPLANATION OF FIGURES O8, A–F*
ODONATA-ZYGOPTERA

Damsel-fly Nymphs (naiads)

Note. Three external paddle-shaped gills are present at the caudal end among nymphs (naiads) of the Zygotera, damselflies.

Figure A. Coenagrionidae. Dorsal view of a nymph possessing three external gills and two pairs wing pads (buds).

Figure B. Lestidae. Lateral view of the head and part of the thorax of a nymph possessing an elongated labium.

Figure C. Coenagrionidae. Lateral view of a nymph possessing three external gills and two pairs of wing pads (buds).

Figure D. Agrionidae. Distal portion of a labium showing two lateral lobes and a mentum with a deep median cleft.

Figure E. Agrionidae. Dorsal view of a head showing the characteristic structure and position of the antennae.

Figure F. Coenagrionidae. Distal portion of a labium showing two lateral lobes and a mentum without a median cleft.

*Figures taken from Wright and Peterson, 1944, (Plate 6).

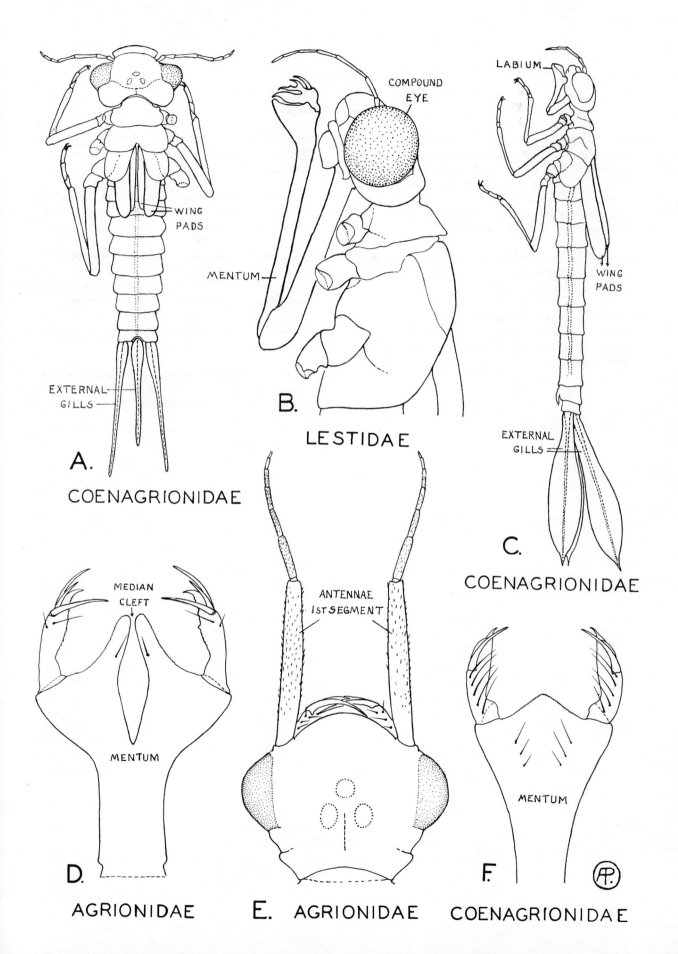

WING PADS

EXTERNAL GILLS

A.

COENAGRIONIDAE

COMPOUND EYE

MENTUM

B.

LESTIDAE

LABIUM

WING PADS

EXTERNAL GILLS

C.

COENAGRIONIDAE

MEDIAN CLEFT

MENTUM

D.

AGRIONIDAE

ANTENNAE 1st SEGMENT

E. AGRIONIDAE

MENTUM

F.

COENAGRIONIDAE

PUPAE
EXPLANATION OF FIGURES O9, A-F
COLEOPTERA

Note. All pupae of the Coleoptera are of typical exarate type with distinct and free antennae, legs and wing cases held close to the body. The wing cases arise from the dorso-lateral aspects of the mesothorax and metathorax and usually extend around the lateral aspects and onto the ventral side.

Figure A. Cerambycidae. Ventral view of a pupa showing the position of the legs, wings, and the elongated antennae.

Figure B. Scarabaeidae, Popillia japonica Newm., Japanese beetle. Ventral view of a pupa showing the typical position of the legs and wings.

Figures C and D. Coccinellidae, Hippodamia convergens Guér., convergent lady beetle pupa.

Figure C. Lateral view showing position and manner of attachment of the pupa to an object and the larval cast skin at its base.

Figure D. Dorsal view showing same.

Figures E and F. Curculionidae, Brachyrhinus sulcatus F. A black vine weevil pupa.

Figure E. Ventral view of pupa showing position of legs and wing cases.

Figure F. Lateral view of pupa showing the mouth parts on the distal portion of the elongated head and the antennae.

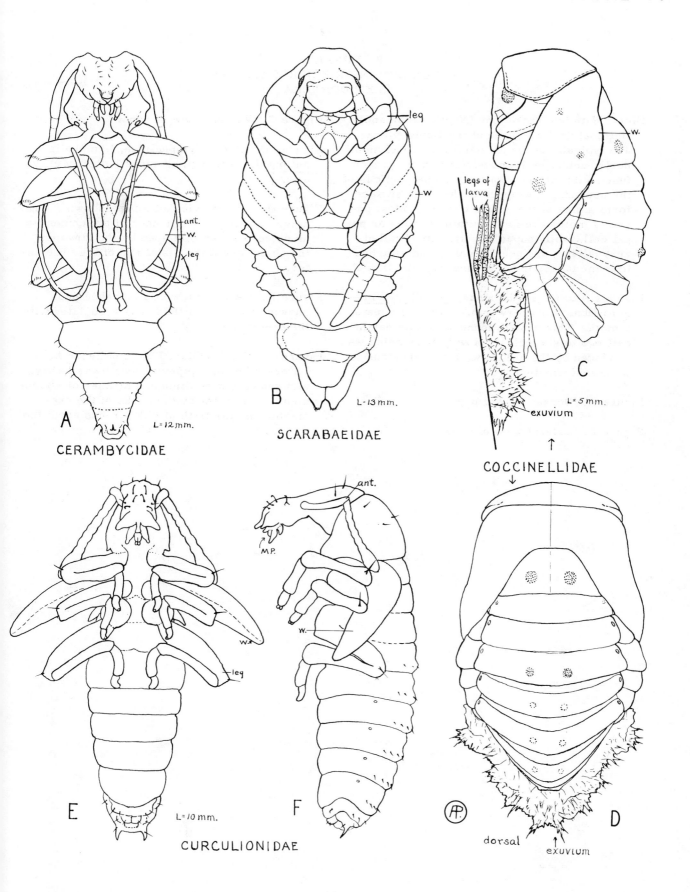

CERAMBYCIDAE

A L=12mm.

ant.
w.
leg

SCARABAEIDAE

B L=13mm.

leg
w.

COCCINELLIDAE

C L=5mm.

w.
legs of larva
exuvium

CURCULIONIDAE

E L=10mm.

w.
leg

F

ant.
M.P.
w.

D

dorsal
exuvium

PUPAE
EXPLANATION OF FIGURES O10, A-F
LEPIDOPTERA

Note. With few exceptions (Nepticulidae and Heliozelidae) all pupae of the Lepidoptera are typically of the obtected type. The mouth parts, antennae, legs and wing cases are fused with the body wall and those portions of the appendages exposed to the ectal surface form a part of the outer covering. Most pupae of moths are found within cocoons or pupal cells while pupae of butterflies, called chrysalides, are usually naked and attached to some object above ground, figures D to F.

Figures A to C. Phalaenidae, Heliothis armigera Hbn., corn earworm. A typical pupa of a moth. This pupa is found within an earthen cell two to six inches below ground which was produced by the full grown larva previous to its transformation.

Figure A. Dorsal view of pupa.

Figure B. Lateral view of pupa.

Figure C. Ventral view of pupa.

Figures D. and E. Nymphalidae, Nymphalis antiopa L., a mourning-cloak butterfly chrysalis.

Figure D. Lateral view of a pupa showing its natural position and manner of attachment to an object and the silk spun by the larva on the object about the distal end of the cremaster.

Figure E. Ventral view of a detached pupa showing position of the hooks associated with the cremaster.

Figure F. Papilionidae, Battus philenor L. Lateral view of a pipevine swallowtail chrysalis showing it position and manner of attachment to an object by the hooks of the cremaster and the girth of silk threads about the thorax.

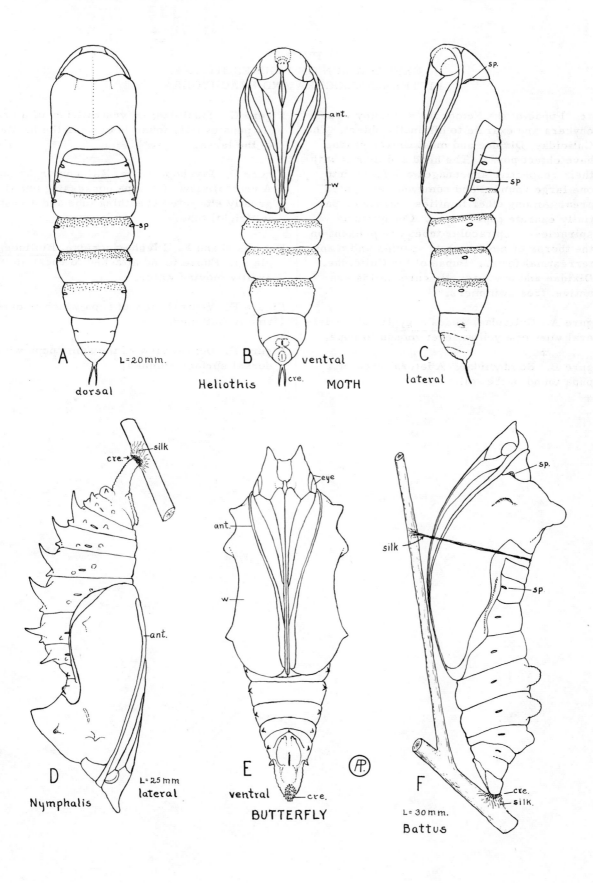

A dorsal   L=20mm.
sp

B Heliothis   ventral   MOTH
ant.
w
cre.

C lateral
sp.
sp

D Nymphalis   lateral   L=2.5mm
cre.   silk
ant.

E ventral   BUTTERFLY
eye
ant.
w
cre.

F Battus   L=30mm.
sp.
silk
sp
cre.
silk.

PUPAE
EXPLANATION OF FIGURES O11, A-F
DIPTERA-NEMOCERA AND BRACHYCERA

Note. Pupae of the Nemocera and many Brachycera are exarate to distinctly obtect. The Culicidae, Dixidae and most Chironomidae have obtect pupae. The head and thorax with their respective appendages are fused into one large rounded and somewhat elongated area. Among other families exarate or partially exarate pupae occur. Conspicuous spiracles or spiracular tubes are present on the thorax of most aquatic species and many terrestrial forms. Pupae of the Culicidae, Dixidae and many aquatic chronomids are active, free swimmers.

Figure A. Culicidae, Aedes aegypti (L), A lateral view of a yellow fever mosquito pupa.

Figure B. Bombyliidae. A lateral view of a pupa found in the soil.

Figure C. Tipulidae. A ventral view of a crane-fly pupa usually found in or near the habitat of the larva.

Figure D. Ptychopteridae, Bittacomorpha sp. A ventral view of a pupa possessing one (left) greatly elongated breathing tube and a vestigial (right) tube.

Figures E and F. Blephariceridae, Biblioceph-ala sp. Pupae found attached to rocks in swiftly moving water.

Figure E. Ventral view of pupa which is distinctly flattened.

Figure F. Dorsal view of the same pupa with dorsal surface humped.

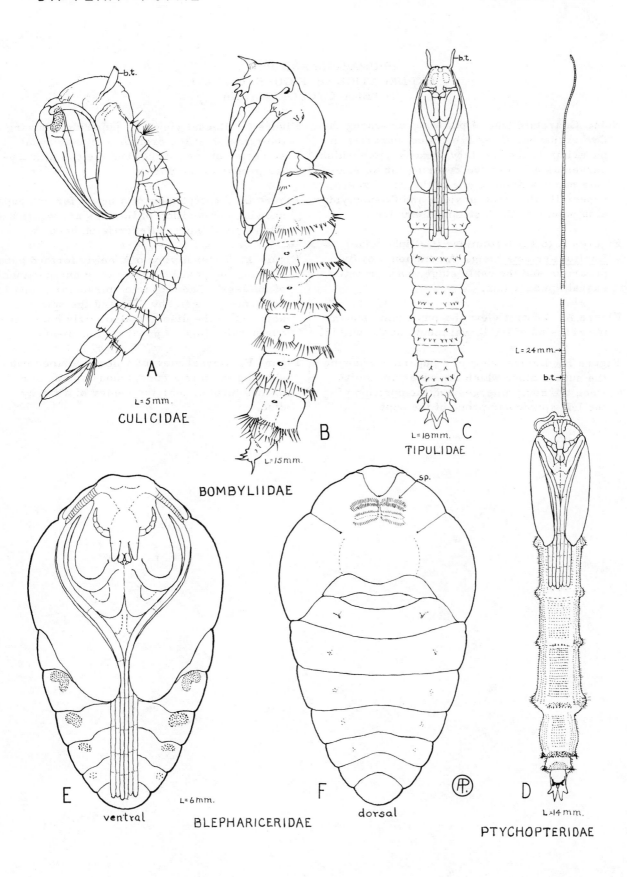

L=5mm.
CULICIDAE

A

B

L=15mm.

BOMBYLIIDAE

L=18mm. C
TIPULIDAE

L=24mm.
b.t.

E
ventral
L=6mm.
BLEPHARICERIDAE

sp.

F
dorsal

D
L=14mm.
PTYCHOPTERIDAE

PUPARIUM AND PUPA
EXPLANATION OF FIGURES O12, A-F
DIPTERA-CYCLORRHAPHA

Note. Coarctate type of pupae occur among the Cyclorrhapha. They are called puparia. A puparium is the last larval exoskeleton which serves as a protective covering for an exarate pupae within. Some of the Brachycera, especially the Stratiomyidae and Coenomyidae also pupate in the last larval exuvium.

Figures A to F. Metopiidae (Calliphoridae), Lucilia sericata Meig. A common blowfly puparium and the early stage, nonpigmented, exarate pupa within.

Figure A. Ventral view of a puparium showing the remains of the larval mouth hooks within.

Figure B. Lateral view of a puparium showing the suture along which the puparium splits when the adult emerges and the position of the left spiracular prong of the pupa

Figure C. Dorsal view of a puparium showing the remains of the prothoracic and caudal spiracles of the maggot and the two spiracular prongs of the pupa.

Figure D. Ventral view of a newly formed pupa showing the position of the legs and wings and the shape of the undifferentiated head.

Figure E. Lateral view of a newly formed pupa showing the position of the wing and portions of the legs. The thoracic spiracular prong in the center of a fleshy disc and the spiracles adjacent to the disc are also fairly conspicuous in this stage of pupal development

Figure F. Dorsal view of a newly formed pupa showing the fairly conspicuous spiracular prongs located near the center of a fleshy disc.

DIPTERA - PUPARIUM AND PUPA

FIGURE O12.

METOPIIDAE

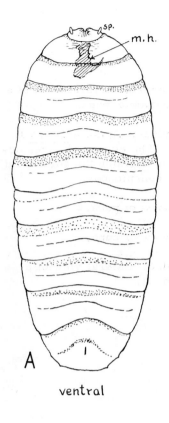

A

ventral

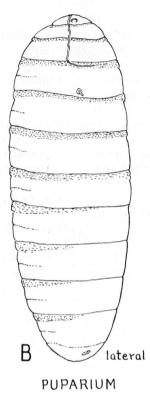

B

lateral

PUPARIUM

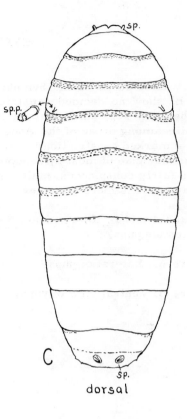

C

dorsal

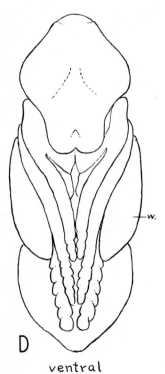

D

ventral

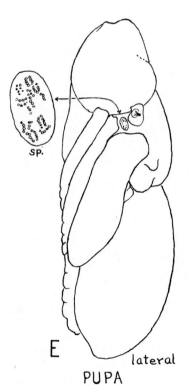

E

lateral

PUPA

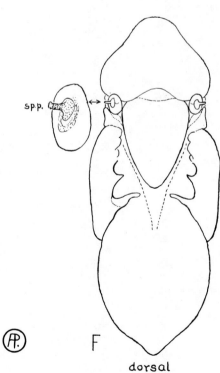

F

dorsal

PUPAE
EXPLANATION OF FIGURES O13, A-F.
HYMENOPTERA

Note. Most pupae of the Symphyta (figures A-B) show no decided constriction in the abdominal segments adjacent to the thorax while among pupae of the Apocrita (figures C-F) a marked constriction is usually present. The antennae of most hymenopterous pupae are fairly conspicuous, multisegmented and may possess more than eleven segments.

Figures A and B. Diprionidae, Neodiprion sp. A female pupa.

Figure A. Lateral of pupa.

Figure B. Ventral view of pupa.

Figure C. Ichneumonidae. Lateral view of a female bagworm parasite pupa.

Figures D and E. Apidae. Apis mellifera L. A honey bee pupa. The elongated cases adjacent to the meson in which the adult mouth parts develop are conspicuous.

Figure D. Lateral view of pupa.

Figure E. Ventral view of pupa.

Figure F. Formicidae. Lateral view of a wingless worker pupa.

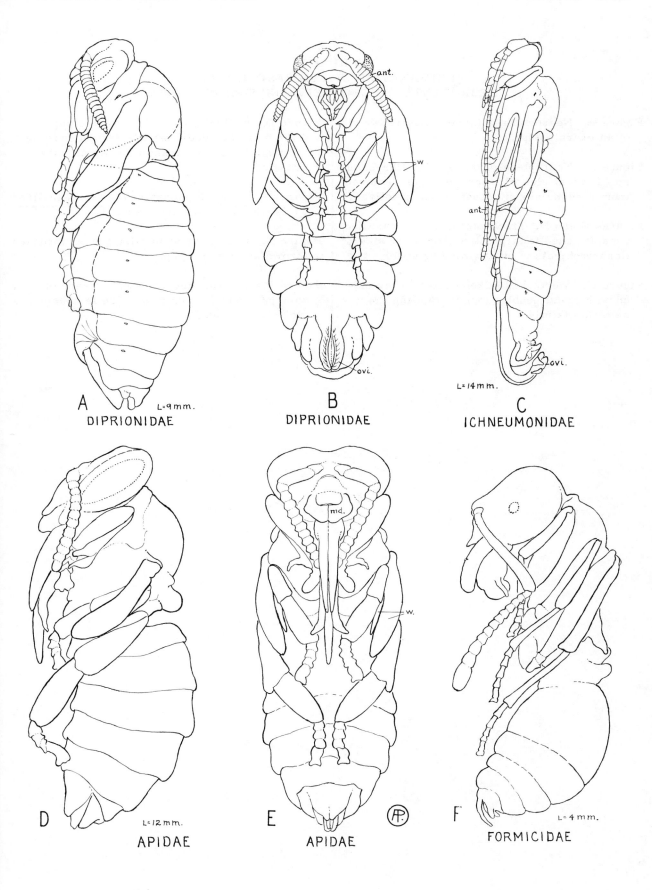

A
DIPRIONIDAE

B
DIPRIONIDAE

C
ICHNEUMONIDAE

D
APIDAE

E
APIDAE

F
FORMICIDAE

PUPAE
EXPLANATION OF FIGURES O14, A-F.
NEUROPTERA. TRICHOPTERA AND SIPHONAPTERA

Figure A. Neuroptera, Sialidae. Lateral view of an exarate pupa.

Figure B. Neuroptera, Chrysopidae, Chrysopa sp. Lateral view of a compact pupa removed from a round silken cocoon found on foliage.

Figures C and D. Trichoptera. Pupal case and pupa attached to large stones or other stationary objects in swiftly moving water.

Figure C. A detached silken cocoon surrounded with small pebbles (sand), showing the pupa within faintly.

Figure D. Ventral view of the exarate pupa after it is removed from the cocoon showing the well developed mandibles which may cross each other.

Figures E and F. Siphonaptera, Ctenocephalides canis (Curt). A dog flea pupa.

Figure E. Ventral view showing the compressed form of an exarate pupa.

Figure F. Lateral view showing absence of wing pads and the position of the legs held close to the body.

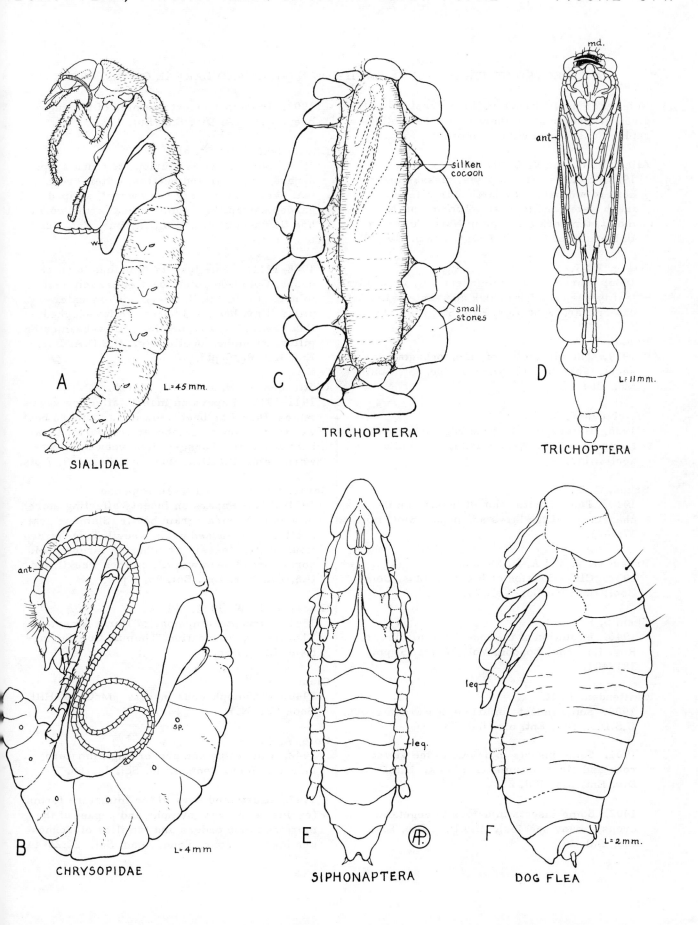

A   SIALIDAE   L.=45 mm.

C   TRICHOPTERA   silken cocoon   small stones

D   TRICHOPTERA   md.   ant.   L.=11mm.

B   CHRYSOPIDAE   ant.   o sp.   L.=4mm

E   SIPHONAPTERA   leq.

F   DOG FLEA   leq.   L.=2mm.

A SELECTED GENERAL BIBLIOGRAPHY ON NYMPHS AND LARVAE OF INSECTS

Note: For publications on larvae restricted to given orders or parts thereof see the bibliographies associated with each order.

Allee, W. C. and V. E. Shelford
1923. Synoptic key to phyla, classes and orders of animals with particular reference to fresh water and terrestrial forms of the moist, temperate region in North America. University of Chicago Press, 63 pp.

Baerg, W. J.
1935. Three shade tree insects, II. great elm leaf beetle, catalpa sphinx and eastern tent caterpillar. Ark. Agr. Exp. Sta. Bul. 317.

Balduf, W. V.
1939. The bionomics of entomophagous insects. John S. Swift and Co., Inc., St. Louis, Mo. 384 pp.

Blatchley, W. S.
1926. Heteroptera or true bugs of eastern North America. Nature Publ. Co., Indianapolis, Ind.

Brues, C. T.
1919. The classification of insects on the characters of the larva and pupa. Biol. Bul. 37:1-21.

Brues, C. T. and A. L. Melander.
1932. Classification of Insects. Mus. Comp. Zool. Harvard Col. Vol. 73.

Chen, S. H.
1946. Evolution of the insect larva. Trans. Roy. Ent. Soc. London. Vol. 97, pt. 15, pp. 381-404.

Chittenden, F. H.
1900. Some insects injurious to garden crops. U.S.D.A. Div. Ent. n.s. Bul. 23.

1901. Some insects injurious to the violet, rose and other ornamental plants. U.S.D.A. Div. Ent. n.s. Bul. 27.

1902. Some insects injurious to vegetable crops, (many species). U.S.D.A. Div. Ent. n.s. Bul. 33.

1903. Principal insect enemies of the sugar beet. U.S.D.A. Div. Ent. Bul. 43.

Chittenden, F. H., et. al.
1910. Some insects injurious to truck crops; asparagus miner and beetles, water-cress leaf beetle, cranberry span worm, striped garden caterpillar, semitropical army worm, hop flea beetle, etc. U.S.D.A. Bur. Ent. Bul. 66, 7 pts.

1908-1911. Some insects injurious to truck crops; Colorado potato beetle, parsnip leaf miner, parsley stalk weevil, celery caterpillar, lima bean pod borer, yellow-necked flea beetle, hop flea beetle, yellow-bean caterpillar, cucumber beetle, etc. U.S.D.A. Bur. Ent. Bul. 82, 7 pts.

Chittenden, F. H. and H. O. Marsh.
1911-1913. Papers on insects affecting vegetables; Hawaiian beet webworm, southern beet webworm, imported cabbage webworm, sugar beet webworm, horse-radish webworm, cutworm, etc. U.S.D.A. Bur. Ent. Bul. 109, 7 pts.

Chittenden, F. H. and C. H. Popenoe
1911-1912. Papers on insects affecting stored products; Mexican grain beetle, Siamese grain beetle, broad-nosed grain weevil, long-headed flour beetle, lesser grain borer, larger grain borer, broad bean weevil, cowpea weevil, etc. U.S.D.A. Bur. Ent. Bul. 96, 6 pts.

Claassen, P. W. 1931. Pl
1931. Plecoptera nymphs of North America. Thomas Say Foundation, Thomas Co., Springfield, Ill. 199 pp.

Clausen, C. P.
1940. Entomophagous Insects. McGraw-Hill Book Co., N.Y.

Cole, A. C.
1942. Collecting and preserving immature insects. Jour. Tenn. Acad. Sci. 14:166.

1947. Illustrated keys to the immature forms (exclusive of eggs, nymphs and pupae) of the more common orders and families of Tennessee insects. Jour. Tenn. Acad. Sci. 22:28-44.

Comstock, J. H.
1947. An introduction to entomology. Comstock Pub. Co., Ithaca, N. Y.

Craighead, F. C. and W. Middleton.
1930. An annotated list of the important North American forest insects (bibliography). U.S.D.A. Misc. Publ. 74.

Crosby, C. R. and M. D. Leonard.
1918. Manual of vegetable insects. Macmillan Co., N. Y.

Dean, R. W.
1939. Anatomy and development of the female reproductive system in Rhagoletis pomonella Walsh. (Types of pupae), Ph.D. dissertation, O.S.U., Columbus, Ohio.

Dustan, A. G.
1932. Vegetable insects and their control. Can. Dept. Agr. Bul. 161. n.s.

Essig, E. O.
1942. College entomology. Macmillan Co., N. Y.

Felt, E. P.
1905. Insects affecting park and woodland trees. N. Y. State Museum, Albany, N. Y., Memoir 8.

1924. Manual of tree and shrub insects. Macmillan Co., N. Y.

Franklin, H. J.
1928. Cape Cod cranberry insects. Mass. Agr. Exp. Sta. Bul. 239.

Frison, T. H.
1929. Fall and winter stoneflies, of Plecoptera of Illinois, Ill. State Nat. Hist. Survey Bul. 18:343-409.

1935. The stoneflies or Plecoptera of Illinois. Ill. Nat. Hist. Survey Bul. 20:281-471.

1937. II. Descriptions of Plecoptera with special reference to Illinois species. Ill. State Nat. Hist. Survey Bul. 21:78-99.

1942. Studies of North American Plecoptera. Ill. Nat. Hist. Survey Bull. 22:235-355.

Frost, S. W.
1942. General Entomology. McGraw-Hill Book Co., N. Y.

Garman, P.
1917. The Zygoptera, or damsel-flies, of Illinois. Bull. Ill. Nat. Hist. Survey, Vol. 12:411-587.

1927. Guide to the insects of Connecticut. Part 5. The Odonata or dragonflies of Connecticut. Conn. Geol. and Nat. Hist. Survey Bul. 39:1-331.

Gibson, A.
1928. Insects of the flower garden and their control. Cannadian Dept. of Agri. Bul. 99. n.s.

Gibson, A. and W. A. Ross.
1922. Insects affecting greenhouse plants. Canadian Dept. of Agri. Bul. 7. n.s.

Gordon, E. L.
1933. Notes on the ephemerid genus Leptophlebia. Bul. Brook. Ent. Soc. 28:116-130.

Harden, P. H.
1942. The immature stages of some Minnesota Plecoptera. Ann. Ent. Soc. Amer. 35: 318-33.

Harrison, A. S. and R. L. Usinger.
1934. A simple device and method for blowing insect larvae. Bul. Brooklyn Ent. Soc., 29:168.

Hayes, W. P.
1941. Some recent works on the classification of immature insects. Jour. Kans. Ent. Soc. 14: 3-11.

Hearle, E.
1938. Insects and allied parasites injurious to livestock and poultry in Canada. Canad. Dept. Agr. Publication 604.

Herms, W. B.
1923. Medical and veterinary entomology. Macmillan Co., N. Y.

Herrick, G. W.
1935. Insect enemies of shade-trees. Comstock Publ. Co., Ithaca, N. Y.

Houser, J. S.
1918. Destructive insects affecting Ohio shade and forest trees. Ohio Agr. Exp. Sta. Bul. 332, p. 161-486.

Imms, A. D.
1925. A general textbook of Entomology. Methuen and Co., Ltd., London, England.

1937. Recent advances in entomology. 2nd. ed. P. Blakiston's Sons & Co., Philadelphia, Pa. (Berlese's theory. p. 51.)

Ingram, J. W.
1927. Insects injurious to rice crops. U.S.D.A. Farmers' Bul. 1543.

Johnson, F., A. G. Hammar, S. W. Foster and J. B. Gill.
1912-1913. Papers on deciduous fruit insects; grapeberry moth, cherry fruit sawfly, fruit tree leaf roller, etc. U.S.D.A. Bur. Ent. Bul. 116, 5 pts.

Leonard, M. D.
1928. A list of the insects of New York with a list of the spiders and certain other allied groups. Cornell Univ. Agr. Ex. Sta. Mem. 101.

Lutz, F. E.
1935. Field Book of Insects. 3rd edition. G. P. Putnam's Sons, N. Y.

Metcalf, C. L. and W. C. Flint.
1939. 2nd ed. Destructive and useful insects, their habits and control. McGraw-Hill Book Co., N. Y.

Needham, J. G., S. W. Frost and B. H. Tothill.
1928. Leaf-mining insects. Williams and Wilkins Co., Baltimore, Md.

Needham, J. G., and H. B. Heywood.
1929. A handbook of the dragonflies of North America. Thomas Co., Springfield, Ill.

Needham, J. G., J. R. Traver and Y. Tsu.
1935. The biology of mayflies with a systematic account of North American species. Comstock Publ. Co., Ithaca, N. Y.

Needham, J. G. and P. R. Needham.
1938. A guide to the study of fresh-water biology. Comstock Publ. Co., Ithaca, N. Y.

Packard, A. S.
1890. Insects injurious to forest and shade trees. Fifth Rept. U. S. Ent. Com., revised ed. Bul. 7.

Park, O., W. C. Allee and V. E. Shelford.
1939. A laboratory introduction to an animal ecology and taxonomy. Univ. of Chicago Press, Chicago, Illinois, Keys to Orders.

Pennak, R. W.
1947. Keys to aquatic insects of Colorado. Univ. of Colo. Studies, Series D, Physical and Biol. studies vol. 2, p. 353.

Peterson, A.
1923. The blackberry psyllid, (Trioza tripunctata Fitch). N. J. Agr. Exp. Station Bul. 378.

1934-37, (revised and combined fifth edition, 1947). A manual of entomological equipment and methods, parts 1 and 2, Edwards Bros., Ann Arbor, Mich.

1939. Keys to the orders of immature stages (exclusive of eggs and pronymphs) of North American insects. Ann. Ent. Soc. Amer. 32:267-278.

1943. Some new killing fluids for larvae of insects. Jour. Econ. Ent. 36:115.

1945. Some insect infants. Sci. Monthly, 6 60:426-442.

Plumb. G. H.
1936. New apparatus and technique for inflating larvae. U.S.D.A., Bur. Ent. and P. 2, ET-75.

Quaintance, A. L., et. al.
1909. Papers on deciduous fruit insects and insecticides; pear thrips, spring canker worm, trumpet leaf miner, lesser peach borer, lesser apple worm, grape root worm, grape leaf skeletonizer and peach-tree barkbeetle. U.S.D.A. Bur. Ent. Bul. 68.

Quayle, H. J.
1938. Insects of citrus and other subtropical fruits. Comstock Publ. Co., Ithaca, N. Y.

Raizenne, H.
1945. How to inflate insect larvae. Canad. Dept. Agri., Div. Ent., Ottawa, Canad., Processed Publ. 32.

Riley, W. A. and O. A. Johannsen.
1938. Medical Entomology. ed. 2. McGraw-Hill Book Co., N. Y.

Sanderson, E. D., and L. M. Peairs.
1921. Insect Pests of Farm, Garden and Orchard. ed. 2. John Wiley and Sons, N. Y. More recent revisions by L. M. Peairs.

Shotwell, R. L.
1930. A study of the lesser migratory grass-hopper. U.S.D.A. Tech. Bul. 190.

Slingerland, M. V. and C. R. Crosby.
1914. Manual of fruit insects. Macmillan Co., N. Y.

Smith, J. B.
1906. Economic entomology. J. B. Lippincott Co., Philadelphia, Pa.

1909. Insects of New Jersey. Ann. Rept. of the New Jersey State Museum. MacCrellish and Quigley, State Printers, Trenton, N. J.

Smith, R. C., E. G. Kelly, G. A. Dean, H. R. Bryson and R. L. Parker.
1943. Common insects of Kansas. Kansas State Bd. Agr. Vol. 62, No. 255.

Swaine, J. M. and C. B. Hutchings.
1926. The more important shade tree insects of eastern Canada and their control. Canad. Dept. of Agr. Bul. 63. n.s.

Torre-Bueno, J. R. de la
1937. A glossary of entomology. Brooklyn Ent. Soc., Brooklyn, N. Y.

Traver, J. R.
1932-33. Mayflies of North Carolina. Jour. Elisha Mitchell Sci. Soc. 47:85-236 and 48:141-206.

1933. Heptagenine mayflies of North America. Jour. N. Y. Ent. Soc. 41:105-125.

Ward, H. B. and G. C. Whipple.
1918. Fresh-water biology. John Wiley & Sons, N. Y.

Webster, F. M.
1903. Some insects attacking the stems of growing wheat, rye, barley and oats. U.S.D.A. Bur. Ent. Bul. 42.

1906. Some insects affecting the production of red clover seed. U.S.D.A. Bur. Ent. Circ. 69.

Webster, F. M. et al.
1910-1911. Papers on cereal and forage insects; lesser clover leaf weevil, slender seed-corn ground beetle, clover root curculio, sorghum midge, New Mexico range caterpillar, smoky crane fly, cowpea curculio, etc. U.S.D.A. Bur. Ent. Bul. 85, 8 pts.

Webster, F. M., J. A. Hyslop, E. O. G. Kelly, T. H. Parks and W. J. Phillips.
1913. Papers on cereal and forage insects; timothy stem borer, "curlew bug," false wire-worms, legume pod moth and maggot, alfalfa looper, etc. U.S.D.A. Bur. Ent. Bul. 95, 7 pts.

Wehrle, L. P.
1939. Grape insects in Arizona. Ariz. Agr. Exp. Sta. Bul. 162:274-292.

Weigel, C. A. and L. A. Baumhofer.
1948. Handbook on insect enemies of flowers and shrubs. U.S.D.A. Misc. Publ. 626.

Wright, M. and A. Peterson.
1944. A key to the genera of Anisopterous dragonfly nymphs in the United States and Canada (Odonata, suborder Anisoptera). Ohio Jour. Sci. 44:151-166.

More than ten thousand species of nearctic Lepidoptera have been described. Larvae of most species of moths, butterflies and skippers are called caterpillars. Some are referred to as slugs, borers or miners. Full-grown caterpillars may be very large (regal moth caterpillars, 135+ mm.) while others are tiny, less than 5 mm. (many leaf mining species). Many common caterpillars are 25 to 50 mm. long. Practically all species are terrestrial in habits; a few pyralids, however live in moving water under webs on stones or on submerged vegetation. Food of most terrestrial species is plant tissue. The majority feed on foliage, stems, roots, buds, blossoms or fruits, while some species bore or produce mines within leaves, stems, buds, fruits, seeds, nuts, roots and woody portions of plants. A number of species live on plant by-products and a few on animal by-products, especially those containing wool, feathers and animal proteins. A few species are predacious on other insects chiefly plant lice and scale insects. Descriptions of various families and notes on individual species give more details on feeding habits.

The basic external morphology of most larvae of Lepidoptera is strikingly similar. Larvae of this order resemble each other more closely than the larvae of the other major orders of holometabolous insects such as the Coleoptera, Diptera or Hymenoptera. This fact at times makes it difficult to differentiate sharply some families, especially those belonging to Tortricoidea and Gelechioidea. One cannot give a basic description of a lepidopterous larva which will be infallible for all forms; the following statement, however, includes the vast majority of species.

All larvae or caterpillars of Lepidoptera possess a distinct head with chewing mouth parts including opposable mandibles. Most species possess several ocelli, adfrontal areas, antennae and a protruding spinneret, three distinct thoracic segments each bearing true segmented legs and spiracles on the prothorax, ten abdominal segments with prolegs bearing crochets usually present on segments three, four, five, six and the last, and spiracles on abdominal segments one to eight. From this point on the various areas and external structures will be discussed in some detail.

Head. (L4) Most species possess a well defined, sclerotized and frequently deeply pigmented head. Among some species, particularly those where head is deeply retracted into prothorax (Limacodidae), the dorsocaudal portion of the head capsule is not as heavily sclerotized or as deeply pigmented as the exposed portion. Heads of most species usually project ventrad (hypognathous) or cephaloventrad. Among leaf mining species and some wood or stem boring forms the head projects cephalad (prognathous).

A well defined epicranial inverted Y-shaped suture occurs on the head of most species, (L4, A-B). The inverted V portion of this suture encloses the frons (front). Laterad of and parallel with the sides of the frons narrow adfrontal sclerites exist. Adfrontal areas occur in most larvae of Lepidoptera and are never found on larvae among other orders. The mesal arm or coronal suture of the Y-shaped epicranial suture may be short or absent. Among those species where the frons extends dorso-caudad to the vertical triangle and the two arms of the inverted V portion of the epicranial suture do not meet the front is said to be open, (L4, F.).

The clypeus (epistoma) and labrum are usually distinct and located in their customary positions ventrad (or cephalad) of the frons. The labrum (L1, A-F) and clypeus (epistoma) may possess distinct setae. The labrum may be deeply or acutely cleft on the meson of its distal margin.

Ocelli or simple eyes are present in groups of one to six and located on the lateral aspect of the head capsule adjacent to the base of the mandibles. When four or more are present they are usually arranged in a semicircle. They are numbered as indicated in figures L4, C and D. Also see S. B. Fracker, 1915 and W. T. M. Forbes, 1923.

Antennae usually possess three segments and as a rule arise from the membranous area between the head capsule and the mandibles. Dethier is of the opinion that the basic structure of antennae of all lepidopterous larvae is the same and characteristic of the order. See drawings by Dethier (L1, R-V).

A distinct protruding spinneret is present on the disto-meson of the labium in practically all species, (L1, G-N). The mouth parts are a generalized chewing type with opposable mandibles. Very little use is made of mouth structures in the key to families; however, good specific characters exist in detailed structure of mandibles

(L1, O-P) and other parts. For information on setae of head capsule see discussion on chaetotaxy.

Thorax. Most species possess three distinct thoracic segments with one pair of straight or slightly curved segmented legs on each segment, (L1, Z). Legs are very small (L22, D) in some groups (Limacodidae) or they may be fleshy nonsegmented protuberances, or completely wanting in many leaf mining species. One pair of spiracles is usually present on the prothorax or it may be located between prothorax and mesothorax. Prothoracic spiracles may be vestigial or absent among aquatic species.

Abdomen. Most larvae of Lepidoptera possess ten abdominal segments. Pairs of fleshy-nonsegmented projections called prolegs usually exist on the ventral aspect of segments three, four, five, six and last. Prolegs on the last or tenth abdominal segment are called anal prolegs while those on all other abdominal segments are referred to as ventral prolegs. Anal prolegs may be absent, rudimentary or exceedingly long (L1, X) and slender (stemapoda). Prolegs may occur among the Nepticulidae and Megalopygidae on segments two to seven inclusive. Among Nepticulidae crochets are absent on all prolegs while among the Megalopygidae they are missing on prolegs of segments two and seven. If the fleshy portion of prolegs appears to be wanting on abdominal segments, yet crochets are present, then prolegs are said to be present. Circular or oval spiracles (L2, I-J) usually occur on the lateral aspects of segments one to eight. They are vestigial, absent or replaced by bunches of tracheal gills among aquatic species.

Crochets. Considerable use is made of the arrangement and distribution of the hooks or crochets (L3, A-P) on the prolegs in determining families of lepidopterous larvae, consequently one needs to have a clear understanding of terminology employed.

A planta is that portion of a proleg which gives rise to the hooks or crochets. In the generalized type of larva it is assumed that the crochets were arranged in circles about the distal end of a proleg, (L3, M). As specialization progressed only one circular row or series of hooks existed. The term series incorporated into the description of crochets refers to the arrangement of the crochets from the point of view of number of rows the bases of crochets produce. The vast majority are uniserial, all in one line; a few are biserial (Plutellidae), in two lines, while others are multiserial (Acrolophidae), three or more lines. Unless stated otherwise in keys or in descriptions of cro-

chets it is assumed that the crochets have a uniserial arrangement. When the term ordinal is employed it refers to the number of rows produced by variation in the lengths of the crochets. If all are of the same length, or approximately so, they are uniordinal, if two alternating lengths of crochets occur they are biordinal while three lengths of crochets produce a triordinal condition.

More primitive families of Lepidoptera probably possessed one or many complete circles of crochets about each proleg. Many families possessing a single circle of crochets about each proleg exhibit one small break or gap in the series of hooks on the lateral or mesal aspect. This incomplete circle or arrangement is called a penellipse. If the lateral portion of the circle of the crochets is complete and a break occurs on the mesal side it is a lateral penellipse or lateropenellipse, (L3, H). When the break in the circle occurs on the lateral side and is complete toward the meson it is called a mesal penellipse or mesopenellipse, (L3, G).

Among other families of Lepidoptera an elliptical circle of crochets may show two breaks or gaps in the circle of hooks, one on the lateral side and one toward the meson. Resulting crochets may then appear as two transverse bands, (L3, E) common among several families of Lepidoptera. One of the bands may disappear leaving only one transverse band on a proleg, (L3, P). A single transverse band situated on ventral prolegs is not very common but is of common occurrence on anal prolegs.

Circles of crochets may again be elliptical with the long axis of each projecting cephalocaudad. As the crochets at the two ends of each ellipse disappear two longitudinal bands are formed, the outer band being called a lateroseries, and the inner band a mesoseries, (L3, K). Very few species possess both a lateroseries and a mesoseries. This condition exists among species of the Libytheidae. Fracker refers to this arrangement as a pseudocircle.

Many larvae of Lepidoptera, especially among the Macrolepidoptera, possess prolegs with one longitudinal band on the mesal side of the planta. This is a mesoseries, (L3, I). This band is usually fairly straight and more or less parallel with the meson; however, in some species it may be curved and resemble a mesopenellipse. If this resemblance exists the open or discontinuous area of crochets usually exceeds one-third or more of the projected circle, and the entire mesoseries on the anal prolegs is usually nearly parallel with the meson. In a mesoseries when all crochets are almost alike in structure and size throughout the band they are said to be homoideous. Again in a meso-series where the crochets near the center are well developed and those near the two ends are very small or mere rudiments they are said to be heteroideous, (L3, J). Crochets of a homoideous mesoseries may be absent or greatly reduced in size near the center (Lycaenidae) and a fleshy lobe may be present laterad of the crochets at this point, (L3, O).

Armature, including setae. (L2, A-F) A wide variety of structures occur on the ectal surface of the various parts of caterpillars. Few species are completely void of armature. One common and simple structure of the armature is a seta. Most setae are simple hairs; however, they may be plumose, knobbed, flattened or disclike. A seta or hairlike organ arises from a small sclerotized ringlike papilla on the ectocuticle and internally connects with at least one hypodermal cell. In exceptional cases it may be hollow and also may exude secretions at its distal end. The ringlike papilla usually permits a seta to be somewhat flexible at its base. If a well defined sclerotized and flattened pigmented area occurs at the base of one or more setae it is called a pinaculum, (L2, A). If this pinaculum is distinctly elevated and conelike it is called a chalaza, (L2, B). A chalaza usually bears one seta; however, according to Fracker, it may bear two to four setae but is never multi-setiferous. If the chalaza is of sufficient size to be multi-setiferous or to give rise to several spines, called spinules, such a structure is called a scolus, (L2, C-D). Where chalazalike structures occur without setae, typical of structures on the suranal plate of some species, they are called cornicula. Some workers call these structures tubercles.

Tufts or dense groups of setae are common among very hairy caterpillars. If the setae are numerous and arise from a rounded wartlike elevation and project in many directions, resembling a pin-cusion, the structure is called a verruca, (L2, E). In case the setae are thickly grouped, brushlike, upright and more or less parallel with each other the brushlike structure is called a verricule, (L2, F). Pencils or tufts of setae (L24, I) are made up of a few, exceedingly long, closely adjacent setae. Setae may arise in numbers from sclerotized plates. These may occur on the dorsal aspect of the caudal segment (suranal plate), on the dorsal aspect of the prothorax (prothoracic shield), or from plates on the lateral aspects of the proleg (proleg plates).

The term gibbosity refers to enlarged dorsal swellings which are more like malforma-

tions than processes, (L25, H). Large rounded swellings without definite outline and usually located on the lateral aspects are sometimes called protuberances, (L26, A-B). The term tubercle, as used by various investigators, is very general and includes such structures as verruca, verricule, scolus, cornicula, etc.

Fleshy, flexible filaments are frequently found arising from various segments of the body especially among the Papilionidae and Danaidae, (L33, I). A caudal horn or scar occurs on the dorsomeson of the eighth abdominal segment among Sphingidae, (L55, G). A caterpillar is said to be sphingiform when it is cylindrical, possesses very short setae (or wanting) and has no other armature except a meso-dorsal horn on the eighth abdominal segment. Anal combs or forks, (L32, C, M-Q) used to eject faeces, are sclerotized prongs with two to seven or more digits. They are located on the meson, caudad of the anus, and usually on the ventral aspect of the overlapping caudal end of the suranal plate. They are common among many species of Olethreutidae, (L29, L30), Tortricidae, (L32, C, M, Q), Gelechiidae, (L15, I, N, S) and Hesperiidae, (L20, M).

If one examines the cuticle of larvae of many species under high magnification (at least 100x) it will be noted that the surface is pigmented, stippled, roughened, granular, or covered with microspines. If granular the bumplike structures may be conical, convex, or flattened. Microspines (L36, D, H, N) are tiny sharp points frequently arising from small pigmented areas. Among Phalaenidae the above characters are very useful in determining genera and species. They may be exceedingly numerous on some parts of the body.

Glands. Several kinds of eversible glands occur on the thorax and abdomen of caterpillars. Among the Papilionidae eversible v-shaped glands (osmeteria) sometimes arise from cephalo-dorso-meson of prothorax, (L2, K). Other larvae possess eversible glands on ventromeson of prothorax (L2, L) and some abdominal segments. They also occur on dorsomeson, especially on the sixth and seventh abdominal segments, (L24, J). Gland openings are also present at other points on the thorax and abdominal segments of various species.

Color. Green is the basic ground color of many caterpillars that feed upon plant tissues containing chlorophyll. The basic ground color of others, especially those found within living or dead parts of plants, may be near white, or varying shades of yellow, orange, pink, red, brown or near black. In addition to the basic color, bright pigmented areas may occur on some or all parts of the body. These areas may be small to large spots, blotches or stripes. If striped they are usually transverse or longitudinal. If longitudinal they may extend from the head to the caudal segment. The longitudinal stripes have been given names according to their position on the body, (L2, M-N). Some of these are called dorsal, addorsal, subdorsal, supraspericular, spiracular (stigmatal) subspiracular, and ventral. For definitions see glossary. Color of some species of caterpillars varies greatly. Distinct differences in color may occur among the successive instars of a given species or among individuals of a given instar. In general the distribution pattern of the color is the same for a given instar of a given species but intensity of color and the actual color itself may be very different. Good examples of this are tomato hornworm, corn earworm and armyworm.

Since color is so variable one cannot place too much reliance upon it in identification of some species. Liquid preserved specimens may be very different in color from living material. A student may be thoroughly familiar with the morphology of a preserved specimen yet when he sees the same insect alive may not recognize it unless he examines it closely for its distinctive morphological characters. Inflated specimens, good colored drawings, colored photographs or films will help the student visualize the natural color of species.

Chaetotaxy - Setal Maps. Setae of caterpillars (L5-L8) fall into three categories, primary, subprimary and secondary. It has been shown by several investigators that primary and subprimary setae have a definite distribution on the head, thorax, and abdomen and have been assigned names or numbers. The difference between primary and subprimary setae is of no significance in the late instars. Fracker, 1915, states that a few important setae, gamma, theta, mu and omega on all segments and eta on the thorax, do not occur in the first larval instar but appear in later instars and show a definite arrangement. Such setae are called subprimary. Secondary setae are usually fine hairlike setae, frequently very numerous and usually without definite distribution. They may be associated with chalazae, verrucae or sclerotized plates. Secondary setae also may vary considerably in length and frequently are restricted to the ventral half of the thorax and abdomen or they may be confined to the prolegs. If confined to the prolegs there are always more than four on each proleg. No names or numbers have been assigned to secondary setae.

Arrangement of setae (primary and subpri-

mary) on the head and body has been studied extensively by a number of workers. So far as the chaetotaxy of the head is concerned it is of little significance in determining families of larvae (Gelechiidae, an exception) yet it is important in determining genera and species especially among the Phalaenidae and Pyralidae. Figure L4, A shows the two systems employed in naming (Heinrich) or numbering (Dyar) the setae and setal punctures on the head. For more detailed discussions see papers by Crumb, 1929 and Whelan, 1935.

Setal arrangement on the thorax and abdomen is used extensively in determining the families of caterpillars (Lepidoptera). There are two systems of nomenclature in vogue, assigning of Greek letters to given setae or use of numbers, usually Roman numerals (caps or lower case). Fracker adopted Greek letters because he found disagreement among investigators using numbers. Table 1 summarizes the names or numbers of the setae of several investigators; namely, S. B. Fracker, W. T. M. Forbes, and Carl Heinrich. The author does not favor any particular system; however, for convenience sake he would be inclined to substitute Arabic numbers for Roman numerals or Greek letters as a few investigators have done. If one describes a larva of a lepidopteron and uses Roman numerals he should state which interpretation he has accepted; namely, the interpretation of W. T. M. Forbes, Carl Heinrich or other workers.

No attempt will be made here to discuss setal maps extensively. An excellent review of the subject is available in S. B. Fracker's paper. At this point a few significant facts will be reviewed which will be of help to beginners using the family key for the first time.

In this publication a number of setal maps of various insects are included. A setal map shows the arrangement of the setae on one half (left) of any thoracic or abdominal segment. In other words, the oblong diagrammatic area or map is bounded at the top by the dorsomeson, at the bottom by the ventromeson, at the left by the cephalic margin and at the right by the caudal margin of the segment, (L5, A).

As an aid to entomologists not thoroughly familiar with the Greek alphabet the author has included at the bottom of figures L5, L6 and L8 of setal maps a key to Greek letters and numerals used by most investigators. Arabic numbers are used in place of Roman numerals on some of the maps. In the family key Greek letters by Fracker and corresponding Arabic numbers in place of Roman numerals are incorporated wherever setae on the abdominal segments are mentioned.

It will be noted that the most decided disagreement among investigators on setal patterns occurs about those on the thoracic segments. Consequently many investigators describing setae in this region, especially those on the prothorax, employ the Greek letters as used by Fracker. Probably the most important group of setae, so far as family determination is concerned, is the Kappa group on the prothorax, frequently referred to as the prespiracular group or wart, (L5, B). This group is usually distinctly separated from all other setae and located cephalad of the spiracle. Among most Microlepidoptera it possesses a maximum of three setae, theta, kappa and eta. The cervical shield on the prothorax usually possesses six pairs of setae and their relative positions may be significant. Again on the prothorax ventrad of the spiracle and immediately dorsad of the prothoracic legs the Pi or sub-ventral group of setae usually exists consisting of setae nu and pi. The Pi group (6) on the mesothorax and metathorax (L7, A-D) immediately dorsad of the legs is also referred to frequently and possesses one or two setae. On the abdomen the Pi group (7) is located on the base of the prolegs and usually consists of three setae, nu, pi and tau. Investigators using numerals assign number 7 to the Pi group on the abdominal segments making no effort to differentiate between the three setae usually present.

Kappa (4) and eta (5) setae on the abdominal segments are referred to as being distant, (L7, K-L) or adjacent, (L7, I-J). When adjacent the setae are very close to each other and may arise from a common pinaculum, if a pinaculum is present.

The relative position of alpha (1) and beta (2) on a number of segments is important. In a generalized segment seta alpha (1) is cephalad of seta beta (2) and closer to or more distant from the dorsomeson than seta beta (2). On the ninth abdominal segment (L8, M-P) seta alpha (1) may be distinctly more distant from the dorsomeson than seta beta (2) and may be only slightly cephalad of or almost directly ventrad of seta beta (2). Under these conditions on segment nine seta alpha (1) is the second seta ventrad of the dorsomeson.

Table 2

CHAETOTAXY OF LEPIDOPTEROUS LARVAE

Thorax and Abdomen

The following table, for classification use only, presents the names and numbers used by S. B. Fracker, W. T. M. Forbes and Carl Heinrich for the various setae on the thorax and abdomen of lepidopterous larvae. Heinrich and Forbes derived most of their respective systems from Dyar and Müller.

ALL SEGMENTS			PROTHORAX			MESOTHORAX METATHORAX		ABDOMEN	
FRACKER groups			FORBES		HEINRICH	FORBES	HEINRICH	FORBES	HEINRICH
alpha	a	B	a	Cerv.	Ia	ιa	Ia	ι	I
beta	β		β	Cerv.	IIa	ιb	Ib	ιι	II
gamma	γ		γ	Cerv.	Ib	x, (4)		x	
delta	δ		δ	Cerv.	IIb				
epsilon	ε	P	ε	Cerv.	Ic	ιιa	IIa	ιιιa	IIIa
rho	ρ		ρ	Cerv.	IIc	ιιb	IIb	ιιι	III
theta	θ		θ	Psp.	III	ιιι	III		
kappa	κ	K	κ	Psp.	IV	ιv	IV	ιv, (6)	IV
eta	η		η	Psp.	V	v	V	v, (7)	V
mu	μ							vι, (8)	VI
pi	π	Π	π	Subv.	VI	vιι, (3)	VI	vιι	VII
nu	ν		ν	Subv.	VI	vιι, (3)	VI	vιι	VII
tau	τ	(2)			VII, (1)	ιx	VII, (1)	vιι	VII
omega	ω							ιx, (5)	
sigma	σ				VIII	vιιι	VIII	vιιι	VIII
lambda	λ								

( ) = see comments.

COMMENTS

The above table submitted to W. T. M. Forbes and Carl Heinrich for criticism brought forth the following comments (1 to 8) which are summarized as follows:

In general the table does not express correctly the existing homology for all of the setae, however, it appears to be satisfactory for use in classifying or describing larvae.

(1). Heinrich's VII on the prothorax and mesothorax is not synonymous with Fracker's tau. Neither Fracker or Forbes has a homologue for Heinrich's thoracic VII. Also Heinrich gives no symbol for Fracker's thoracic tau or Forbes' thoracic ix.

(2). On the abdomen tau belongs to the Pi group and is part of the VII group of Heinrich or Forbes. The homologies of VI and VII between the thorax and abdomen are disputed by Fracker and Heinrich.

(3). In all probability vii of Forbes on the mesothorax and metathorax should be vi as interpreted by Heinrich.

(4). x of Forbes on the mesothorax and metathorax may include three or four small setae, xa, xb, xc, and xd.

(5). Some or all may have two setae here.

(6). Equals theta among Jugatae.

(7). Equals kappa among Jugatae.

(8). Equals eta among Jugatae.

Keys. S. B. Fracker in 1915 gave us the first satisfactory key to families for all of the known nearctic larvae of the Lepidoptera. Since then W. T. M. Forbes, 1924 and A. Gerasimov, 1937 have published keys which are largely modifications of Fracker's key. The key included in this volume is a rearrangement and a partial revision of the dichotomous inset key prepared by S. B. Fracker (1930 revision) with some help derived from the keys of W. T. M. Forbes, 1923 and A. Gerasimov, 1937. It includes nearly all families where larval stages of one or more species are known.

Family names used in the key are those found in J. McDunnough's check list of the Lepidoptera of Canada and the United States, 1938-39. For a fairly complete listing of family names accepted by S. B. Fracker; W. T. M. Forbes, J. McDunnough and the Bureau of Entomology and Plant Quarantine (Carl Heinrich) see prepared list of family names of the Lepidoptera pages 78 to 80.

The key is most useful in determining last or late instar larvae found in Canada and the United States. It is not perfect, consequently one may occasionally experience difficulty in reaching a satisfactory determination, especial-ly among some of the Microlepidoptera. Some of the difficulties with economic forms are noted. For other keys to families see S. B. Fracker, 1915 (revised 1930), W. T. M. Forbes, 1923, C. T. Brues and A. L. Melander, 1932, A. Gerasimov, 1937, and E. O. Essig, 1942.

Arabic numerals in parenthesis, following Greek letters assigned to setae by Fracker are the numbers assigned to the same setae by W. T. M. Forbes, (Roman numerals, lower case), Carl Heinrich (Roman numerals, caps) and other investigators.

The numbers on the left margin in parentheses are useful in tracing major steps taken in the key. The abbreviation f.g.l. equals full grown larva or length. The sizes are tiny, under 5 mm.; very small, under 10 mm.; small, 10 to 25 mm.; medium size, 25 to 50 mm.; large, 50 to 75 mm.; and very large, greater than 75 mm. (L1 to L58) refer to figures.

Before attempting to use this key one should be thoroughly familiar with the terminology of the exoskeleton of caterpillars. Beginning students should read carefully the general discussion on larvae of Lepidoptera pages 60 to 64 in this publication and pages 30 to 46 of "Lepidopterous Larvae" by S. B. Fracker, 1915, (or 1930 revision.

SECTION A.

Section A includes primarily small larvae generally possessing some modification in the usual structure of the thoracic legs (3) or prolegs on abdominal segments 3, 4, 5, 6 and 10. Many species are leaf-miners or live within plant tissue and may produce galls. All belong to the Microlepidoptera.

A 1. —— Segmented thoracic legs absent; fleshy and nonsclerotized protuberances may be present A2

A 1a. Segmented, distinctly sclerotized, thoracic legs present; prolegs usually present (most specimens with prolegs bearing crochets see B1) . . . . A 9

A 2. —— Body cylindrical or depressed; if somewhat fusiform the front reaches the vertical triangle or is very broad at the caudal end . . . . A 3

A 2a. Body fleshy, swollen at middle (fusiform) or cyphosomatic; the front does not reach the vertical triangle . . . . (L58), Prodoxidae

A 3. —— Head with several small ocelli, usually six and subequal in size . . . . A 8

A 3a. Head with one or two large ocelli on each side or without ocelli . . . . A 4

A 4. —— Ocelli absent or one large ocellus on each side . . . . A 5

A 4a. Two ocelli on each side; front usually triangular and may not reach the vertical triangle; f.g.l. under 6 mm.; chiefly leaf miners producing blotch mines with pupation in an oval cut from leaf at end of mine . . . . (L19), Heliozelidae

A 5. —— Front triangular; ocelli cephalic adjacent to lateral angles of the clypeus; adfrontal areas broad with antennae located at their cephalic ends; f.g.l. small, 8 to 10 mm., leaf miners (Betula) .... Eriocranidae

A 5a.   Front quadrangular; ocelli distant from lateral angles of clypeus; adfrontal areas narrow with antennae remote from their cephalic ends .... A 6

A 6.   —— Front narrower at caudal end; body always cylindrical; prolegs absent or borne on segments 2 to 7 inclusive without crochets .... A 7

A 6a.   Front wider at caudal end; body usually depressed and moniliform; ventral prolegs, if present, on segments 3 to 5. .... Gracilariidae

A 7.   —— Prolegs absent; body long and slender; length at least 10X diameter of abdomen; mine under bark of stems of many plants .... Opostegidae

A 7a.   Prolegs usually present on segments 2 to 7, f.g.l. very small, under 5 mm., not exceedingly slender; larvae mine in leaves, bark or fruit or produce galls on twigs or petioles. .... Nepticulidae

A 8(3).   —— Transverse bands or crochets located on segments 3 to 6 with fleshy portion of proleg vestigial; head depressed; front with sides more or less parallel; f.g.l. under 7 mm.; chiefly leaf miners usually producing blotches. .... Tischeriidae

A 8a.   No crochets or prolegs present or with crochets present on segments 3 to 5 only; f.g.l. very small; leaf miners, at least in early instars .... Gracilariidae

A 9,(1a) —— Antennae normal, no longer than the head; no scalelike setae .... A 10

A 9a.   Antennae longer than the head; setae replaced by large ovate scales arranged in pairs; head retractile; 8 pairs of prolegs with suckers on the ninth and tenth segments; f.g.l. under 5 mm., live in moss and lichens .... Micropterygidae

A 10.   —— Prolegs with distinct crochets absent; fleshy swellings, ventral suckers or mucous secreting discs may exist .... A 11

A 10a.   Prolegs with crochets present; the fleshy portion of the prolegs may be vestigial.. B1

A 11.   —— Front not reaching vertical triangle; body usually fusiform or sluglike; head small, not greatly depressed, may be retractible .... A 12

A 11a.   Front extending to vertical triangle; body usually cylindrical; head depressed, not narrowed; f.g.l. usually under 5 mm., casebearers .... Coleophoridae

A 12.   —— Intersegmental incisions distinct; head exposed; body usually a pale color; f.g.l. under 10 mm. .... A 13

A 12a.   Intersegmental incisions usually indistinct; head retracted; scoli or lateral setaceous filaments usually present; frequently brightly colored; f.g.l., 15 to 30 mm., many sluglike. .... (L22-23), Limacodidae

A 13.   —— Kappa (4) and eta (5) of abdominal segments distant or all setae wanting; fleshy prolegs without crochets may occur; f.g.l. 12 mm. ....(L58), Prodoxidae

A 13a.   Kappa (4) and eta (5) of abdominal segments segments adjacent; setae small but distinct; ocelli six; live in seeds or mine in grasses .... a few Gelechiidae

SECTION B.

Section B includes larvae without secondary setae, mostly naked species and chiefly families belonging to the Microlepidoptera. All Macrolepidoptera are indicated by an asterisk.

B 1.   —— Primary setae only; no tufted or secondary setae present; mu group (6) of abdomen usually unisetose, never a verrucae; pi group (7) on prolegs usually trisetose, rarely with four or five setae. .... B 2

B 1a.   Primary and numerous secondary setae usually present, setae may be tufted and secondary setae may be confined to the prolegs or ventral aspect, secondary setae may be very inconspicuous or absent if larva only possesses two pairs of functional prolegs; mu group (6) of abdomen if present at least bisetose or associated with several subprimaries, usually a verruca; generally many (more than 4) setae on the prolegs; chiefly Macrolepidoptera. .... C 1

B 2.   —— Prolegs always present on the sixth abdominal segment .... B 3

B 2a.   Prolegs absent on sixth abdominal segment, yet present on segments 3, 4 and 5; f.g.l. 3 to 7 mm., leaf miners at least in early instars, leaf rollers or in a leaf ball. (This bracket also includes a few species of case bearing Coleophoridae) ....
.... (L19), Gracilariidae

B 3. ——— Crochets on ventral prolegs arranged in a circle, penellipse or transverse bands, never in a mesoseries; if arranged as a mesopenellipse the gap free of crochets is usually distinctly less than one-third the circumference of the projected circle, also the entire series (planta) of crochets on each anal proleg is more nearly perpendicular than parallel to the meson . . . . B 4

B 3a. Crochets on ventral prolegs arranged in a mesoseries or pseudocircle, if a mesoseries on a ventral proleg resembles a mesopenellipse (some Phalaenidae, Epiplemidae and Ethmiidae) then the gap, free of crochets, is usually equal to or greater than one-third the circumference of the projected circle; also the entire series (planta) of crochets on each anal proleg is more nearly parallel than perpendicular to the meson; also kappa (4) on the abdominal segments is caudad (Epiplemidae an exception) of the spiracle . . . . B 35

B 4. ——— Kappa group (prespiracular, kappa-4 and eta-5) of setae on the prothorax bisetose; may be unisetose, especially if the prothoracic spiracles are vestigial or absent (aquatic pyralids) . . . . B 5

B 4a. Kappa group (prespiracular, theta-3, kappa-4, and eta-5) of setae on the prothorax trisetose; may be unisetose if larvae are casebearers or if crochets are few in number or reduced to rudiments . . . . B 8

B 5. ——— Crochets of ventral prolegs uniordinal . . . . B 6

B 5a. Crochets of ventral prolegs biordinal or triordinal, if uniordinal (Chrysauginae) the Pi group (6) on mesothorax and metathorax is bisetose . . . . B 7

B 6. ——— Large caudo-projecting spiracles of the eighth abdominal segment nearer the dorsomeson than seta alpha (1) of the seventh abdominal segment; f.g.l. of most species very small, within fruits of Rosa, Barberis, etc. . . . . Carposinidae

B 6a. Spiracles of the eighth abdominal segment normal in size and position; f.g.l. very small within stems, fruits and flowers of Compositae and Lonicera, often producing galls . . . . Alucitidae

B 7(5a) —— Pi group (6) unisetose on mesothorax and metathorax. If bisetose crochets are usually uniordinal or triordinal; pinacula about setae may be conspicuous; setae alpha (1) of ninth abdominal segment farther apart than setae beta (2), f.g.l. 10 to 35 mm. with varied habits. . . . . (L44-53), Pyralidae

B 7a. Pi group (6) bisetose on mesothorax and metathorax; setae alpha (1) of ninth abdominal segment closer together than setae beta (2); f.g.l. very small to small, within rolled leaves and stems of cruciferous plants (Clematis and Phaseolus) . . . . . . Thyrididae

B 8(4a) —— Kappa group (prespiracular) of setae on the prothorax distinctly separated from the cervical shield and are usually bunched together on a separate and frequently distinct sclerotized area cephalad of the spiracle . . . . B 12

B 8a. Kappa group (prespiracular) of setae on the prothorax and usually all six setae dorsad of this group located on one continuous sclerotized area, however, the Kappa group may be on the ventral edge of the prothoracic shield. If the Kappa group appears to be on a separate distinct sclerotized area then this area surrounds the spiracle and the crochets on the ventral prolegs are distinctly multiserial . . . . B 9

B 9. ——— Pi group (6) of setae unisetose on the mesothorax and metathorax; crochets of ventral prolegs multiserial or biserial circles or transverse bands, never a penellipse. . B 10

B 9a. Pi group (6) of setae bisetose on the mesothorax and metathorax; crochets of ventral prolegs arranged as a uniordinal latero- penellipse; long axis of prothoracic spiracles horizontal; casebearers (if the crochets are biserial or multiserial and the prothoracic spiracle is perpendicular see B 19a - Plutellidae) . . . . (L42), Psychidae

B 10. ——— Crochets of ventral prolegs a multiserial crossband; larvae within leaves, needles or seeds of food plants . . . . Adelidae

B 10a. Crochets of ventral prolegs a multiserial or biserial circle . . . . B 11

B 11. ——— Setae beta on prothorax closer to dorsomeson than alpha; six ocelli arranged in an irregular semi-circle with the first and second somewhat remote from the third and fourth which are close together; seta theta absent on abdomen; f.g.l. 25 mm.* . . . . Acrolophidae

B 11a. Setae beta on prothorax much farther from dorsomeson than alpha; six ocelli arranged in two vertical rows of three each; seta theta (3) present on abdomen; f.g.l. small to medium sized; within roots of plants. . . . . Hepialidae

B 12(8).—— Crochets of ventral prolegs arranged in transverse bands or reduced to mere rudiments . . . . B 13
B 12a.   Crochets of ventral prolegs arranged in a circle or penellipse . . . .   B 18
B 13. —— Crochets of ventral prolegs in two transverse rows; anal shield with eight setae..B 14
B 13a.   Crochets of ventral prolegs in a single transvers row, rarely two bands; anal shield with six setae; f.g.l. very small, within buds, terminals, fruits and leaves of bushes and trees . . . . (L57), Incurvariidae
B 14. —— Setae kappa (4) and eta (5) adjacent on abdominal segments . . . . B 15
B 14a.   Setae kappa (4) and eta (5) remote on abdominal segments; f.g.l. under 10 mm., mining foliage or free on surface . . . . pars Lyonetiidae
B 15. —— Crochets of each anal proleg a continuous series . . . . B 16
B 15a.   Crochets of each anal proleg divided into two groups; an anal comb (fork) frequently present . . . . (L15), pars Gelechiidae
B 16. —— Front extends two-thirds or more to the vertical triangle, f.g.l. small or medium size. . . . . B 17
B 16a.   Front extends half way to the vertical triangle, prothorax bears a large dorsal semicircular rugose plate; spiracles on eighth abdominal segment much larger than others; f.g.l. large, chiefly wood borers . . . . Cossidae
B 17. —— Spiracles usually elliptical, the eighth pair of the abdomen usually larger and more dorsad than those of segments 1 to 7; f.g.l. usually 20 to 35 mm., borers in deciduous trees, bushes and other plants . . . . (L9), Aegeriidae
B 17a.   Spiracles circular, small and all in the same line; crochets of opposite prolegs almost continuous; f.g.l. under 10 mm., some species are casebearers. . . . . (L13-14), Coleophoridae
B 18(12a)—Setae kappa (4) and eta (5) remote on abdominal segments or eta (5) is wanting (in very small larvae) . . . . B 19
B 18a.   Setae kappa (4) and eta (5) adjacent on abdominal segments, may be on the same pinaculum . . . . B 22
B 19. —— Crochets of ventral prolegs arranged in a uniserial circle or lateropenellipse, if arranged as a uniserial lateropenellipse also see description of the very small leaf mining Elachistidae omitted in this key . . . . B 20
B 19a.   Crochets of ventral prolegs arranged in a biserial or multiserial circle or penellipse which may be biserial on mesal aspect only; the circle of larger crochets may be incomplete; prothoracic spiracles never distinctly elliptical and horizontal; (also includes the Yponomeutidae) . . . . (L42), Plutellidae
B 20. —— Kappa group (prespiracular) of setae on prothorax all close together, one and one-half to two times as far from the spiracle as from each other. . . . . B 21
B 20a.   Kappa group (prespiracular) of setae on the prothorax distant, all about as far from the spiracle as from each other; setae alpha (1) of abdomen closer together than setae beta (2); f.g.l. tiny, chiefly plant miners. Lyonetiidae
B 21. —— Front extends more than halfway to the vertical triangle, attenuate at tip; setae alpha (1) of abdomen usually much farther apart on dorsum than setae beta (2); f.g.l. very small, living in fungi, animal tissues (by-products) and legume seeds, frequently within silken cases . . . . (L57), Tineidae
B 21a.   Front extends less than half way to the vertical triangle; setae alpha (1) of the abdomen not as far apart on dorsum as setae beta (2) . . . . Heliodinidae
B 22(18a)— Setae beta (2) of the ninth abdominal segment often on the same pinaculum and usually as near (Cossidae) or distinctly nearer to one another than setae alpha (1) on the eighth abdominal segment. If all setae on the ninth segment are in a more or less straight line the setae nearest the meson are beta (2) . . . . B 23
B 22a.   Setae beta (2) of the ninth abdominal segment not on same pinaculum and as far apart as setae alpha (1) on the eighth abdominal segment. If they are not as far apart seta rho (3) of the eighth abdominal segment is somewhat dorsad of and not distinctly cephalad of the spiracle . . . . B 27
B 23. —— Seta rho (3) of the eighth abdominal segment usually located almost cephalad of the spiracle . . . . B 24
B 23a.   Seta rho (3) of the eighth abdominal segment located almost above the spiracle. . B 25
B 24. —— No series of spines on the caudal margin of the prothoracic cervical shield; f.g.l.

10 to 30 mm. located in rolled, folded or bunched leaves, within twigs, stems, roots, flower buds, fruits, etc., of many plants (also includes the Olethreutidae) . . . . (L29-32), Tortricidae

B 24a. A series of spines on the caudal margin of the prothoracic cervical shield; f.g.l. medium size to large, chiefly wood borers. . . . . Cossidae

B 25. —— Abdominal prolegs short . . . . B 26

B 25a. Abdominal prolegs very long with uniordinal crochets; seta beta on prothorax closer together than setae alpha; f.g.l. very small, under silken webs on foliage or within grass. . . . . Glyphipterygidae

B 26. —— Larvae medium size to large, f.g.l. 30+ mm., two or more secondary setae may occur dorsad of the spiracles; chiefly borers in branches and stems of woody plants . . . . Cossiadae

B 26a. Larvae small, f.g.l. under 12 mm.; secondary setae absent (also includes the Yponomeutidae) . . . . Plutellidae

B 27(22a) — Seta L1 on the head is closer to A3 than A3 to A2 or the distances are subequal, ocelli one to four frequently unevenly spaced . . . . B 28

B 27a. Setae L1 on the head usually farther away from setae A3 than A3 is away from A2; ocelli one to four usually evenly spaced; crochets of anal prolegs may be in two groups, f.g.l. small, 10 to 25 mm. with diversified habits; in general resemble tortricids. . . . . (L17), Gelechiidae

B 28. —— Distance between the metathoracic coxae distinctly less than one and one-half to two times the width of the coxae . . . . B 29

B 28a. Distance between the metathoracic coxae one and one-half to two times the width of the coxae; setae may be indistinct; spiracles and prolegs usually small; f.g.l. small, living within plant shoots, fruits and leaves . . . . (L13), Cosmopterygidae

B 29. —— Setae alpha (1) and beta (2) remote on abdominal segments . . . . B 30

B 29a. Setae alpha (1) and beta (2) adjacent on abdominal segments; f.g.l. are very small to small. . . . . Heliodinidae

B 30. —— Adfrontals reach the vertical triangle or nearly so and the front extends two-thirds the distance; if shorter the front forms an antenuate point or the head is depressed and prognathous . . . . B 32

B 30a. Adfrontals reach two-thirds and the front extends less than one-half the distanct to the vertical triangle. . . . . B 31

B 31. —— Setae kappa (4) and eta (5) of abdominal segments on a common pinaculum; front blunt, head depressed . . . . Stenomidae

B 31a. Seta kappa (4) and eta (5) of abdominal segments located on separate pinacula; large borers in plants. . . . . (L11), pars Cossidae

B 32. —— Prothoracic coxae separated, not touching each other . . . . B 33

B 32a. Prothoracic coxae touch each other; seta rho (3) of segment 8 caudodorsad of spiracle . . . . Blastobasidae

B 33. —— Anal prolegs and anal segment (on each side excluding anal plate) bears no more than nine setae; crochets on ventral prolegs uniordinal . . . . B 34

P 33a. Anal prolegs and anal segment (on each side excluding anal plate) bears more than nine setae; crochets on ventral prolegs usually biordinal; f.g.l. under 25 mm. with diverse habits. . . . . (L28), Oecophoridae

B 34. —— Seta beta (2) of abdominal segments much lower than seta alpha (1) and subequally distant from alpha (1) and rho (3) or nearer rho (3); f.g.l. small, on leaves of Umbelliferacea . . . . Epermeniidae

B 34a. Seta beta (2) of abdominal segments, if lower than seta alpha (1) always further from seta rho (3) than from alpha (1); f.g.l. small, usually living within bulbs, stems or webbed leaves of evergreens and deciduous plants. . . . . (also includes the Yponomeutidae) Plutellidae

B 35(3a) — Kappa group (prespiracular) of setae bisetose on prothorax; occasionally unisetose; kappa (4) and eta (5) of abdomen remote especially on segments 4 to 8 . . . . . . B 38

B 35a. Kappa group (prespiracular) of setae trisetose on prothorax, also with epsilon below alpha and gamma, not near rho. . . . . B 36

B 36. —— Kappa (4) and eta (5) adjacent on abdominal segments; crochets arranged in a mesoseries which may resemble a mesopenellipse. . . . . B 37

B 36a. Kappa (4) and eta (5) remote on abdominal segments; if adjacent setae beta (2) on pro-thorax much closer together than setae alpha (1); crochets of ventral prolegs usually uniordinal sometimes in a pseudocircle..(also includes the Yponomeutidae) Plutellidae

B 37. —— Pi group (6) bisetose on mesothorax and metathorax; primary setae prominent; pro-legs slender usually elongated; ocelli 2 to 4 more conspicuous than 1 and 5; f.g.l. very small. . . . . (L43), a few Pterophoridae

B 37a. Pi group (6) unisetose on mesothorax and metathorax; setae beta of prothorax about as far apart as setae alpha, prolegs usually short; f.g.l. under 30 mm. . . . Ethmiidae

B 38(35).—— Pi group (6) bisetose on mesothorax and metathorax, if unisetose seta lambda is pres-ent . . . . B 39

B 38a. Pi group (6) unisetose on mesothorax and metathorax, lambda usually absent . . B 41

B 39. —— Setae well developed, plumose and borne on chalazae or on somewhat elevated pina-cula. . . . . B 40

B 39a. Setae small, simple and borne on minute papillae; head very wide and prolegs re-duced . . . .(L42), Thyatiridae*

B 40. —— Chalazae rho (3) bisetose on abdominal segments; f.g.l. medium sized, feeding on lichens (Lithosiidae) . . . . Arctiidae*

B 40a. Chalazae rho (3) unisetose on abdominal segments; f.g.l. near 25 mm.; Utetheisa . . . . (L10), Arctiidae*

B 41. —— Ventral prolegs present on fifth abdominal segment . . . . B 42

B 41a. Ventral prolegs absent or vestigial on fifth abdominal segment . . . . . . Geometridae

B 42. —— Each Pi (7) group of setae on ventral prolegs usually possesses two or three setae, if four or occasionally five setae occur the crochets are uniordinal and arranged in a mesoseries, also all spiracles are usually subequal in size . . . . .B 43

B 42a. Each Pi (7) group of setae on ventral prolegs usually possesses four setae; kappa (4) and eta (5) on the abdomen are close together on segments 1 to 3 and remote on seg-ments 4 to 8; on the prolegs the biordinal crochets are so arranged that they resemble a mesopenellipse; spiracles are elliptical with those on the prothorax and eighth ab-dominal segment twice as high and wide as those on other segments . . . . Epiplemidae

B 43. —— Transversely striped and spotted black by large contrasting pinacula and chalazae; eighth abdominal segment gibbose; f.g.l. 35+ . . . . (L28), Agaristidae

B 43a. May be longitudinally or transversely striped, if striped transversely the eighth ab-dominal segment is not gibbose and prominent chalazae are absent; f.g.l. medium to large; most species feed on external parts of plants, some live in the soil. . . . . (L34-40), Phalaenidae

SECTION C.

Section C includes mostly medium size to very large larvae possessing secondary setae which may be confined to the prolegs. Most of the families belong to the Macrolepidoptera (see asterisk) including butterflies and skippers.

C 1. —— Four distinct pairs of ventral prolegs and usually one anal pair (very few exceptions). . . . . C 4

C 1a. Six or less than four pairs of ventral prolegs and usually one pair of anal prolegs .C 2

C 2. —— Three or less pairs of ventral prolegs . . . . C 3

C 2a. Six pairs of ventral prolegs on segments 2 to 7 and one anal pair; the prolegs on seg-ments 2 and 7 without crochets; verrucae present bearing numerous fine setae . . . . (L23), Megalopygidae

C 3. —— One pair of fully developed ventral prolegs on the sixth abdominal segment and one pair of anal prolegs, all others rudimentary if present; most species are practically hairless; a living larva in motion has a looping movement; f.g.l. small to medium size. . . . . (L18, L56), Geometridae*

C 3a. Three pairs of ventral prolegs and one anal pair on segments 4, 5, 6 and 10 bearing crochets in a uniordinal or biordinal mesoseries; verrucae with few setae . . . . Nolidae*

C 4. —— Anal prolegs always present, however they may be rudimentary or elongated taillike structures . . . . C 5

C 4a. Anal prolegs absent; crochets of ventral prolegs in a pseudocircle; suranal plate

terminating in a process; f.g.l. medium sized, living on deciduous trees . . . .
. . . . Drepanidae*

C 5. —— Crochets on ventral prolegs uniordinal never greatly reduced in length near center. .
. . . . C 6

C 5a. Crochets on ventral prolegs biordinal or triordinal . . . . C 20

C 6. —— Verrucae absent, reduced or obscured by development of secondary setae . . . . C 7

C 6a. Verrucae, at least mu (6), well developed, distinct and possessing many setae; secondary setae sparse or absent except on prolegs. . . . . C 14

C 7. —— Anal plate simple, not bifurcate, head not definitely muricate and third ocellus usually
normal. . . . . C 8

C 7a. Anal plate bifurcate; head muricate; third ocellus very large; f.g.l. medium sized living on grasses . . . . Satyridae*

C 8. —— Body cylindrical or slightly depressed, not parasitic . . . . C 9

C 8a. Body very small, hemispherical in shape, head retractible; crochets in a complete
circle; parasites of fulgorids. . . . . Epipyropidae

C 9. —— Spiracles large and elliptical, ventral prolegs short . . . . C 10

C 9a. Spiracles small and circular; secondary seta may be numerous; ventral prolegs frequently long and slender with enlarged planta; chiefly leaf rollers, rarely within plant
stems. . . . . (L43), Pterophoridae

C 10. —— Secondary setae usually numerous, may obscure primary setae and verrucae. . C 11

C 10a. Secondary setae absent or sparse dorsad of prolegs; primary setae distinct, sometimes small . . . . C 12

C 11. —— Anal prolegs as well developed as ventral prolegs; notch of labrum deep with parallel
sides; verrucae, tufts and pencils of setae may be present but never cornicula on anal
plate or conspicuous dorsal humps . . . . (L38-39), Phalaenidae*

C 11a. Anal prolegs may be rudimentary or greatly elongated and narrow, with or without
crochets; elongated, scattered, secondary setae may be present but no tufts or pencils
of setae; dorsal humps (gibbose areas) may be present on one or more abdominal segments, cornicula may be present on anal plate . . . . (L25-26), Notodontidae*

C 12. —— Kappa (4) seta on seventh abdominal segment located a greater distance (usually ventrad) from the spiracle than on segments 6 or 8; gibbosities, horns, cuticular processes and stemapoda may be present . . . . C 13

C 12a. Kappa (4) seta on seventh abdominal segment located about the same distance (usually
ventrad) from the spiracle as occurs on segment 6 and 8; no humps, horns, or minute
cuticular processes present (Doa) . . . . Pericopidae*

C 13. —— Cuticle not shagreened or covered with minute processes; gibbosites, horns, and
stemapoda may occur; f.g.l. usually medium size and frequently highly pigmented . .
. . . . (L25-26), Notodontidae*

C 13a. Cuticle shagreened and covered with minute processes; form cylindrical except for a
dorsal gibbosity on the eighth segment; one species near Pacific coast . . . Dioptidae*

C 14 (6a) —No eversible glands present on dorsomeson of abdominal segments 6 and 7. . . . C 15

C 14a Eversible glands present on dorsomeson of abdominal segments 6 (may be absent) and
7; hairy, often with tufts and hair pencils; f.g.l. medium size to large, chiefly on deciduous trees. . . . . (L24), Liparidae*

C 15. —— Spiracles small, usually circular . . . . C 19

C 15a. Spiracles large, usually elliptical . . . . C 16

C 16. —— Kappa (4) verruca of seventh segment same distance from the spiracle as occurs on
segment 6 and 8 . . . . C 17

C 16a. Kappa (4) verruca of seventh segment a greater distance from spiracle than on segments 6 and 8; kappa may be reduced to one or a few setae or wanting on segment 7. .
. . . . C 18

C 17. —— Mesothorax with one large verruca above the spiracle line; f.g.l. medium size, chiefly
on shrubs . . . . (L10), Amatidae*

C 17a. Mesothorax with two or three verrucae above the spiracle line; most setae are plumose . . . . (L10), Arctiidae*

C 18. —— Crochets homoideous; mesothorax bearing two verrucae above the spiracle line (or
kappa verruca); labrum with a deep parallel sided notch; setae simple not plumose;
f.g.l. medium size to large. . . . . (L38), Phalaenidae*

C 18a.　　Crochets heteroideus; mesothorax usually bearing only one verruca above the spiracle line (or kappa verruca); verrucae conspicuous; f.g.l. small to medium size . . . . Pericopidae*

C 19(15).── Head small, retractible; prolegs short with crochets in a straight mesoseries; gland-like lobes may occur dorsad of prothoracic legs. . . . . (L58), Zygaenidae*

C 19a.　　Head exposed; prolegs usually long, slender and cylindrical bearing crochets in a circle or penellipse; secondary setae short and numerous on dorsal and ventral aspect on most segments . . . . (L43), Pterophoridae

C 20(5a).── Secondary setae present, at least numerous (more than eight) on each proleg . . . C 26

C 20a.　　Secondary setae almost absent, with no more than eight setae on each proleg . . . C 21

C 21. ── Crochets in a complete circle . . . . C 22

C 21a.　　Crochets in a mesoseries or pseudocircle. . . . . C 24

C 22. ── Alpha (1) and beta (2) simple on abdomen . . . . C 23

C 22a.　　Alpha (1) and beta (2), in form of verrucae, at least bisetose on abdomen. . .Scythridae

C 23. ── Head surface rough; body fusiform; larvae may build nests of leaves and later construct portable cases . . . . Lacosomidae*

C 23a.　　Head surface smooth; first abdominal segment widest; casebearers. . . . . Stenomidae

C 24. ──- Kappa group (prespiracular) of setae bisetose on prothorax; setae kappa (4) and eta (5) remote at least on abdominal segments 4 to 8. C 25

C 24a.　　Kappa group (prespiracular) of setae trisetose on prothorax; setae kappa (4) and eta (5) adjacent on abdominal segments . . . . (L28), Ethmiidae

C 25. ── Spiracles on prothoracic and eighth abdominal segments twice as large as those on other segments . . . . Epiplemidae*

C 25a.　　Spiracles all subequal in size. . . . . (L42), Thyatiridae*

C 26(20). ── Secondary setae usually short and more or less uniform in length; distinct verrucae or scoli may be present if secondary setae are long and irregular . . . . C 28

C 26a.　　Secondary setae very irregular in length, very long setae mixed with others one-tenth their length; distinct verrucae (a few exceptions) and scoli absent; thorax and abdomen often bear lateroventral, blunt, fleshy protuberances . . . . C 27

C 27. ── Labrum with an obtuse (shallow) notch never extending to base; may be very hairy or somewhat depressed with fleshy lateral protuberances; larvae may live in a communal web on deciduous trees. . . . . (L21), Lasiocampidae*

C 27a.　　Labrum with a deep notch which may be continued as a groove to its base; several unpaired pencils of hairs on the dorsomeson often present; usually cylindrical . . . . (L26), Zanolidae*

C 28. ── Eighth segment of abdomen armed with a mid-dorsal horn, scolus, chalaza, tubercle or scar. . . . . C 29

C 28a.　　Eighth segment of abdomen not armed with a mid-dorsal horn, scolus, chalaza, tubercle or scar . . . . C 33

C 29. ── Body usually armed with numerous branching scoli or enlarged verrucae (tubercles); primary setae on verrucae may be reduced to two fairly conspicuous setae . . . . C 30

C 29a.　　Body without numerous branching scoli, never more than two pairs of small spines on thorax; all setae short and inconspicuous . . . . C 32

C 30. ── Head rounded without scoli or spines . . . . .C 31

C 30a.　　Head distinctly conical or angulate or armed dorsally with scoli or spines, or abdomen with several mid-dorsal scoli; crochets usually triordinal . . . . .(L27), Nymphalidae*

C 31. ── Ninth abdominal segment not bearing a mid-dorsal scolus, if a scolus is present then scolus alpha (1a) of mesothorax is usually profusely branched (Hemileuca) and not distinctly longer than abdominal scoli; body spines usually subequal, may possess long poisonous spinules; anal plate smooth. . . . . (L54), Saturniidae*

C 31a.　　Ninth abdominal segment bearing a mid-dorsal scolus; scolus alpha (1a) on mesothorax at least twice the length of same scoli on abdominal segments 1 to 6; scoli never profusely branched; anal plate bearing at least one pair of small sclerotized processes. . . . .(L12), Citheroniidae*

C 32(29a).── Segments divided into 6 to 8 annulets; distance between bases of ventral prolegs usually no greater than length of each mesoseries of crochets; f.g.l. usually large, (hornworms) . . . . (L55-56), Sphingidae*

C 32a.　　Segments not divided into many annulets, never exceeding 3; distance between bases of

ventral prolegs greater than length of each mesoseries (silkworm). . . . .
. . . . (L58), Bombycidae*

C 33 (28a)—Head usually rounded, not distinctly triangular, may be rough and possesses scoli or
spines. . . . . C 34

C 33a.   Head elevated, smooth and distinctly triangular, cone shaped. .(L55), pars Sphingidae*

C 34. —— Ninth abdominal segment without a mid-dorsal scolus or spine. . . . . C 35

C 34a.   Ninth abdominal segment with an inconspicuous mid-dorsal scolus . . . .
. . . . (L12), (Anisota) Citheroniidae*

C 35. —— Crochets arranged in a continuous or interrupted mesoseries or pseudocircle; lateral
crochets (lateroseries), when present, rudimentary; long setae and scoli sometimes
present . . . . C 37

C 35a.   Crochets in a circle (rarely a mesopenellipse) usually triordinal with lateral crochets
about as well developed as mesal; secondary setae small or absent on dorsal-half of
body, never long or borne on scoli . . . . C 36

C 36. —— Body widest within region of ventral prolegs and distinctly tapering toward both ends;
head usually much larger than prothorax; an anal comb may be present; f.g.l. small to
medium size . . . . (L20), Hesperiidae*

C 36a.   Body cylindrical; head smaller than prothorax and partially retracted; f.g.l. large;
borers in Yucca and Maguey. . . . . (L20), Megathymidae*

C 37. —— Mesoseries of crochets on ventral prolegs without an interruption or fleshy lobe near
center. . . . . C 39

C 37a.   Mesoseries of crochets on ventral prolegs interrupted or reduced near center and
with a spatulatelike lobe located near the interruption; head small. . . . . C 38

C 38. —— Head one-half diameter of the body; secondary setae usually prominent; f.g.l. medium-
size living on Primula, Rumes, etc. . . . . Riodinidae*

C 38a.   Head rarely more than one-third diameter of body, distinctly retractible; secondary
setae may be numerous but not very prominent; f.g.l. very small to small . . . .
. . . . (L23), Lycaenidae*

C 39. —— No forked eversible gland (osmetarium) present on mid-dorsal area of prothorax; may
possess ventral prothoracic glands . . . . C 40

C 39a.   A forked eversible gland (osmetarium) present on mid-dorsal area of prothorax; if
retracted a dorsal groove occurs on the meson close to the head; no ventral prothoracic glands; f.g.l. medium size. . . . . (L33), Papilionidae*

C 40. —— Scoli or fleshy filaments well developed and conspicuous on body; if reduced large
scoli may occur on the head. . . . . , C 41

C 40a.   Scoli and fleshy filaments never present on body. . . . . .C 42

C 41. —— Mesothorax and frequently other segments, usually the eighth abdominal, possess long,
paired, fleshy filaments; secondary setae short and confined to prolegs. . . . .
. . . . (L33), Danaidae*

C 41a.   Mesothorax and other segments without fleshy filaments; distinct scoli on body segments which may also occur on the head . . . . (L27), Nymphalidae*

C 42. —— Suranal plate rounded, not bifurcate . . . . C 43

C 42a.   Suranal plate bifurcate at tip, bearing two distinct processes . . . . Satyridae*

C 43. —— Crochets of ventral prolegs arranged in a mesoseries. . . . . C 44

C 43a.   Crochets of ventral prolegs arranged in a pseudocircle with the lateroseries less conspicuous than mesoseries; most setae borne on chalazae; head small . . .Libytheidae*

C 44. —— Head distinctly larger than prothorax and may possess scoli or conspicuous chalazae
. . . . (L27), Nymphalidae *

C 44a.   Head subequal to but not distinctly larger than prothorax; most setae borne on chalazae
each segment usually divided into six annulets . . . . (L41), Pieridae*

KEY TO PYRALIDAE INJURIOUS TO STORED FOOD PRODUCTS

For additional Lepidoptera in stored food products see Hinton, 1943.

1. —— Distinct sclerotized areas (pinacula) about all setae (except epsilon, 3a in some cases) immediately dorsad and ventrad of the spiracles on abdominal segments 1-6 inclusive; pinacula may be darker or lighter than surrounding area 3

1a. No distinct sclerotized areas (pinacula) about setae immediately dorsad and ventrad of the spiracles on abdominal segments 1-6 inclusive 2

2. —— Spiracles conspicuous, somewhat elliptical with a thick dark peritreme; on the eighth abdominal segment the spiracle is much nearer seta rho (3) than seta eta (5); thoracic segments distinctly more deeply pigmented (stippled) than the abdominal segments; frequently found in moist waste grain, bran, or in mouldy grain; last instar 20± mm. . . . . (L49, P-S), meal moth, Pyralis farinalis L.

2a. Spiracles inconspicuous, circular with a narrow light colored peritreme; on the eighth abdominal segment the spiracle is approximately half way between setae rho (3) and eta (5); thoracic and abdominal segments uniformly light colored, no pigmented stippling; found in a wide variety of stored and prepared food products especially if nuts or protein are present; last instar 12± mm. . . . . (L49, A-B), Indian meal moth, Plodia interpunctella Hbn.

3. —— Entire body deeply pigmented brown to black due to the presence of numerous microscopic pigment spots stippled in the cuticle; peritremes of spiracles black; mandible with two sharp pointed dentes . . . . (L53, 1-L), murky meal caterpillar, Aglossa caprealis Hbn.

3a. Entire body lightly pigmented usually near white, cream, greenish yellow to pink, never a deep brown or near black; peritremes of spiracles light in color; mandibles usually possessing at least three dentes 4

4. —— On the eighth abdominal segment the greatest diameter of the spiracle is distinctly less than the distance between setae kappa (4) and eta (5); on the prothorax the diameter of the spiracle is distinctly less than the distance between the two setae of the kappa (prespiracular) group; most setae of considerable length; found in cured tobacco, nuts, chocolate and dried vegetable products; last instar 12 mm. . . . . (L49, J-M), tobacco moth, Ephestia elutella Hbn.

4a. On the eighth abdominal segment the greatest diameter of the spiracle equals or is somewhat greater than the distance between kappa (4) and eta (5) 5

5. —— All setae of moderate length; length of seta rho (3) on abdominal segments 1 to 7 usually less than one half the greatest diameter of any abdominal segment; on the eighth abdominal segment the distance between seta epsilon (3a) and the spiracle usually twice the diameter of the spiracle; found in stored grain, flour, cereals, pollen in beehives, etc.; last instar 15 mm. . . . . (L49, E-I), Mediterranean flour moth, Ephestia kuehniella Zell.

5a. All setae of unusual length; length of seta rho (3) on abdominal segments 1-7 usually much longer than one-half the greatest diameter of any abdominal segment; on the eighth abdominal segment the distance between seta epsilon (3a) and the spiracle subequal to the diameter of the spiracle; found in dried fruits etc.; last instar 11 mm. . . . . (L49, N-O), raisin moth, Ephestia figulilella Greg.

Note. Ephestia cautella Walk., the almond moth, from all reports resembles closely E. figulilella. Reared larvae of Ephestia cautella have not been seen by the author. For further information on all stages of Ephestia species see H. E. Hinton, 1943.

KEY TO PYRALIDAE INJURIOUS TO CORN, SUGARCANE AND RELATED PLANTS

Chiefly late instar larvae of Crambus, Diatraea, Elasmopalpus and Pyrausta. Many larvae of other families also attack these hosts.

1. —— Larvae spotted especially on dorsal aspect; all setae on the abdominal segments 1 to 8 arise from well defined usually disklike pigmented pinacula (hibernating forms may be without spots 2

1a. Larvae striped longitudinally on dorsal aspect; setae may arise from pigmented areas but these are not disklike pinacula. Living larvae are reddish brown on dorsal aspect and greenish blue on ventral areas. F.g.l. 18 mm. lesser corn stalk borer........ .... (L47,A-C) Elasmopalpus lignosellus (Zell).

2. —— On the dorsal aspect of abdominal segments 1 to 6 inclusive the distance between the sclerotized (usually pigmented) pinacula of setae alpha (1) of each segment usually less than one-half the lateromesal width of each pinaculum; coronal suture as long or longer than mesal length of the front (frons); the eighth abdominal spiracles distinctly elliptical (diameter measurement ratios somewhere between 1 to 4 and 3 to 4) and each possesses a deeply pigmented peritreme. (Crambus and Diatraea)............ 5

2a. On the dorsal aspect of abdominal segments 1 to 6 inclusive the distance between the sclerotized (usually pigmented) pinacula of setae alpha (1) of each segment always more than one-half (frequently subequal to or greater than) the lateromesal width of each pinaculum; coronal suture much shorter than the mesal length of the front (frons); the eight abdominal spiracles almost circular (diameter measurement ratios somewhere between 3 to 4 and 4 to 4) and each possesses a light amber colored peritreme (Pyrausta) 3

3. —— On the dorsal aspect of abdominal segments 2 to 6 the distance between the sclerotized (usually pigmented) pinacula about setae alpha (1) on each segment usually slightly less than the lateromesal width (not under one-half) of each pinaculum; no distinct pigmented spot adjacent to the spiracle on the prothoracic pinaculum; epicranial setae, A^1 and A^2, and puncture A^a form an obtuse angle with the puncture mesad of a line drawn through epicranial setae A^1 and A^2; length 20 mm. .... (L52, J-M), smartweed borer, Pyrausta ainsliei Hein.

3a. On the dorsal aspect of abdominal segments 2 to 6 the distance between the sclerotized (usually pigmented) pinacula about setae alpha (1) on each segment usually as great or greater than the lateromesal width of each pinaculum; epicranial setae A^1 and A^2 and puncture A^a usually located in a straight line or with puncture A^a somewhat laterad of seta A^2 4

4. —— Mandibles distinctly longer than wide; no distinct pigmented spot adjacent to the spiracle on the prothoracic Kappa (prespiracular) group pinaculum; length 20 mm........ .... (L52, N-P), lotus borer, Pyrausta penetalis Grt.

4a. Mandibles square, as wide as long; usually a distinct pigmented spot adjacent to the spiracle on the prothoracic Kappa (prespiracular) group pinaculum; length 27 mm. .. .. (L52, A-I), European corn borer, Pyrausta nubilalis Hbn.

5,(2).—— Pigmented pinaculum about seta rho (3) on abdominal segments 1 to 8 spot like and does not surround the spiracle, also the sclerotized area of the Kappa (prespiracular) group located cephalad of the spiracle and does not surround the spiracle 6

5a. Pigmented pinaculum about seta rho (3) on abdominal segments 1 to 8 irregular in shape and nearly surrounds the spiracle; sclerotized area of the Kappa (prespiracular) group enlarged and nearly surrounds the spiracle; larvae found in soil on roots .... (L47, I-K), corn root webworm, Crambus calliginosellus Clem.

6. —— On each half of the prothoracic cervical shield seta delta (2b) is distinctly closer to seta beta (2a) than seta rho (2c), also a line drawn through the two setae of the prespiracular (Kappa) group is almost parallel with a line drawn through the two setae of the subventral (Pi) group, lines drawn through setae alpha (1) and seta beta (2) on each half of abdominal segments 2 to 6 inclusive converge at sharp angle, approximately 30°;

length 25 mm. . . . . (L44, A-D), sugarcane borer, <u>Diatraea</u> <u>saccharalis</u> F.

6a. On each half of the prothoracic cervical shield seta delta (2b) is usually equally distinct from setae beta (2a) and rho (2c); also a line drawn through the two setae of the prespiracular (Kappa) group is distinctly not parallel with a line drawn through the two setae of the subventral (Pi) group; lines drawn through setae alpha (1) and seta beta (2) on each half of abdominal segments 2 to 6 inclusive converge at an obtuse angle, 45° or greater 7

7. —— Among summer forms of larvae the pigmentation of the head, the prothoracic cervical shield and especially the pinacula about the setae of the prespiracular (Kappa) and subventral (Pi) groups dark colored, also about the same degree of pigmentation as the pinacula of most setae of the thorax and abdomen; pigmentation of pinacula of setae sigma (8) on ventral aspects of abdominal segments 1, 2, 7 and 8 distinct; lines drawn through setae alpha (1) and seta beta (2) on each half of abdominal segments 2 to 6 inclusive converge at an angle approximately 45°, length 28 mm. . . . .(L44, I-P), southwestern corn borer, <u>Diatraea</u> <u>grandiosella</u> Dyar.

7a. Among summer forms of larvae the pigmentation of the prothoracic cervical shield and especially the pinacula about the setae of the prespiracular (Kappa) and subventral (Pi) groups light colored, not nearly as dark as the pigmentation of the pinacula about most setae of the thorax and abdomen; pigmentation of pinacula of setae sigma (8) on ventral aspects of abdominal segments 1, 2, 7 and 8 indistinct or absent; lines drawn through setae alpha (1) and seta beta (2) on each half of abdominal segments 2 to 6 inclusive converge at an angle of 50° or greater; length 30 mm. . . . .(L44, E-H), southern cornstalk borer, <u>Diatraea</u> <u>crambidoides</u> Grote.

The following alphabetical list of families of North America (larvae that are known) attempts to show the interrelationships existing between the family names accepted by (Fa.) S. B. Fracker 1915, (Fo.) W. T. M. Forbes 1923, (M.) J. McDunnough 1936 and (B.E.) Bureau of Entomology and Plant Quarantine (1942 list provided). The family names used in this publication are those found in J. McDunnough's 1938-39 check list of the Lepidoptera of Canada and the United States of America. The author is indebted to H. W. Capps, Carl Heinrich, W. T. M.

Forbes and J. McDunnough for assisting in the preparation of this list.

The Rhopalocera and the Heterocera-Jugate are indicated in the list. All others belong to the Heterocera-Frenate. An asterisk before a family name indicates that it belongs to the Macrolepidoptera while those without an asterisk, according to McDunnough 1936, belong to the Microlepedoptera.

Fa = S. B. Fracker, Fo = W. T. M. Forbes, BE = Bureau of Entomology and Plant Quarantine and M = McDunnough.

List of Families

Accepted by

Fa,		BE, M.	Acrolepiidae; pars Yponomeutidae of Fa and Fo, pars Plutellidae of M.
		BE, M.	Acrolophidae; pars Tineidae (Acrolophinae) of Fo.
Fa, Fo,	BE, M.	Adelidae; includes or equals Incurvariidae of Fa and Fo.
Fa,			Aegeriidae; equals Sesiidae of authors.
Fa, Fo,	M.	*Agapetidae; pars Nymphalidae of Fo, BE and M; equals Satyridae of authors.
		BE, M.	*Agaristidae; pars Phalaenidae of BE.
		BE, M.	Alucitidae; equals Orneodidae of Fa and Fo; equals Pterophoridae of authors.
			*Amatidae; equals Syntomidae of Fa, equals Euchromidae of Fo.
Fa, Fo,	BE, M.	Anthroceridae; includes Pyromorphidae and equals Zygaenidae of authors.
			*Arctiidae; includes Lithosiidae of authors.
			Argyresthiidae; pars Yponomeutidae of Fa, Fo, and M.
Fa, Fo,	BE, M.	Auzatidae; pars Drepanidae of Fo.
Fa, Fo,	BE, M.	Blastobasidae; pars Gelechiidae of authors.
Fa,			*Bombycidae (for introduced Bombyx mori L. only)
	Fo,	BE, M.	Bucculatrigidae; pars Lyonetiidae of Fo, BE and M.
Fa,			Carposinidae; pars Tortricidae or Gelechiidae of authors.
			*Ceratocampidae; equals Citheroniidae of Fo, BE and M.
		BE,	Choreutidae; equals or pars Glyphipterygidae of Fa and BE.
	Fo,	BE, M.	Crysaugidae; equals Chrysauginae of Pyralidae of Fa, Fo, and M.
Fa,			*Citheroniidae; equals Ceratocampidae of Fa.
Fa, Fo,	BE, M.	Cochlidiidae; equals Eucleidae of Fo, equals Limacodidae of BE and M.
			Coleophoridae;
Fa,		BE, M.	Conchylidae; equals Phaloniidae of Fo, BE and M.
Fa, Fo,	BE, M.	Cosmopterygidae; equals Laverniidae of Fo.
		BE,	Cossidae; includes Zeuzeriidae.
	Fo,		Crambidae; equals Crambinae-Pyralidae of Fa, Fo, and M.
			Cycnodiidae; equals Elachistidae of Fa, BE and M.
		BE, M.	*Cymatophoridae; equals Thyatiridae of Fa, Fo, BE, and M.
		BE, M.	Dalceridae
			*Danaidae; equals Lymnadidae of Fa; pars Nymphalidae of Fo; includes Ithomiidae in part of Fa.
Fa, Fo,	BE, M.	Depressariidae; equals or pars Oecophoridae of Fa, Fo, BE, and M.
	Fo,	BE, M.	*Dioptidae.
			Douglasiidae; pars Elachistidae and pars Glyphiterygidae of authors.
	Fo,	BE, M.	Drepanulidae; equals Drepanidae of Fo, equals Platypterygidae of Fa.
Fa,		BE, M.	*Drepanidae; equals Platypterygidae of Fa.
		M.	Elachistidae; equals Cycnodiidae of Fo;
			Epermeniidae

				Epiblemidae; pars Tortricidae of authors.
		BE,		Epipaschiidae; equals Epipaschininae-Pyralidae of Fo. and M.
Fa,	Fo,	BE,	M.	*Epiplemidae
Fa,	Fo,	BE,	M.	Epipyropidae
				Eriocephalidae; equals Micropterygidae of Fo.
	Fo,	BE,	M.	Eriocraniidae; pars Micropterygidae of Fa (Heterocera-Jugate)
	Fo,			*Erycinidae; equals Riodinidae of Fa, BE and M.
Fa,		BE,	M.	Ethmiidae; pars Oecophoridae of Fo.
	Fo,			*Euchromiidae; equals Syntomidae of Fa, Amatidae of BE and M.
	Fo,			Eucleidae; equals Cochlidiidae of Fa; equals Limacodidae of BE and M.
				Eucosmidae; equals Oleuthreutidae of BE; pars Tortricidae of authors.
Fa,	Fo,			*Eupterotidae; pars Zanolidae of BE and M.
		BE,		Galleriidae; equals Gallerinae and Macrothecinae-Pyralidae of Fa, Fo, and M.
Fa,	Fo,	BE,	M.	Gelechiidae;
Fa,	Fo,	BE,	M.	*Geometridae
	Fo,	BE,	M.	Glyphipterygidae; equals Hemerophylidae of Fa; equals Choreutidae and includes Douglasiidae of authors.
Fa,	Fo,	BE,	M.	Gracilariidae; pars Tineidae of authors.
				Grapholithidae; pars Tortricidae of authors.
Fa,				*Heliconiidae; pars Nymphalidae of Fo, BE, and M.
Fa,	Fo,	BE,	M.	Heliodinidae; Fa includes Heliozelidae;
	Fo,	BE,	M.	Heliozelidae; pars Heliodinidae of Fa.
Fa,				Hemerophilidae; equals or pars of Glyphipterygidae of Fo, BE and M.
Fa,				*Hemileucidae; pars Saturniidae of Fo, BE and M.
Fa,	Fo,	BE,	M.	Hepialidae (Heterocera-Jugatae)
Fa,	Fo,	BE,	M.	*Hesperiidae; Fa and M exclude Megathymidae.
		BE,		*Hyblaeidae; pars Phalaenidae of M. belongs to micro pyraloids by BE
		BE,		Hyponomeutidae; equals Yponomeutidae of Fa and Fo except Scythrididae, includes Yponomeutidae and Plutellidae of M.
Fa,	Fo,		M.	Incurvariidae; equals or includes Adelidae and Prodoxidae of BE.
Fa,				*Ithomiidae; pars Nymphalidae and Danaidae of authors.
				*Lachneidae; equals Lasiocampidae.
Fa,	Fo,		M.	*Lacosomidae; equals Mimallonidae of BE, a micro.
				Lagoidae; equals Megalopygidae.
Fa,	Fo,	BE,	M.	*Lasiocampidae; equals Lachneidae of authors.
	Fo,			Lavernidae; equals Cosmopterygidae of Fa, BE and M.
Fa,		BE,	M.	*Libytheidae; pars Nymphalidae of Fo; (Rhopalocera)
		BE,	M.	Limacodidae; equals Eucleidae of Fo, equals Cochlidiidae of Fa.
Fa,	Fo,		M.	*Liparidae; equals Lymantriidae of BE.
Fa,	Fo,			*Lithosiidae; pars Arctiidae of BE and M.
Fa,	Fo,	BE,	M.	*Lycaenidae; Fo includes Riodinidae; (Rhopalocera)
		BE,		*Lymantriidae; equals Liparidae of Fa, Fo, and M.
Fa,				*Lymnadidae; equals Danaidae of BE and M, pars Nymphalidae of Fo; (Rhopalocera)
Fa,	Fo,	BE,	M.	Lyonetiidae, Fa excludes Bucculatrix-Bucculatrigidae.
Fa,	Fo,	BE,	M.	Megalopygidae; equals Lagoidae of authors.
Fa,			M.	*Megathymidae; pars Hesperiidae of Fo and BE.
Fa,	Fo,	BE,	M.	Micropterygidae; Fa includes Eriocraniidae of Fo, BE and M; (Heterocera-Jugate).
		BE,		Mimallonidae; equals Lacosomidae of Fa, Fo and M.
		BE,		Momphidae, equals Lavernidae of Fo., equals or pars Cosmopterygidae of Fa and M.
Fa,	Fo,	BE,	M.	Nepticulidae.
Fa,	Fo,			*Noctuidae; equals Phalaenidae of BE and M.
Fa,	Fo,	BE,	M.	*Nolidae.
Fa,	Fo,	BE,	M.	*Notodontidae.
Fa,	Fo,	BE,	M.	*Nymphalidae; Fa excludes Agapetidae, Libytheidae, Lymnadidae and Heliconiidae; Fo includes Satyridae; (Rhopalocera).

Fa,	Fo,	BE,	M.	Oecophoridae; Fo includes Ethmiidae; includes Depressariidae of authors
			M.	Oinophilidae (may be a tineid BE).
		BE.	M.	Oleuthreutidae; pars Tortricidae of Fa and Fo; equals Eucosmidae of authors.
	Fo,	BE.	M.	Opostegidae, pars Neptidulidae of Fa.
Fa,	Fo,			Orneodidae; equals Alucitidae of BE and M.
Fa,	Fo,	BE,	M.	*Papilionidae; includes Parnassiidae of Fa; (Rhopalocera)
Fa,				*Parnassiidae; pars Papilionidae of Fo, BE, and M; (Rhopalocera)
Fa,	Fo,	BE,	M.	*Pericopidae
		BE,	M.	*Phalaenidae; equals Noctuidae and Agaristidae of Fa and Fo; BE includes Agaristidae and excludes Hyblaeidae.
	Fo,	BE,	M.	Phaloniidae; pars Tortricidae of Fa.
		BE,		Phycidae; pars Phycitinae and Anerastiine-Pyralidae of Fa, Fo and M.
Fa,	Fo,	BE,	M.	*Pieridae; (Rhopalocera)
Fa,				*Platypterygidae; equals Drepanidae of Fo, BE and M.
			M.	Plutellidae; pars Yponomeutidae of Fa and Fo and Hyponomeutidae of BE.
Fa,		BE,	M.	Prodoxidae; pars Incurvariidae of Fo.
Fa,	Fo,	BE,	M.	Psychidae.
Fa,	Fo,	BE,	M.	Pterophoridae; equals Alucitidae of authors.
Fa,	Fo,	BE,	M.	Pyralidae; BE excludes the Chrysaugidae, Crambidae, Epipaschiidae, Galleriidae, Phycitidae, Pyraustidae and Schoenobiidae which have sub-family rating by M.
		BE,		Pyraustidae; equals Glaphyriidae, Nymphulinae, Pyraustinae and Scopariinae of Pyralidae of authors.
Fa,	Fo,			Pyromorphidae; equals Zygaenidae of BE and M; pars Anthroceridae of authors.
Fa,		BE,	M.	*Riodinidae; pars Lycaenidae of Fo; (Rhopalocera)
Fa,	Fo,	BE,	M.	*Saturniidae; Fa excludes Hemileucidae.
		BE,	M.	*Satyridae; equals Agapetidae of Fa, pars Nymphalidae of Fo; (Rhopalocera).
		BE,		Schoenobiidae, pars Schoenobiinae-Pyralidae of Fa, Fo and M.
		BE,	M.	Scythrididae or Scythridae; pars Yponomeutidae of Fa and Fo.
				Sesiidae; equals Aegeriidae of Fa, Fo, BE and M.
				Sparganothidae; pars Tortricidae of Fa, Fo, Be and M.
Fa,	Fo,	BE,	M.	*Sphingidae
Fa,		BE,	M.	Stenomatidae (Stenomidae) equals Xylorictidae of Fo.
Fa,				*Syntomidae; equals Euchromidae of Fo; equals Amatidae of BE and M.
Fa,	Fo,	BE,	M.	*Thyatiridae; Cymatophoridae of authors.
Fa,	Fo,	BE,	M.	Thyrididae; equals Thyridae of authors.
Fa,	Fo,	BE,	M.	Tineidae; Fo includes Acrolophidae.
Fa,	Fo,	BE,	M.	Tischeriidae.
Fa,	Fo,	BE,	M.	Tortricidae; Fo excludes Carposinidae and Phaloniidae; BE and M exclude Carposinidae, Oleuthreutidae and Phaloniidae; include Carposinidae, Epiblemidae, Eucosmidae, Grapholithidae, Oleuthreutidae, Phaloniidae, Sparganothidae of authors.
	Fo,			Xylorictidae; equals Stenomidae of Fa, BE and M; Uzuchidae of authors.
Fa,	Fo,		M.	Yponomeutidae; equals Hyponomeutide of BE with Scythrididae excluded; Fa, and Fo include Scythrididae; M excludes Plutellidae and Scythrididae; also includes Acrolepiidae, Argyresthiidae and pars Glyphipterygidae of authors.
		BE,	M.	*Zanolidae; equals Eupterotidae of Fa and Fo; pars Notodontidae of authors.
				Zeuzeriidae; included in Cossidae of authors.
		BE,	M.	Zygaenidae; equals Pyromorphidae of Fa and Fo; equals Anthroceridae of authors.

DESCRIPTIONS OF THE LARVAE OF MOST FAMILIES OF LEPIDOPTERA

The families are presented in alphabetical order. The names accepted are those found in McDunnough's, 1938-39, "Check List of the Lepidoptera of Canada and the United States of America." For other names accepted by S. B. Fracker, W. T. M. Forbes, the Bureau of Entomology and Plant Quarantine (Carl Heinrich) and various investigators see list of family names, page 78. For the taxonomic position of the families see McDunnough 1938-39. The description of a few families are omitted (Epermenidae and Riodinidae) because the author has not seen representatives or very little published information exists about the larvae. The number of species recorded after each family name is the number of species recorded by McDunnough, 1938-39.

The information of habits of the family is very general, restricted largely to the feeding habits of the larvae. For those families the author has not seen he has derived most of the information presented from various authors especially from Fracker, 1915 and Forbes, 1923. The descriptions present the most significant morphological characters of late instar larvae common to most members of each family. The size character, tiny and very small to very large, refer to the length of full grown larvae (f.g.l.). For details see f.g.l. in glossary. In most cases the morphological characters are presented in the following order, size, shape and color, head, thorax, abdomen, body armature, particularly the distribution of primary and and secondary setae, spines, verrucae, scoli, etc., spiracles, prolegs and the crochets and anal structures. The term primary setae used in the descriptions includes all subprimary setae if present.

ACROLOPHIDAE, L3, L6, L11.

Tineoidea, 46 species, burrowing web-worms etc.

Habits. A few known larvae feed on grasses, corn and leaves, some species constructing tubular webs near the surface of the ground.

Description. Full grown larvae are small to medium sized, approximately 20 to 30 mm. On the head the adfrontal areas are unusually wide and reach the vertical triangle. Six ocelli are present on each side with the first and second distinctly remote from the third and fourth which are adjacent to each other. The nine most dorsal setae on the prothorax (including the Kappa group) are usually located on a continuous sclerotized area. Seta kappa of the prothoracic Kappa group is nearer theta (seta nearest the spiracle) than eta which is the most cephalic of the three setae. The most striking character of the family is the multiserial arrangement of the crochets in a circle or ellipse on the ventral prolegs. The innermost set of crochets is uniordinal and of average size and shape while the crochets in all other rows are minute hooks or rudimentary sclerotized pieces.

ADELIDAE

Incurvarioidea, 12 species, flat casebearers.

Habits. The larvae live in leaves, needles, flowers and seeds of a number of plants. When nearly mature most species form a lenticular case of two, flat, oval pieces of leaf in which they pupate.

Description. Full grown larvae are small, very small or tiny. The body is cylindrical with shallow intersegmental incisions. The head is as high as broad bearing a triangular front, which extends two-thirds of the way to the vertical triangle, and distinct adfrontal areas that reach the vertical triangle. All setae are primary. Some are indistinct or absent dorsad of the spiracles on the prothorax and most abdominal segments. The prothoracic Kappa (prespiracular) group is trisetose. On the abdomen kappa (4) and eta (5) are adjacent and near the caudal edge of the spiracle. Thoracic legs present. Two multiserial transverse bands of crochets on ventral prolegs 3 to 6. Crochets may be reduced on sixth segment and anal prolegs absent.

AEGERIIDAE, L6-9

Yponomeutoidea, 122 species, borers, clear wing moths.

Habits. The larvae are chiefly wood borers attacking stems. trunks, crowns, or roots of many plants some of which are peach, plum, locust, poplar, willow, spruce, pine, dogwood, currant, gooseberry, strawberry, cucurbs, etc.

Description. Full grown larvae are 20 to 35 mm. The body color is usually near white with rather deep intersegmental incisions. The head is smaller than the prothorax and pigmented, frequently brown. Primary setae only are present. On the prothorax seta beta is more mesad than alpha, seta rho is closely associated with gamma and epsilon, also three setae are present in the Kappa (prespiracular) group. On abdominal segments 1 to 7 setae kappa (4) and eta (5) are adjacent while on segment 9 all setae are arranged in nearly a single row. The somewhat elliptical spiracles on abdominal segments 1 to 7 are on the same line while the spiracles on the eighth abdominal segment are larger and more dorsad. The four ventral prolegs on segments 3 to 6 bear two transverse rows of uniordinal crochets while the anal prolegs possess only one transverse row of uniordinal crochets. The number, size and position of the crochets is of some value in determining species.

AGARISTIDAE, L1-3, L28.

Noctuoidea, 16 species, foresters, wood moths.

Habits. The larvae are chiefly leaf feeders especially on grape, Virginia creeper, fireweed and Mertensia.

Description. Full grown larvae are medium sized, 25 to 40 mm. All species examined possess a distinct tooth or ridgelike retinaculum on the inner (oral) aspect of each mandible. They closely resemble some of the larvae of the Phalaenidae in that they possess a bisetose Kappa (prespiracular) group on the prothorax and a unisetose Pi (6) group on the mesothorax and metathorax. Nearly all species are transversely striped and usually possess primary setae located on conspicuous pinacula or chalazae. The eighth abdominal segment may be much enlarged or humped (gibbose). The ventral prolegs bear uniserial, uniordinal crochets arranged in a mesoseries.

ALUCITIDAE

Pyralidoidea, 1 species, many-plume moth.

Habits. Larvae reported from flowers or Centaurea and Knautia, also from stems, fruits, and flowers of Compositae and Lonicera.

Description. Full grown larvae are small, rough and granulose. Each possesses a small prognathous head, a front which extends two-thirds of distance to the vertical triangle and inconspicuous adfrontal areas. The cylindrical, pale, colored body bears primary setae only. Prothoracic Kappa (perspiracular) group and Pi (subventral) group are bisetose. Also prothoracic seta rho is caudad of and slightly below epsilon. On the abdomen alpha (1) is nearer the dorsomeson than beta (2), rho (3) is dorsad of the spiracle, kappa (4) and eta (5) are adjacent and mu (6) is present. Spiracles are circular, slightly larger on the prothorax and more dorsad on segment 8 than on segments 1 to 7. Short prolegs occur on segments 3 to 6 bearing uniordinal crochets arranged in a complete circle on the ventral prolegs.

AMATIDAE, L10.

Noctuoidea, 25 species.

Habits. Larvae of a number of species feed on grasses, lichens, oleander and other plants.

Description. Full grown larvae are small and they resemble Arctiidae. The smooth head bears a small front in the form of an equilateral triangle, inconspicuous secondary setae (rarely wanting) and a labrum somewhat acute at tip. Verrucae on the body are usually well developed. On the prothorax Kappa (prespiracular) and Pi (subventral) verrucae are large but rho is rudimentary. On the mesothorax and metathorax all setae above the Kappa and Pi groups are merged into one verruca which is distinctive of the family (Pericopidae the only exception). On abdominal segments 1 to 8, alpha (1), beta (2), rho (3), kappa (4), eta (5) and mu (6) are distinct and separate verrucae. Kappa (4) may be small but in the same position on segment 7 as on other segments. Verrucae alpha (1) are usually contiguous on the abdominal segments and secondary setae are rare or absent. Thoracic legs present. Prolegs present on segments 3 to 6 but may be reduced or wanting on 10. Crochets are uniordinal and arranged in a homoideous or heteroideous mesoseries.

ARCTIIDAE; L3, L6-8, L10.

Noctuoidea, 201 species, woolly bears, webworms, hedgehog, tussock moth and tiger moth caterpillars.

Habits. The larvae are foliage feeders of a wide variety of plants namely grasses, weeds, cultivated garden crops, shrubs, deciduous trees, etc. Some species live within silken webs or nests.

Description. Full grown larvae vary considerably in size, however, most species are medium sized, 25 to 50 mm. The head is smooth but may possess a few secondary setae. Front about as wide as high and extends half way to vertical triangle. Except for Utetheisa and most Lithosiinae many plumose setae arising from verrucae cover the entire body of most species. The setae may be more or less uniform in length or prominent paired tufts may exist. Verrucae beta and rho of the mesothorax and metathorax are distinct (not fused). Kappa verrucae of the abdominal segments 1 to 8 are located near the spiracles and rarely is the kappa verruca on segment 7 further removed from the spiracle than on segments 6 or 8. If verrucae are absent then the setae, usually plumose, are borne on chalazae or somewhat elevated pinacula, also the pi group (6) of the mesothorax and metathorax is bisetose. Among the Lithosiinae chalazae rho (3) of most abdominal segments is bisetose and unisetose among the Utetheisa. Prolegs are present on abdominal segments 3 to 6 and 10. The four ventral prolegs possess uniordinal crochets arranged in a heteroideous mesoseries (homoideous among the Lithosiinae). The tarsi of the thoracic legs may possess spatulate setae near the distal ends.

BLASTOBASIDAE

Gelechioidea, 102 species, blastobasids.

Habits. The few larvae known are found in nuts, acorns, fruit mummies, phylloxera galls, apple buds, sumac heads, and elsewhere. Some species are scavengers while others are predacious on insect borers and scale insects.

Description. Full grown larvae are small. They closely resemble Oecophoridae and Gelechiidae. All setae are primary. On the prothorax the kappa (prespiracular) group is trisetose. On the abdomen kappa (4) and eta (5) are adjacent. On the eighth abdominal segment rho (3) is caudodorsad of the spiracle while kappa (4) is cephaloventrad. Thoracic legs are present with the coxae of the prothoracic pair touching each other. Prolegs occur on segments 3 to 6 and 10 bearing uniordinal crochets arranged in a complete series (circle) which may be irregular.

BOMBYCIDAE, L58.

Bombycoidea, 1 species, silkworm.

Habits. The larvae feed on mulberry foliage and spin cocoons from which the silk is obtained.

Bombyx mori L.

Description. Full grown larvae are medium

sized, approximately 45 mm. A silkworm resembles a sphingid larva in that it has a caudal horn, however the numerous annulets, so characteristic of sphingids, are absent in Bombyx mori. Numerous small secondary setae occur on all segments and the head. They are somewhat longer on the prolegs and the ventrolateral areas. Prolegs occur on segments 3 to 6 and 10 bearing biordinal crochets arranged in a mesoseries. The bases of the ventral prolegs are far apart usually more distant than the length of a given mesoseries of crochets.

CARPOSINIDAE

Tortricoidea, 7 species, borers, fruit worms.

Habits. The larvae are fruit borers of several plants namely, currants, peaches and species of Rosa, Barberis, etc.

Description. Full grown larvae are small, usually under 12 mm. Primary setae only are present. On the prothorax the Kappa (prespiracular) group is bisetose, also the Pi (subventral) group is bisetose. Pi groups unisetose, on mesothorax, metathorax and eighth abdominal segment, bisetose on first and seventh and trisetose on second to sixth abdominal segments. On the abdomen kappa (4) is above eta (5) on segments 1 to 6. On the ninth segment setae beta (2) are well separated but on a single piniculum. Spiracles on the eighth abdominal segment are conspicuous, project caudad and are nearer the dorsomeson than seta alpha (1) of the seventh segment. Prolegs are present on segments 3 to 6 and 10 bearing uniordinal crochets arranged in a circle.

CITHERONIIDAE; L7, L12.

Saturnioidea, 19 species, royal moths.

Habits. The larvae feed on foliage of shrubs and trees especially on oaks, hickory, pine, butternut and other forest trees.

Description. Full grown larvae are medium sized to very large. Late instar larvae possess a mid-dorsal spine, often rudimentary, usually in the form of a scolus on the ninth abdominal segment. The anal plate is spined or tuberculate. On the mesothorax scoli alpha are at least twice as long as any scoli on abdominal segments 1 to 6. The scoli are not profusely branched. Short or long secondary setae may be present on the head and all segments. They are always present and conspicuous on the prolegs. Prolegs occur on segments 3 to 6 and 10 bearing biordinal crochets arranged in a mesoseries.

COLEOPHORIDAE, L13-14.

Tineoidea, 109 species, leaf miners, casebearers.

Habits. The larvae may be leaf miners at least in their early instars may produce portable cases frequently made from leaf tissues. Some common species feed on the foliage or seeds of many plants including pomaceous and stone fruit trees. Some other plants are aster, elm, hickory, larch, pecan willows, Alnus, Polygonum, Stellaria, Solidago, Viburnum, Tilia and Juncus (seeds).

Description. Full grown larvae are cylindrical and tiny or very small, most species under 5 mm. The head, cervical shield of the prothorax, suranal plate and some pinacula on the thorax may be deeply pigmented, brown or near black. The head possesses adfrontal areas that reach the vertical triangle and several ocelli which are close together. On many species the primary setae are inconspicuous or absent. The coxae on the thorax are far apart, usually a distance greater than the width of the respective coxae. The spiracles are small and circular with the eighth pair larger and more dorsad than the remainder. Prolegs, if present, occur on segments 3 to 6 and 10. The crochets on the ventral prolegs are uniordinal and arranged in two transverse rows. The bands of crochets on the right and left ventral prolegs of a given segment may be so close to each other that they appear to be continuous. On the ventral prolegs the number of crochets in each band may be small, 1 to 6 or absent. Each anal proleg bears a single transverse row of crochets.

LEPIDOPTERA

COSMOPTERYGIDAE, L13.

Gelechioidea, 92 species, leaf miners, borers.

Habits. Many species feed on the surface of plant foliage while others are miners or borers in leaves, stems, flower parts, seeds and fruit of various plants. Some of the host plants are palmetto, cat-tails, thorns of locust, fruit of evening primrose, etc.

Description. Full grown larvae are small or very small, most species under 12 mm. They are cylindrical or somewhat depressed especially the head. Adfrontal areas almost reach the vertical triangle and the ocelli are close together with the distances between the fourth, fifth and sixth subequal. Small primary setae only are present. On the ninth abdominal segment setae beta (2) are much farther apart than the distance between beta (2) and alpha (1) on each side, also beta (2), alpha (1) and rho (3) are arranged in nearly a transverse line. The thoracic legs are far apart with the distance between the metathoracic coxae usually one and one-half to two times the diameter of each coxa. Prolegs are far apart and usually occur on segments 3 to 6 and 10. The ventral prolegs bear a complete circle of uniordinal or biordinal crochets.

COSSIDAE, L11.

Tortricoidea, 42 species, cossids, carpenter moth, wood moth and leopard moth.

Habits. The larvae of most species are borers in wood of several shrubs and many common deciduous trees including pomaceous and stone fruit species.

Description. Full grown larvae of most species are large usually 50+ mm. Their general color is near white, yellow to pink and some possess a dorsal dusky pigmentation. The head is conspicuous, deeply pigmented and broad yet smaller than the enlarged thorax (usually the prothorax) which is the broadest of the body. Front one-third to one-half the length of the head capsule. Labrum truncate with a slight emargination. Mandibles very large.

The setal pattern, except for details noted (see key), is very similar to that of the Tortricidae. Except for a few (two or more) secondary setae dorsad of the spiracles, among some species, primary setae only are present. On the prothorax seta rho is directly caudad of epsilon and the Kappa (prespiracular) group is trisetose while on the abdomen setae kappa (4) and eta (5) are adjacent and epsilon (3a), if present, is usually cephalad of the spiracle. On segment nine beta (2) is located dorsad of alpha (1). Prolegs occur on segments 3 to 6 and 10 bearing biordinal or triordinal crochets arranged in a complete circle or uniordinal crochets arranged in two transverse rows (Cossula).

DANAIDAE, L2, L33.

Papilionoidae, 7 species, milkweed and monarch caterpillars.

Habits. The larvae feed on foliage of several plants chiefly milkweek, oleander and Ficus.

Description. Full grown larvae are medium sized, 35 to 50 mm. Transverse black and green stripes occur on most segments and on the head. The head is as large as the prothorus deeply pigmented with black stripes and covered with numerous short secondary setae. The primary setae of the body are inconspicuous and most secondary setae are confined to the prolegs. Paired fleshy filaments occur on the dorsal aspect. Among North American species paired fleshy filaments are never found on more than three segments with one pair always present on the mesothorax. Prolegs occur on segments 3 to 6 and 10, bearing triordinal crochets arranged in a mesoseries.

LEPIDOPTERA

DIOPTIDAE

Noctuoidea, 1 species, California oak worm.

Habits. The larvae feed on foliage of several oaks and occasionally on chestnut, eucalyptus and other plants near the Pacific Coast. Phyganidia californica Pack.

Description. Full grown larvae are medium sized. They are cylindrical, noctuiform and olive green with black and yellow longitudinal stripes on the dorsal and lateral aspects. The head is reddish brown. Primary setae are inconspicuous while the secondary setae are confined to the prolegs. Microscopic cuticular projections are present, only visible under high magnification, producing a shagreened surface. Prolegs are present on segments 3 to 6 and 10 bearing uniordinal crochets arranged in a mesoseries. See Burke and Herbert, 1920.

DREPANIDAE, L1, L3.

Drepanoidea, 6 species, long-tailed caterpillars.

Habits. The larvae feed on the foliage of several deciduous shrubs and the trees, some of these are birch, alder, Viburnum and Cornel.

Description. Full grown larvae are small most species not exceeding 30 mm. Head about as high as wide and somewhat bigibbous. No secondary setae present (Fracker, 1915). On the prothorax the Kappa (prespiracular) group is bisetose, setae epsilon and rho are much more cephalad than in most Macrolepdoptera, also the Pi (subventral) group possesses several setae located on fleshy protuberances. On the metathorax the setae above the spiracular level have the usual distribution while below eta (5) of mu (6) setae are variously arranged usually two on a level with mu (6) of the abdomen and several in a Pi group near the base of the legs. On the abdomen alpha (1), beta (2) epsilon (3a) and rho (3) separate and above the spiracles, kappa (4) caudad of the spiracle and eta below, mu (6) also present. At the base of the prolegs three setae are present and three more on the lateral aspect of each proleg. Setae are usually borne on small chalazae with great variation on the ventral aspect, though never numerous. All spiracles are elliptical with those on the prothorax about twice the size of all others. Prolegs occur on segments 3 to 6. Anal prolegs are absent. The crochets are biordinal or uniordinal arranged in a mesoseries and a rudimentary lateroseries producing a psuedocircle. The suranal plate terminates in an acute spine or process.

ELACHISTIDAE, L14.

Cycnodioidea, 46 species, grass leaf miners.

Habits. Among most species, especially the Elachista and Dicranocletes, all instars of the larvae of North American species are leaf miners on various grasses and sedges, especially species of Carex, Elymus, Glyveria, Hystria, Poa, and Juncaceae.

Description. Full grown larvae of most species are very small probably none exceeding 10 mm. in length. The entire body is spindle-shaped, somewhat cylindrical and deeply segmentes. The general color is usually near white, pale yellow or pale green. The head is prognathous, somewhat elongated, definitely depressed, distinctly sclerotized, pigmented and narrower than the prothorax. Five pairs of ocelli may be present adjacent to the sharp lateral margins of the head capsule and near the antennae. The front and adfrontal areas reach the vertical triangle. Primary setae may occur on the various segments. These may be inconspicuous especially on the dorsal aspect. Spiracles occur in the usual position. They are circular inconspicuous and all approximately the same size. On the thorax three pairs of segmented legs occur which may be very small. Also on the thorax pigmented sclerotized areas may exist especially on the ventral and dorsal aspects of the prothorax. Prolegs occur on segments 3 to 6 and 10. The crochets are uniserial, uniordinal and frequently arranged in a partial circle which may form a lateropenellipse.

LEPIDOPTERA

EPIPLEMIDAE

Uranioidea, 5 species, epiplemids.

Habits. The larvae feed on Viburnum pru-nifolium, Lonicera dioica, etc. usually living in a web in their early development.

Description. Full grown larvae are small. The usual minutely rugose head, about as high as wide and somewhat bilobed, possesses a front which extends halfway to the vertical triangle and a moderately emarginate labrum. Only primary setae exist on the various segments. On the prothorax the Kappa (prespiracular) group and the Pi (subventral) group are bisetose. On the abdomen kappa (4) and eta (5) are below the spiracle and approximately at the same level. On segments 1 to 3 they are close together while on segments 4 to 8 they are separated. Also mu (6) on the abdomen is bisetose. The additional seta is a subprimary called lambda. The Pi group consists of one seta on segment A1, two setae on segment A2, four setae on segments A3 to A6 and one seta on segments A7 to A9. On the ninth abdominal segment beta (2) is nearest the dorso meson with alpha (1) as far from beta (2) as from rho (3). All spiracles are elliptical with those on the prothorax and on segment 8 two times as high and wide as those on all other abdominal segments. Prolegs occur on segments 3 to 6 and 10 bearing biordinal crochets arranged in a curved mesoseries closely resembling a penellipse.

EPIPYROPIDAE

Zygaenoidea, 2 species, fulgorid caterpillars.

Habits. The larvae are parasitic on fulgorids.

Description. Full grown larvae are very small. The body is hemispherical and depressed with a retractible head. Secondary setae are sparsely scattered over the entire body. Each claw of the thoracic legs bears a long spinelike structure near its base. The prolegs bear uniordinal degenerate claws somewhat irregular in position and length yet arranged in a complete circle.

ERIOCRANIIDAE

Jugate, 5 species, leaf miners.

Habits. The larvae produce blotch mines in leaves of deciduous trees especially oak, chestnut, chinquapin, and Amentiferae.

Description. Full grown larvae are small, under 10 mm. They are distinctly flattened and broadest at the prothorax and gradually becoming smaller to the tiny caudal end. The large prognathous head bears broad adfrontal areas adjacent to a front which extends to the vertical triangle and antennae located at the cephalic ends of the adfrontal areas. Ocelli, when present, are reduced to one large pair located at the cephalic ends of the epicranial sutures. Setae are reduced, however, alpha (1) and beta (2) are present on the abdomen. Segmented, thoracic legs are absent. Rudimentary prolegs, may be present on abdominal segments 1 to 8.

ETHMIIDAE, L28.

Gelechioidea, 31 species, ethmiids.

Habits. The larvae feed on several plants of the Borginaceae and Hydrophyllaceae, some of which are species of Thalictrum, Phacelia and Lithospermum. They are social and may spin a light web. Information from A. F. Braun.

Description. Full grown larvae are small to medium sized and may be striped with deep pigmented areas. The head is somewhat smaller than the prothorax bearing primary setae only. The adfrontal areas do not reach the vertical triangle. On most species (Ethmia) only primary setae are present while other species possess secondary setae (never more than eight) on the prolegs. On the prothorax alpha is nearer the dorsomeson than beta and the Kappa (prespiracular) group is trisetose. On the mesothorax and metathorax the Pi group is unisetose. On abdominal segments 1 to 7 alpha (1) is nearer the dorsomeson than beta (2), rho (3) is dorsad of the spiracle while on segment 8 it is cephalad of the spiracle, kappa, (4) and eta (5) are adjacent, mu (6) is present, the Pi (7) group is present and variable and sigma (8) is present. Spiracles elliptical, slightly larger on segment A8 but no higher. Prolegs occur on segments 3 to 6 and 10 bearing crochets that are usually biordinal and arranged in a mesoseries which may resemble a mesopenellipse.

GELECHIIDAE, L8, L15-17.

Gelechioidea, 578 species, leaf miners, leafrollers, webworms, seed worms, and fruit worms.

Habits. The larvae feed on living and dead plant tissues. They infest twigs, stems, flower parts, seeds, fruits and tubers of many wild and cultivated plants. They may mine, roll or web together leaves of various plants. Some species produce galls while others are important pests in stored seeds, cereals and tubers.

Description. Full grown larvae of most species are small very few exceeding 15 mm. Larvae of many species are more or less uniformly colored, namely shades of white, yellow, pink, brown, purple, etc. or they may be longitudinally striped. They may be slender or of moderate thickness. The pigmented head possesses a front and adfrontal areas which are dorsally very acute with the adfrontals frequently reaching the verticle triangle. Ocelli 1 to 4 as a rule evenly distributed. The setae on the head (see Gerasimov, 1937, or key) are somewhat useful in separating this family from closely related families. However, some species do not fit the character noted in the key (fig. L17). In general the primary setal map resembles the arrangement in many of the more important families of Microlepidoptera. On the prothorax the Kappa (perspiracular) group is trisetose while on the ninth segment in almost all species setae beta (2) are not on the same pinaculum nor are they closer together than setae alpha (1) on the eighth segment. The spiracles are circular with those on the eighth segment larger and usually more dorsad than those on segments 1 to 7. An anal comb may be present. Prolegs when present occur on segments 3 to 6 and 10. On the ventral prolegs the crochets are usually biordinal and arranged in a complete circle or two transverse bands. If arranged in two transverse rows the bands on the anal prolegs are divided into two groups (Anarsia etc.). Crochets are rudimentary, vestigial or wanting among the Sitotroga and Metzneria.

GEOMETRIDAE, L18, L56.

Geometroidea, 1200 species, loopers, measuring worms, inch worms and span worms.

Habits. The larvae feed chiefly on foliage of many native and cultivated plants. When a living larva crawls the middle portion of the body forms a distinct loop each time the functional prolegs are carried forward.

Description. Full grown larvae are small to medium sized, 20 to 50 mm. The body is cylindrical and slender and may bear processes, humps or protuberances of various shapes. Usually short primary setae are present above the spiracles while secondary setae may be abundant below the spiracles, especially on the prolegs. A subanal fleshy process projecting is caudad frequently present on the meson between the anal prolegs. The most striking character is the absence of normal, fully developed, ventral prolegs on segments 3, 4 and 5. Among a few species rudimentary prolegs may occur on some of these segments. Only two pairs of fully developed prolegs are present namely one pair on the sixth abdominal segment and an anal pair on the last segment. The crochets on the well developed prolegs are usually biordinal and arranged in a continuous or broken mesoseries. If a broken mesoseries exists a fleshy lobe is present on each proleg at the center of the mesoseries.

LEPIDOPTERA

GLYPHIPTERYGIDAE

Yponomeutoidea, 52 species, leaf skeletonizers, etc.

Habits. The larvae feed on plant tissue particularly foliage of wild and cultivated plants. Some species live in or under webs on leaves or between leaves and may produce skeletonized foliage.

Description. Full grown larvae are small, most species under 10 mm. The elongated head possesses a narrow sharp pointed front bounded by narrow adfrontal areas. All ocelli are close together. The setae on the prothorax show alpha more distant from the meson than beta, rho distant from epsilon, the Kappa (pre-spiracular) group trisetose and the Pi (subventral) group bisetose. On the abdomen alpha (1) is nearer the meson than beta (2) on all segments except nine where alpha is much further from the meson than beta, also on the abdomen kappa (4) and eta (5) are adjacent. The spiracles are circular or broadly elliptical. The prolegs occur on segments 3 to 6 and 10. They are usually long and slender bearing uniordinal, strongly sclerotized, or rudimentary crochets arranged in a complete circle.

GRACILARIIDAE, L3, L14, L19.

Tineoidea, 238 species, leaf, cambium, skin or blotch miners.

Habits. Early instar larvae of most species mine leaves, bark or fruit of various wild and cultivated plants especially deciduous trees and shrubs. Late instars of some of the genera feed externally but may be concealed by folded or rolled leaf parts.

Description. Full grown larvae are tiny or very small many species not exceeding 5 mm. Early instar larvae are greatly flattened and usually possess horizontal wheellike or sawtoothed mandibles. Late instar larvae of many species are cylindrical and possess a normal head and mouth parts. Ocelli reduced in size and number, frequently to one pair. Distinctive pigmented areas may occur on the dorsal and ventral aspects of the various segments. Thoracic legs present or absent. All setae are exceedingly small or absent. Kappa (4) and eta (5) on abdomen usually remote. Ventral prolegs may be represented by suckerlike discs. Prolegs when present occur on segments 3, 4, 5 and 10. The absence of prolegs on the 6th segment is distinctive. Crochets are uniordinal and arranged in transverse rows or in a lateropenellipse or both (see Fracker, 1915, p. 103).

HELIODINIDAE

Yponomeutoidea, 22 species, sun moths.

Habits. Some larvae are parasitic (Euclemensia) on oak scales (Kermes), however most species feed on plants, some of the hosts are, sumac (racemes), Panicum clandestinum, Oxybaphus nyctagineus, Orthocarpus, etc.

Description. Full grown larvae are small. The head is slightly depressed and possesses a short front which usually extends less than half the distance to the vertical triangle. All setae are primary. On the prothorax the kappa (prespiracular) group is trisetose with the three setae close together. On the abdomen seta kappa (4) and eta (5) are far apart and not on the same swelling. The spiracles are small. Prolegs occur on segments 3 to 6 and 10 bearing uniordinal or biordinal crochets arranged in a complete circle.

HELIOZELIDAE, L19.

Cycnodioidea, 28 species, leaf miners and shield or case bearers.

Habits. The larvae are leaf miners of deciduous trees, shrubs, grasses, so far as known, especially in their early instars, when full grown the larvae may construct cases, frequently disclike, from the leaves they mine which they attach to a branch or trunk. They transform and hibernate in these cases.

Description. Full grown larvae are tiny or very small, most species under 5 mm. The head is flattened, possessing two ocelli which may exist as pigment spots, a prominent vertical triangle and a triangular front which usu- ally reaches the vertical triangle. Pigmented areas on the dorsal and ventral aspects of the thorax and abdomen may exist. Some primary setae are present. Kappa (4) and eta (5) on the abdomen are fairly prominent, both may be located on the same swelling and fairly close together. Thoracic legs and prolegs are absent.

HEPIALIDAE, L6.

Jugate, 19 species, plant borers, swifts, macrojugatae.

Habits. The larvae are borers in the roots, trunks, stalks and stems of many plants chiefly annuals, perennial grasses, shrubs and trees, including alders, eucalyptus, ferns, etc.

Description. Full grown larvae are medium sized to large. The larvae are slender, cylindrical and possess an elongated head. The six ocelli on each side do not have the usual crescent arrangement but may be arranged in two vertical rows. All setae are primary. On the prothorax all nine dorsal setae on each side, including the Kappa group and the spiracles, are on one continuous sclerotized area. Also on the prothorax beta, delta and rho are close together and usually more ventrad of the dorsomeson than alpha or beta. On the abdomen setae theta are present. Prolegs occur on abdominal segments 3 to 6 and 10. bearing multiserial, uniordinal crochets arranged in a continuous circle on the ventral prolegs.

HESPERIIDAE, L2, L20.

Hesperioidea, 208 species, skipper caterpillars.

Habits. The larvae feed on foliage of many plants chiefly cereals, grasses, palms, and legumes which they may roll or web together.

Description. Full grown larvae are medium sized to large, 20 to 70 mm. The head is large or appears to be conspicuous because the thoracic region, especially the prothorax, is usually distinctly narrower than the head or abdominal segments. The head is deeply pigmented and bears numerous secondary setae which may be plumose or borne on chalazae. Front extends approximately two-thirds distance of head capsule. The body is frequently distinctly fusiform, widest in the vicinity of the ventral prolegs and in some instances somewhat flattened. All segments are divided into indistinct annulets. Secondary setae usually abundant and frequently short. Small flattened plates occasionally present. Prolegs present on segments 3 to 6 and 10, bearing triordinal or biordinal crochets arranged in an irregular but complete circle on all of the ventral prolegs. An anal comb usually present.

INCURVARIIDAE, L3, L57.

Incurvarioidea, 32 species, leaf miners and casebearers.

Habits. The larvae in their early instars are chiefly leaf miners and during their late stages become casebearers feeding on the leaves of deciduous herbs, shrubs and trees.

Description. Full grown larvae are small most species under 10 mm. The body and head are cylindrical. The head is distinct, as high as broad and not retractile. The front extends two-thirds the distance between the clypeus and the vertical triangle while the adfrontal areas extend to the vertical triangle. Primary setae are present on the thorax and in their usual position. On the abdomen all setae dorsad of kappa are indistinct. Kappa (4) and eta (5) are close together and adjacent to the caudoventral edge of the spiracle. Prolegs are present on segments 3 to 6 and 10, bearing uniserial crochets usually arranged in one transverse band.

LEPIDOPTERA

LACOSOMIDAE

Uranioidea, 3 species, sac-bearers.

Habits. Early instar larvae make silken nests between two leaves. Late instars build roomy portable cases of leaves with round openings at each end. The larvae feed on the foliage of various species of oak. Full grown larvae hibernate in their cases on the surface of the ground.

Description. Full grown larvae are small, 25± mm. The head is large, rounded, heavily sclerotized and rough. It is wider and much higher than the prothorax and projects nearly as far ventrad as the legs are long. On the head the ocelli are close together, the labrum possesses a small notch and no secondary setae occur. The body is lightly sclerotized, slightly flattened and widest in the region of the ventral prolegs. On the prothorax seta epsilon is below alpha and gamma, also rho is located distinctly cephalad and the kappa (prespiracular) group is bisetose. On the abdominal segments 1 to 9 inclusive alpha (1) is closer to the dorsomeson than beta (2), also kappa (4) and eta (5) are adjacent. The Pi (7) group has two to three setae on segments 1 and 2, four to eight setae on each proleg, two setae on segments 7 and 8 and one seta on segment 9. Short prolegs occur on segments 3 to 6 each bearing a complete circle of biordinal crochets.

LASIOCAMPIDAE, L21.

Bombycoidea, 31 species, tent caterpillars, lappet moths, etc.

Habits. The larvae feed on the foliage and young fruit of deciduous trees, shrubs and some evergreens. Some species construct extensive webs which may envelop large portions of the plant.

Description. Full grown larvae are medium sized to large, often brightly colored and many possess many long setae. The head is smaller than the thorax, often retractile and depressed. The labrum is notched in most species to at least one-half its mesal length. The prothorax usually bears one or two pairs of blunt fleshy protuberances or swellings dorsad of the legs. These may also be present on other segments especially when the setae are short. A blunt gibbosity may also occur on the dorsomeson of the eighth abdominal segment. Secondary setae are usually numerous and distinctly irregular in size some being very long. Setae are never in pencils, tufts, or verricules. Distinct verrucae rarely present. Prolegs occur on segments 3 to 6 and 10 bearing biordinal crochets arranged in a mesoseries which may somewhat resemble a mesopenellipse.

LIBYTHEIDAE

Papilionoidea, 1 species, snout butterflies.

Habits. The larvae of Libythea bachmanii Kirt. feed on hackberry (Celtis occidentalis).

Description. Full grown larvae approximate 25 to 30 mm. In general the larva resemble those of the Pieridae. The head is small and and somewhat retracted into the greatly swollen thorax especially the mesothorax and metathorax. The head is more or less covered with secondary setae and possesses the usual number of ocelli with the 3rd, 4th and 5th ocelli located on papillae while the others are reduced in size. The labrum has a shallow depression on the meson. Each abdominal segment is divided into four or five annulets. Primary setae are absent or inconspicuous but secondary setae may be present especially a group at the base of each leg and one on the first annulet of each segment borne on chalazae. Prolegs occur on segments 3 to 6 and 10 bearing biordinal or triordinal crochets arranged in a pseudocircle with the lateroseries of crochets rudimentary.

LEPIDOPTERA

LIMACODIDAE, L22-23.

Zygaenoidea, 50 species, slug caterpillars.

Habits. The larva feed primarily on foliage of shrubs and trees, chiefly forest species. Some of the host plants are oak, willow, cherry pear, apple, flowering blackberry, corn, etc.

Description. Full grown larvae of most species are small, 10 to 30 mm. The head is small, partially or deeply retracted into the prothorax. The body is usually thick, fleshy, sluglike or fusiform. The body covering may be smooth, well sclerotized, brightly colored and without distinct intersegmental incisions. Among some species verrucaelike structures, prominent scoli, or elongated hairy protuberance, bearing poisonous spines or setae, may be present. Thoracic legs are always present but may be very inconspicuous. Prolegs are absent, however, suckerlike discs or mucous secreting areas may exist in their place.

LIPARIDAE, L24.

Noctuoidea, 28 species, tussock moths, gypsy moth, brown-tail moth caterpillars, etc.

Habits. The larvae feed primarily on the foliage of deciduous shade, forest and some fruit trees.

Description. Full grown larvae are medium sized to large, 25 to 70 mm. The most distinctive character is the presence of eversible glands on the dorsomeson of segments 6 (may be absent) and 7. Groups of setae in the form of verrucae, verricules or elongated tufts (some clavate plumed) may be present on the thorax and abdomen. The unusual setae and the striking colors of verrucae, setae and pigmented areas produce vivid specific characteristics. Prolegs occur on segments 3 to 6 and 10 bearing uniordinal crochets arranged in a homoideous mesoseries.

LYCAENIDAE, L3, L23.

Papilionoidea, 124 species, larvae of blues, coppers or hairstreaks.

Habits. The larvae of most species feed on foliage and twigs of plants, chiefly Leguminosae while others are myrmecophilous or predacious on Homoptera especially scale insects.

Description. Full grown larvae are small, 10 to 20 mm. Their shape is somewhat fusiform and may be slightly depressed. The head is frequently very small and distinctly retractible and protrusible. Primary setae are absent or inconspicuous. Short secondary setae are very numerous and may be more or less evenly scattered over the entire body. Prolegs occur on segments 3 to 6 and 10 bearing triordinal or biordinal crochets arranged in a mesoseries with the crochets near the middle usually reduced in size or absent. Adjacent to and laterad of the break in the continuity of crochets a spatulate or clavate fleshy lobe exists typical of all lycaenids.

LYONETIDAE

Tineoidea, 74 species, leaf miners, ribbed case bearers.

Habits. Larvae of a number of species are leaf miners and feed on a number of trees and other plants, namely willows, poplar, tulip, aspens, sweet yam, oak, grape, Ambrosia, Ampelopsis, Solidago, Compositae, Aster, etc.

Description. Full grown larvae of most species are tiny to very small. The body is cylindrical with moderate intersegmental incisions. The head is more or less depressed except in Bucculatrix. The front is triangular and does not reach the vertical triangle, however, the adfrontal areas do. Primary setae only are present and are arranged as in many Microlepidoptera. On the prothorax the Kappa (prespiracular) group is trisetose with the setae widely separated. On the abdomen alpha (1) is closer to the dorsomeson than beta (2), rho (3) is above the spiracle, kappa (4) and eta (5) are widely separated with kappa some distance caudad of the spiracle. Among the Bucculatrix alpha (1) is below the level of beta (2) on segments 8 and 9. Spiracles are circular.

Prolegs, frequently slender and long, occur on segments 3 to 6 and 10 and bear uniordinal crochets arranged in a circle or two transverse bands of uniordinal well developed crochets (Bucculatrix) on the ventral prolegs.

MEGALOPYGIDAE, L23.

Zygaenoidea, 11 species, flannel moth caterpillars, puss caterpillars, etc.

Habits. The larvae feed on foliage of several shrubs and trees, namely oak, hackberry, etc.

Description. Full grown larvae are small to medium size, 20 to 30 mm. They are fusiform, cyphosomatic and frequently very hairy. The head is small and deeply retractible into the prothorax. Fourth and fifth ocelli much larger than others. Two kinds of setae are most common, namely short, straight, simple, spinelike, structures and greatly elongated, flexible, plumose setae. On the dorsal part of the body the setae arise chiefly from prominent somewhat flattened verrucae. On each half of the mesothorax four distinct verrucae occur dorsad of the legs while on the metathorax only three exist. On each abdominal segment possessing spiracles, two prominent verrucae occur dorsad of each spiracle and one immediately ventrad. The spiracles are prominent and nearly circular with a radial arrangement of parts within the peritreme. Adjacent to and usually caudad of each spiracle a prominent fleshy lobe or cone-shaped protuberance usually exists. Prolegs occur on segments 2 to 7 and 10. No crochets occur on ventral prolegs 2 and 7. The others possess crochets which are uniserial and uniordinal and arranged in a mesoseries. The mesoseries may be distinctly angulate or subdivided into two areas.

MEGATHYMIDAE, L20.

Hesperioidea, 9 species, giant skippers.

Habits. The larvae are wood borers living in the pith and roots of various species of Yucca and Agave in the Western part of North America.

Description. Full grown larvae are large, $60\pm$ mm. The head is rounded, rugose, partially retractile and smaller than the prothorax. It possesses a triangular front with the sides almost straight and reaching about half way to the vertical triangle, small inconspicuous ocelli and a labrum with a small acute mesal notch. The setae of the head and body are much reduced apparently wanting on the dorsal part of the thorax and abdomen. The setae are numerous on the ventral half of the prothorax and mesothorax but rare on the abdomen except on the prolegs. All spiracles are large with those on segment 8 somewhat more dorsal than the others. The thoracic legs bear numerous setae on their caudomesal surfaces. Prolegs occur on segments 3 to 6 and 10 bearing biordinal crochets arranged in a complete ellipse sometimes broken at the mesal and lateral ends.

MICROPTERYGIDAE

Jugate, 3 species, moss caterpillars.

Habits. The larvae feed on wet moss, liverworts and Hypnum.

Description. Full grown larvae are small, thin skinned and sluglike. The head is retractible, depressed and prognathous bearing antennae which are longer than the head. The front extends to the vertical triangle. One pair of ocelli. Setae are replaced by large ovate scales usually arranged in pairs. Normal thoracic legs are present. Prolegs are represented by conical processes on abdominal segments 1 to 8. Suckerlike structures may be present on segments 9 and 10.

LEPIDOPTERA

NEPTICULIDAE

Nepticuloidea, 72 species, serpentine miners.

Habits. The larvae produce linear mines especially in their early instars in leaves, bark and fruit of many plants. In their late instars each larva usually produces a small blotch area at the end of the linear area.

Description. Full grown larvae are very small, many species under 5 mm. They are somewhat flattened with a compressed head which possesses a somewhat triangular front that does not reach the vertical triangle. One large ocellus is present on each side of the head. Setae are inconspicuous or absent. Segmented thoracic legs usually absent. Prolegs without crochets may occur on segments 2 to 8 and 10.

NOLIDAE

Noctuoidea, 19 species, nolids.

Habits. The larvae feed on foliage of several wild and cultivated plants including apple.

Description. Full grown larvae are small, some not exceeding 15 mm. They closely resemble the Arctiidae. The body is cylindrical bearing sparsely setaceous verrucae but no secondary setae except on prolegs. The small head bearing primary setae is partially retractile. It possesses a broad front which extends less than half way to the vertical triangle. The most ventrocephalic ocellus, probably number 6, is located some distance from the other five forming a distinct semicircle. On the prothorax the dorsal verrucae are united. On the mesothorax four verrucae occur in a transverse row on each side. On the abdominal segments 1 to 9 verrucae Beta, Rho and Kappa groups are present. On segments 1, 2, 3 and 7 mu (6) and Pi (7) are small verrucae and sigma is a single seta while on segments 4, 5, and 6 mu (6) exists but the Pi (7) group are scattered over the proleg and united with sigma. On segments 8 and 9 mu (6) is wanting but Pi (7) is present. Prolegs occur on segments 4, 5, 6 and 10 bearing uniordinal or biordinal crochets arranged in a mesoseries.

NOTODONTIDAE, L1, L25-26.

Noctuoidea, 119 species, hump-backed caterpillars, prominents, etc.

Habits. The larvae feed primarily on the foliage of deciduous shrubs and forest, shade and fruit trees.

Description. Full grown larvae of most species are medium sized, 25 to 50 mm. and may possess distinctive color patterns and unusual contours, especially along the dorsomeson. Early instars may differ decidedly in color from full grown larvae. Primary setae occur on most sepcies but no verrucae are present. All species possess secondary setae on the prolegs while a few show many secondary setae on the head and elsewhere. Seta kappa (4) on segment 7 is usually distinctly more ventrad of the spiracle than on segments 6 or 8. Among species possessing few or no dorsal secondary setae gibbosities, horns and odd shaped structures may be present on the dorsal aspect of some abdominal segments. All species possess four ventral prolegs on segments 3 to 6. The anal prolegs may be rudimentary or greatly elongated and with or without crochets. The crochets on the ventral prolegs are uniordinal and arranged in a mesoseries.

NYMPHALIDAE, L2, L27.

Papilionoidea, 181 species, brushfooted, fritillaries, tortoise shells, leaf butterflies, etc.

Habits. The larvae of this family feed primarily on the foliage of a wide variety of native and cultivated plants. Some of these are willows, aspen, poplar, balm of gilead, birches, hackberry, elm, apple, currant, wild gooseberry, asters, passion flower, everlasting, pansies, hop, nettles, etc.

Description. Full grown larvae of most species are medium sized, 25 to 30 mm. and frequently deeply pigmented. All species possess scoli on the head or body except Apaturinea-Anaea. This distinguishes them from all larvae of butterflies, however, to separate them from the Saturniidae and Citheronidae is more difficult. Among the nymphalids, when mediodorsal scoli occur on the abdomen, they are not confined to the 8th or 9th segments. Among the Euptoieta, Speyeria and Anaea scoli are absent on the head and along the dorsomeson. Among the Euptoieta the subdorsal scoli of the prothorax are very conspicuous and among the Anaea the head is very large. The suranal plate of most nymphalids is rounded while among the Asterocampa it is forked. Prolegs occur on segments 3 to 6 and 10. The crochets on each are uniserial, triordinal (rarely biordinal) and arranged in a mesoseries.

OECOPHORIDAE, L7, L28.

Gelechioidea, 124 species, webworms, leaf rollers, etc.

Habits. The feeding habits vary considerably. The larvae of most species feed on foliage, terminals and blossom heads of many wild and cultivated annuals, perennials, deciduous shrubs and trees. They may roll the leaves or web together the foliage. Other species are found in decayed wood, stored products and elsewhere.

Description. Full grown larvae are small, usually under 25 mm. On the head the adfrontals extend to the vertical triangle. The fourth ocellus is much closer to the third than to the fifth and the second is always farther from the first than from the third. They may be distinctly spotted with deeply pigmented pinacula or chalazae at the base of most setae. The primary setae pattern closely resembles that of most Microlepidoptera. The prolegs are short, stout and possess circles of biordinal crochets. In general it is difficult to name characters distinctive enough to separate all species from closely related families. An attempt is made in the key to do this.

OLETHREUTIDAE and TORTRICIDAE, L2, L6-8, L14, L17, L29-32.

Tortricoidea, 714 and 212 species respectively, leaf rollers, twig borers, tortricids, etc.

Note: No satisfactory characters have been observed which will definitely separate all larvae of these two families.

Habits. The larvae feed on living plant tissue, especially foliage, rolling, folding or webbing leaves together, or they may feed within twigs, flower buds, fruits, and nuts of many wild and cultivated plants. Some of the common fruits and nuts attacked are apple, pear, peach, cherry, quince, strawberry, cranberry, haws, English walnut, hickory, filberts and acorns.

Description. Full grown larvae are small, 10 to 25 mm., occasionally larger. The somewhat cylindrical body is frequently more or less uniform in color, near white, pink, green, purple or brown, and may possess a pigmented cervical shield, suranal plate and pinacula. The rounded, pigmented head is distinct possessing a front covering one-fourth to three-fourths of the distance between the clypeus and the vertical triangle, adfrontal areas usually touching the vertical triangle, and six ocelli, usually unevenly distributed with the sixth always close to the fourth and fifth. Setae are primary and their arrangement typical of many Microlepidoptera. On the prothorax the Kappa (prespiracular) group is trisetose. On the mesothorax and metathorax the Pi group is unisetose or bisetose. Kappa (4) and eta (5) on abdomen adjacent to each other and obliquely or vertically placed. On the ninth abdominal segment setae beta (2) are usually on the same pinaculum and closer together than setae beta on preceding segments. On the eighth segment rho is directly cephalad of the spiracle with few exceptions. Spiracles are usually broadly elliptical with the eighth pair usually somewhat larger and more dorsad. Prolegs are present on segments 3 to 6 and 10 bearing uniordinal or biordinal crochets arranged in complete circles on the ventral prolegs.

LEPIDOPTERA

OPOSTEGIDAE

Tineoidea, 6 species, cambium or bast-miners.

Habits. The larvae mine under the bark of stems and stalks of several plants.

Description. Full grown larvae are small, cylindrical and extremely slender. Their length is fully ten times the greatest diameter. The head is flattened with divergent longitudinal ridges on the lateral and dorsal aspects of the epicranium. Ocelli are single or absent and some distance from the lateral angles of the clypeus. The mandibles are thin and possess a membranous process. All setae are reduced or absent. If present they are arranged in circles about the body. Segmented thoracic legs and prolegs are absent.

PAPILIONIDAE, L2, L33.

Papilionoidea, 27 species, swallow tail caterpillars.

Habits. The larvae feed on the foliage of a number of plants namely carrots, celery, citrus, pipevine, parsley, poison hemlock, sweet fennel, water hemlock, and other deciduous vines, shrubs and trees.

Description. Full grown larvae are medium sized to large, 26 to 60 mm. The head occasionally bearing short secondary setae is usually smaller than the prothorax and frequently somewhat retracted. The front extends half way to the vertical triangle. The labrum bearing many setae is notched about one-half its mesal diameter. Six ocelli, subequal in size and distribution, are present on each side of the head. The body is cylindrical and smooth with inconspicuous conjunctiva. Its greatest diameter is usually in the vicinity of the first abdominal segment tapering gradually toward a small caudal end. On the meson of the prothorax a distinct and characteristic Y or V-shaped eversible osmeterium (gland) exists. When the osmeterium is retracted its location is indicated by a transverse groove. Setae are reduced or absent on most parts of the body except on the lateral aspects of the prolegs where many secondary setae occur. Porlegs occur on the usual segments 3 to 6 and 10 bearing triordinal (rarely biordinal) crochets arranged in a mesoseries. Frequently a biordinal lateroseries of small crochets may be present producing a so-called pseudocircle arrangement.

PERICOPIDAE

Noctuoidea, 6 species, pericopids.

Habits. The food plants of the larvae are not well known. One species feeds on Mertensia.

Description. Full grown larvae are small usually not exceeding 30 mm. They may be highly colored with black and yellow bands and steel blue verrucae. The head is distinct (very small among Doa) and rarely bears secondary setae. All genera possess distinct verrucae except Doa where they are reduced to chalazae bearing single setae. When verrucae are present the arrangement is similar to Amatidae. On the mesothorax and metathorax one or two verrucae occur above the Kappa group and setae sigma close to the coxae are large and distinct. On the abdomen verruca kappa is not reduced in size and it is a greater distance from the spiracle (Doa an exception) on segment 7 than on segments 6 or more. Prolegs occur on segments 3 to 6 and 10 bearing uniordinal crochets arranged in a heteroideus mesoseries.

PIERIDAE, L2, L41.

Papilionoidea, 61 species, pierids, white, sulfur, orange tip and other caterpillars.

Habits. The larvae feed on the foliage of many host plants, particularly species belonging to the Cruciferae, Copparidaceae and Leguminosae.

Description. Full grown larvae of most species are small to medium sized, 20 to 40 mm. In general they are moderately slender, uniformly colored (green, yellow or dusky shades) with no conspicuous armature. The head is distinct and about the size of the prothorax and not retractible except in Phoebis. Front extends half way to the vertical triangle.

Labrum moderately emarginate. The body segments are distinctly annulate, usually six, and covered with rows of numerous secondary setae borne on microscopic papillae to conspicuous chalazae. The ventral prolegs, similar in size, are present on segments 3 to 6 and 10 bearing biordinal or triordinal crochets arranged in a mesoseries.

PHALAENIDAE, L1-2, 4, 6-8, L34-40, L56.

Noctuoidea, 2693 species, cutworms, armyworms, budworms, loopers, millers, noctuids.

Habits. Larvae of this large family feed largely on foliage, attacking the leaves of many kinds of cultivated crops, fruit, shade and woodland trees, shrubs and wild plants. Other species live on or within buds, flowers, fruits, stems, leaves (leaf miners) and the crown portions of cultivated and wild plants. A few species breed in dead or decaying vegetation, especially dead leaves and rotten logs. Some larvae are aquatic to the extent that they feed on or within the submerged portions of aquatic plants.

Description. The larvae of this large family, more than one-fourth of the known species of Lepidoptera in North America, are medium sized, 25 to 50 mm. The gross structure of the vast majority of species resembles that of cutworms. Exceptions to this condition are noted. The cutworm type of larva possesses primary setae only. On the prothorax beta is closer to the meson than alpha, epsilon is associated with rho and located between delta and the spiracle and the Kappa (prespiracular) group is bisetose. On the mesothorax and metathorax alpha is associated with beta, epsilon with rho, kappa with eta while theta is separate and the Pi (subventral) group is unisetose. On abdominal segments 1 to 6 and 8 alpha (1) is nearer the meson than beta (2), rho (3) is dorsad of the spiracle, epsilon (3a), if present, is cephalodorsad of the spiracle, kappa (4) and eta (5) are distinctly remote, mu (6) present, the Pi (7)

group usually trisetose and sigma present. Among a few species gamma and a few setae of the Tau group may be present. Segment 7 is similar to others except kappa (4) is lower and also closer to eta (5). On segment 9, alpha (1), beta (2) and rho (3) form a triangle. Prolegs are usually present on segments 3 to 6 and 10, however they may be reduced in size on segments 3 to 5 or absent on segments 3 and 4. They bear uniordinal (rarely biordinal) crochets arranged in a mesoseries. If the mesoseries resembles a mesopenellipse the gap at the ends of the crochets is usually greater than one-third the projected circumference of the circle also the entire series of crochets of the anal prolegs is more nearly parallel than perpendicular with the meson.

Among species possessing well developed verrucae or numerous nonplumose secondary setae which may obscure the verrucae the prolegs resemble the above description. Also the notch in the labrum is usually deep with parallel sides and a rounded bottom. Among species that resemble arctiids kappa (4) on segment 7 is further removed from the spiracle than on segments 6 or 8. For more details and a few other variations in this family see Fracker, 1915. Detailed characters may be found in microscopic structures on the exocuticle, mandibles, tarsal parts and setal pattern on the head which are useful in separating genera and species.

PLUTELLIDAE and YPONOMEUTIDAE, L3, L6-8, L42.

Yponomeutoidea, 51 and 66 species respectively, plutellids, leaf miners, etc.

Note: No satisfactory characters have been observed which will definitely separate the larvae of these two families.

Habits. The larvae feed on the foliage and flowers or bore within twigs, buds and fruits of various wild and cultivated plants. Some of the

more common host plants are crucifers, cabbage, kale, chestnut, Ailanthus, Persea, Lonicera, Umbelliferae, smilax, birch, alder, red maple, juniper, apple, cherry, short needle pine, grasses, etc.

Description. The larvae of most species

are 8 to 25 mm. They vary in color from a uniform light green to a deeply pigmented striped condition. No secondary setae occur. The following arrangement of the setae is typical for the two families. On the prothorax seta beta is below alpha. The Kappa (prespiracular) group is trisetose and in some species not located on a sclerotized area distinctly separated from the cervical shield. On the abdomen kappa (4) and eta (5) are well separated (a few exceptions). Prolegs occur on segments 3 to 6 and 10 bearing uniordinal of biordinal crochets arranged in circles that are uniserial, biserial or triserial (rarely multiserial).

PRODOXIDAE, L58.

Incurvarioidea, 15 species, prodoxids, yucca seedpod caterpillars, etc.

Habits. The larvae feed in flowers, stems, seed capsules, or the flesh of the fruit of Agave, Yucca, etc.

Description. Full grown larvae are small usually under 15 mm. The body is cylindrical, short and fleshy, fusiform and frequently cyphosomatic, without prominent setae and usually a near white or pink. The head is much smaller than the prothorax and of average shape with the front almost reaching the vertical triangle. Some species are entirely legless while others possess thoracic legs and abdominal swellings on segments 3 to 6 without crochets.

PSYCHIDAE, L3, L6, L42.

Tineoidea, 26 species, bagworms, basketworms, casemoths, etc.

Habits. A given larva lives its entire life (if a female) within a portable silken bag which it constructs about its body. The outside of the bag may have incorporated into its surface bits of plant tissue, namely leaves, twigs, and flower parts. The larvae feed on the foliage of many kinds of evergreens and deciduous trees and shrubs.

Description. Full grown larvae are small to medium sized, 20 to 50 mm. The dorsal portion of the prothorax extends over the head. The setae on the head are prominent and their distribution is useful in determining genera. All body setae are primary and inconspicuous especially in the last instar. On the prothorax the dorsal nine pairs of setae are located on one continuous sclerotized area. This includes the Kappa (prespiracular) group which is trisetose, also epsilon and rho are far removed from each other. On the mesothorax and metathorax the Pi (6) group is bisetose. On the abdominal segments alpha (1), beta (2) and rho (3) are in a straight line and on the same annulet, also kappa (4) and eta (5) are adjacent and mu (6) is present. All spiracles are elliptical with the enlarged prothoracic pair in a horizontal position which is a distinctive character for the family. The prothoracic legs are large. Inconspicuous prolegs occur on segments 3 to 6 and 10 bearing crochets that are uniordinal and arranged in a lateropenellipse on the ventral and anal prolegs.

PTEROPHORIDAE, L43.

Pyralidoidea, 141 species, plume moth caterpillars, leaf rollers, webworms and stem borers.

Habits. The larvae feed on deciduous wild and cultivated plants especially ornamentals and food producing species. Many are leaf rollers and leaf webbers and a few are stem borers.

Description. Full grown larvae are small, most species under 15 mm. The larvae vary considerably in their detailed structure. Most species possess verrucae and numerous secondary setae while some are without secondary setae. On the prothorax the Kappa (prespiracular) group is bisetose or trisetose. On the mesothorax the pi (6) group is usually bisetose. Most species possess long (occasionally short) slender, stemlike prolegs on segments 3 to 6 and 10 bearing uniordinal crochets arranged in a mesoseries which may resemble a mesopenellipse.

LEPIDOPTERA

PYRALIDAE, L3, L6-7, L44-53.

Pyralidoidea, 1133 species, leafrollers, leaftiers, webworms, borers, waxworms, cereal worms, dried fruit worms, pyralids, etc.

Habits. The family, as interpreted by Mc-Dunnough, is a large one comprising a number of subfamilies given family status by several entomologists. The feeding habits of the larvae are diverse, among the Chrysauginae leaf rollers, among the Pyraustinae (the largest subfamily) leaf feeders and stem borers of many native and cultivated species particularly monocotyledons, among the Crambinae leaf, stem or root feeders of grasses and many Graminaceae, among the Phycitinae and Epipaschinae, leaf rollers and crumplers and stored food pests, among the Galleriinae inhabitants of nests of Hymenoptera especially the combs of the honey and also attack stored food products, particularly fruits and vegetables, among the Pyralidinae stored products pests, scavengers and plant feeders, among the Schoenobiinae and Nymphalinae aquatic species frequently living on or within marsh plants and submerged vegetation.

Description. Full grown larvae are small to medium sized, 10 to 35 mm. Many species have a more or less uniform color (shades of green, yellow, pink, brown, near white, etc.) while others are spotted due to conspicuous pigmented pinacula at the base of most primary setae. These spots may disappear in the hibernating instar especially among some species of the Crambinae and Pyraustinae. The setae present are primary with few or no secondary setae. The Kappa (prespiracular) group on the prothorax is bisetose except among some aquatic species possessing vestigial or no prothoracic spiracles it may be unisetose. The Pi (6) group on the mesothorax and metathorax is unisetose except among the Galleriinae and some Crambinae (Diatraea) it is bisetose. Short prolegs are present on segments 3 to 6 and 10. They may bear uniserial biordinal crochets (rarely uniordinal,) some Galleriinae, and occasionally triordinal, some Crambinae) arranged in two transverse bands (Chrysauginae) in a complete circle or in a mesopenellipse (Pyraustinae). For more details see Fracker, 1915 and Forbes, 1923.

SATURNIIDAE, L1, L3, L6, L54.

Saturnioidea, 42 species, giant or wild silkworms, cecropia, luna and others.

Habits. The larvae feed chiefly on the foliage of many deciduous trees and shrubs.

Description. Full grown larvae are medium sized to very large. Early instars usually possess some to many bristly spines. If the late instars are without numerous spines or profusely branched scoli, the ninth abdominal segment bears no scolus on the dorsomeson, also the middorsal scolus of the eighth segment is never associated with a pair of smaller scoli laterocaudad of it. If the various segments of late instar larvae bear scoli which are profusely branched (Hemileuca) the ninth segment bears a scolus on the dorsomeson. Also the anal plate is smooth and the scolus alpha on the mesothorax is no longer than the abdominal scoli. Numerous small secondary setae may occur on all segments. They are most conspicuous on the prolegs and the ventral half of most segments. Prolegs occur on abdominal segments 3 to 6 and 10 bearing biordinal crochets arranged in a mesoseries. Each anal proleg is usually flattened on the lateral aspect producing a triangular sclerotized area.

SATYRIDAE, L1, L7.

Papilionoidea, 59 species, meadow browns, greylings, heaths, satyrs, etc.

Habits. The larvae feed chiefly on cereals and grasses in open meadows.

Description. Full grown larvae are small to medium sized. Most species are more or less uniform in color, shades of green, yellow or brown. The body is fusiform and terminates in a bifurcate suranal plate. The head is usually as large or larger than the prothorax, frequently rugose, bilobed or horned, labrum deeply emarginate, and the third ocellus much larger than the remainder. Most body segments, especially those of the abdomen, are subdivided into annulets, usually six, and bear numerous secondary setae arising from lenticlelike papillae. Prolegs occur on segments 3 to 6 and 10 with uniordinal, biordinal or triordinal crochets arranged in a mesoseries. Suranal plate is bifurcate.

SCYTHRIDAE

Yponomeutoidea, 31 species, scythrids, leaf miners, etc.

<u>Habits</u>. The larvae are not too well known, some are leaf miners in grass while others are found in the tops of thistle.

<u>Description</u>. Full grown larvae are small. Their setal arrangement for the most part resembles that of the Yponomeutidae except the primary setae are represented by verrucalike plates each bearing two or more setae especially alpha (1) and beta (2) on the abdominal segments. Also Pi (7) group on the abdomen consists of four to eight setae. Prolegs occur on segments 3 to 6 and 10 and bear biordinal crochets arranged in a complete uniserial circle.

SPHINGIDAE, L1, L55-56.

Sphingoidea, 107 species, hornworms, sphinx caterpillars, sphingids, etc.

<u>Habits</u>. The larvae feed on the foliage of many plants chiefly cultivated species especially native trees, vines and garden crops. Some of these are catalpa, poplar, willow, cottonwood, elm, ash, pine, apple, plum, Virginia creeper, morning glory, snowberry, hawthorn, bush honeysuckle, tobacco, sweet potato, tomato, etc. Most species are not gregarious in their feeding habits.

<u>Description</u>. Full grown larvae are medium sized to very large, 35 to 100 mm. All hornworms are cylindrical, plump, smooth, without conspicuous setae and frequently brightly colored. The head is usually smaller than the prothorax and in some species partially retractible. It may be covered with numerous minute setae. In the genus <u>Lapara</u> the head is high, smooth and distinctly conical. Primary setae greatly reduced or wanting. If present kappa (4) and eta (5) remote with eta (5) almost even with spiracle. Secondary seta present on prolegs but rare or absent on body. The abdominal segments possess 6 to 8 annulets on the dorsal aspect. Most species possess a distinct spine or horn on the dorsomeson of the eighth abdominal segment. In the last instar this horn may be reduced to a scar or corniculum and in the genus <u>Lapara</u> it is complete wanting. Prolegs occur on segments 3 to 6 and 10 bearing biordinal crochets arranged in a mesoseries. The anal prolegs are flattened forming a triangular pyramid with the suranal plate.

STENOMIDAE

Gelechioidea, 27 species, stenomids, case bearers, webworms, etc.

<u>Habits</u>. The larvae feed on foliage or they are borers in a number of shrubs, trees and other plants some of which are maple, apple, blackberry, oak, hazel, <u>Tsuga</u> and timothy. Some species are casebearers.

<u>Description</u>. Full grown larvae are small, usually brightly colored and somewhat depressed and prognathous. The front and adfrontals do not reach the vertical triangle. Six ocelli and a distinctly emarginate labrum are present. Primary setae only exist. On the prothorax the Kappa (prespiracular) group is trisetose and rho is located near epsilon and below gamma. On the abdomen kappa (4) and eta (5) are adjacent, alpha (1) is nearer the dorsomeson than beta (2) on segments 1 to 7 while on segment 8 they are at the same level. On segment 9 kappa (4), eta (5) and mu (6) are usually on the same pinaculum. Thoracic legs are adjacent. Short prolegs occur on segments 3 to 6 and 10 bearing biordinal crochets arranged in a complete circle on the ventral prolegs. Anal prolegs bear a single somewhat transverse series of crochets along the cephalic margin.

LEPIDOPTERA

THYATIRIDAE, L8, L42.

Drepanoidea, 13 species, thyatirids, leaf rollers, leaf folders etc.

Habits. The larvae feed on foliage usually loosely rolling or folding the leaves. Some of the host plants are blackberry, cornel, thimbleberry, oak and Rosaceae.

Description. Full grown larvae are small to medium sized. The head is hypognathous and distinctly wider than high possessing a small front, prominent adfrontals and a deeply notched labrum with parallel sides. The cylindrical body bears small primary and subprimary setae usually arising from minute papillae. Their arrangement is similar to that of the Epiplemidae except the Pi group on the prolegs is made up of three setae while on segments 1, 2, 7 and 8 only two occur. According to Forbes, 1923, on the abdomen kappa (4) is above the level of the spiracles and close to rho (3). Seta eta (5) is usually associated with one or two subprimaries. Prolegs are present on segments 3 to 6 and 10 with the anal pair much smaller than the ventral prolegs. Each proleg bears biordinal crochets arranged in a curved mesoseries with a rudimentary lateroseries occasionally present.

THYRIDIDAE, L4.

Pyralidoidea, 11 species, leaf rollers, stem borers, window winged moths.

Habits. Larvae are leaf rollers and stem borers of cruciferous and other plants. Some hosts are beans, grape, clematis, etc.

Description. Full grown larvae are very small to small and cylindrical with shallow intersegmented incisions. The head is smaller than the prothorax bearing a triangular front which extends more than half way to the cervical triangle, six ocelli in a semicircle and a slightly emarginate labrum. All setae are primary. On the prothorax the Kappa (prespiracular) group is bisetose and seta rho is near epsilon and below alpha and gamma. On the mesothorax and metathorax the Pi group (6) is bisetose. On abdominal segments 1 to 8 seta beta (2) is nearer the dorsomeson than alpha (1), epsilon is minute or absent, kappa (4) and eta (5) are adjacent and on the same pinaculum and the Pi group is bisetose on segments 1 and 7, trisetose on segments 2 to 6 and unisetose on segment 8. On the ninth segment alpha (1) is closer to the dorsomeson than beta (2). Spiracles oval and small. Moderately long prolegs occur on segments 3 to 6 and 10 bearing biordinal crochets arranged in a complete circle on the ventral prolegs and in a transverse series on the anal prolegs.

TINEIDAE; L57

Tineoidea, 133 species, clothes moth larvae, tineids.

Habits. The larvae of many species are casebearers or webspinners, feeding on feathers, fish scraps, wool and products derived from animals and legume seeds. Other species live in fungi or decayed wood.

Description. Full grown larvae of most species are very small usually distinctly under 10 mm. On the head the front is triangular and closed. Only primary setae are present. On the prothorax setae beta are closer together than setae alpha, also the Kappa (prespiracular) group is trisetose and the setae are close together. On the abdomen setae beta (2) are closer together than setae alpha (1) also kappa (4) and eta (5) are distinctly remote. Prolegs occur on segments 3 to 6 and 10 bearing uniordinal crochets arranged in a uniserial circle.

TISCHERIDAE, L19.

Tineoidea, 31 species, tischerids, leaf miners, etc.

Habits. The larvae are leaf miners in foliage of several cultivated and wild trees and bushes and other plants. On oak they produce blotch mines chiefly. They also infest leaves of apple, chestnut, blackberry, raspberry, rose, Solidago, Heliopsis, Ambrosia, etc., producing trumpet shaped mines on some.

Description. Full grown larvae are very small or small, most species under 10 mm. The head is prognathous, deeply depressed, much longer than high, with a front extending to the vertical triangle and possesses six pairs of ocelli uniform in size. The body also is depressed and somewhat moniliform from a dorsal view. Thoracic legs are absent while prolegs usually occur on segments 3 to 6, and each proleg bears two (occasionally one) transverse uniserial rows of very small uniordinal crochets.

TORTRICIDAE, see Olethreutidae

YPONOMEUTIDAE, see Plutellidae

ZANOLIDAE, L26.

Bombycoidea, 3 species, zanolids.

Habits. The larvae of Apatelodes (one genus) feed on the foliage of various deciduous shrubs and trees.

Description. Full grown larvae are medium sized, 35 to 50 mm. The head is of moderate size, densely covered with secondary setae and possesses a labrum with a deep (usually two-thirds the mesal diameter) notch. No distinct verrucae or protuberances exist, yet the body is densely covered with more or less uniformly scattered secondary setae which vary greatly in length. Those on the thorax and usually those on the ventral aspect of the abdomen are longest except for several, greatly elongated, median, unpaired, mesodorsal tufts on the thorax and abdomen. Prolegs are found on segments 3 to 6 and 10 bearing biordinal crochets arranged in a mesoseries.

ZYGAENIDAE, L8, L58.

Zygaenoidea, 21 species, leaf skeletonizers, smoky moth caterpillars, etc.

Habits. The larvae feed on the foliage of several deciduous wild and cultivated plants, especially vines. Some of these are grapes, Virginia creeper, etc.

Description. Full grown larvae are small, usually under 25 mm. Some species are near white with distinct transverse or lateral bands of black, brown or red. The verrucae may be deeply pigmented. The head is small, somewhat retractible with the caudal portion lightly sclerotized. The body is cylindrical and covered with flat verrucae bearing primary setae. Glandlike protuberances may be present dorsad of the prothoracic legs. On the prothorax numerous setae occur on the cervical shield and the Kappa (prespiracular) group is large. On the mesothorax and metathorax verrucae of the Kappa and Pi groups are single and dorsad of these on each side three verrucae exist. On the abdomen verrucae alpha (1) and beta (2) are fused while rho (3) kappa (4) and mu (6) are distinct and the Pi (7) group may be single or double. All spiracles are circular. Prolegs occur on segments 3 to 6 and 10 bearing uniordinal crochets arranged in a mesoseries.

LEPIDOPTERA

SOME COMMON, IMPORTANT OR UNUSUAL SPECIES

Note. The species marked with an asterisk are figured (*) or described (**). The author has not seen the unmarked (no asterisk) species or the material on hand is unsatisfactory. In a future revision it is hoped that most of these and others may be incorporated. The scientific and common names, with a few exceptions, are taken from the list approved by The American Association of Economic Entomologists, C. F. W. Muesebeck 1946, Jour. Econ. Ent. 39:427 or McDunnough, 1938-39. In this list parentheses are placed about the describers name when the genus differs from the original description. Elsewhere in this publication parenthesis about describers names are omitted.

ACROLOPHIDAE

*Acrolophus prob. arcanellus Clem. L11,
   from ester stems.

AEGERIIDAE

Aegeria apiformis (Clerck),
   hornet moth.
Bembecia marginata (Harr.),
   raspberry root borer.
*Melittia cucurbitae (Harr.), L6, L9,
   squash borer.
Podesesia syringae fraxini (Lug.),
   ash borer.
*Podosesia syringae syringae (Harr.), L9,
   lilac borer.
Ramosia bibionipennis (Bdvl.),
   strawberry crown moth.
Ramosia rhododendri (Beut.),
   rhododendron borer.
Ramosia tipuliformis (Clerck),
   currant borer.
Sannina uroceriformis Wlkr.,
   persimmon borer.
*Sanninoidea exitiosa (Say), L7, L8, L9,
   peach tree borer.
Sanninoidea exitiosa graefi (Hy. Edw.),
   western peach tree borer.
Sylvora acerni (Clem.),
   maple callus borer.
*Synanthedon pictipes (G. & R.), L9,
   lesser peach tree borer.
Thamnosphecia pyri (Harr.),
   pear borer.
*Thamnosphecia scitula (Harr.), L9,
   dogwood borer.
Vespamima pini (Kell.),
   pitch mass borer.
Vespamima sequoiae (Hy. Edw.),
   sequoia pitch moth.

Vitacea polistiformis (Harr.),
   grape root borer.

AGARISTIDAE

*Alypia octomaculata (F.), L1, L28,
   eight-spotted forester.

AMATIDAE

*Syntomeida epilais jucundissima Dyar, L10,
   oleander caterpillar

ARCTIIDAE

Diacrisia virginica (F.),
   yellow woollybear.
*Estigmene acrea (Drury), L10,
   salt-march caterpillar.
**Halisidota caryae (Harr.), L10,
   hickory tussock moth.
*Halisidota harrisii Walsh, L10,
   sycamore tussock moth.
Halisidota maculata (Harr.),
   spotted tussock moth.
Halisidota tessellaris (A. & S.),
   pale tussock moth.
*Hyphantria cunea (Drury), L6, L7, L8, L10,
   fall webworm.
*Hypoprepia fucosa Hbn.,
   painted lichen moth.
**Isia isabella (A. & A.), L10,
   banded woollybear.
*Utetheisa bella (L.), L8, L10,
   bella moth.
*Utetheisa venusta Dal., L10,
   false bella moth.

LEPIDOPTERA

BOMBYCIDAE

*Bombyx mori (L.), L58,
  silkworm.

CITHERONIIDAE

*Anisota rubicunda (F.), L12,
  green-striped mapleworm.
*Anisota senatoria (A. & S.), L7, L12,
  orange-striped oakworm.
*Anisota stigma (F.), L12,
  spiny oakworm.
*Citheronia regalis (F.), L12,
  hickory horned devil, regal moth.
*Citheronia sepulchralis G. and R., L12,
  pine needle citheronid.
*Eacles imperialis (Drury), L12,
  imperial moth.

COLEOPHORIDAE

Coleophora caryaefoliella Clem,
  pecan cigar casebearer.
Coleophora fletcherella Fern,
  cigar casebearer.
*Coleophora laricella (Hbn.), L13,
  larch casebearer.
Coleophora limosipennella (Dup.),
  elm casebearer.
*Coleophora malivorella Riley, L13,
  pistol casebearer.
*Coleophora pruniella Clem., L6, L13-14,
  cherry casebearer.
Coleophora salmani Heinr.,
  birch casebearer.

COSMOPTERYGIDAE

Homaledra sabalella (Chamb.),
  palm leaf skeletonizer.
*Pyrodercus rileyi Wishm., L13,
  pink scavenger caterpillar.
*Walshia amphorphella Clem., L13,
  on Amorpha fructicosa.

COSSIDAE

Cossula magnifica (Stkr.),
  pecan carpenterworm.
Prionoxystus macmurtrei (Guer.),
  little carpenterworm.
*Prionoxystus robiniae (Pack), L11,
  carpenterworm.

*Zeuzera pyrina (L.), L11,
  leopard moth.

DANAIDAE

*Danaus plexippus (L.), L33,
  monarch butterfly.

DIOPTIDAE

Phryganidia californica Pack.,
  California oakworm.

ELACHISTIDAE

*Elachista albicapitella Engel., L14,
  on grass.

ETHMIIDAE

*Ethmia fuscipedella Wlsm., L28,
  on Lithospermum Gmelini (Michx).

GELECHIIDAE

*Anarsia lineatella Zell., L15 and 17,
  peach twig borer.
Dichomeris ligulella Hbn.,
  palmerworm.
*Dichomeris marginella (F.), L15, L17,
  juniper webworm.
Exoteleia pinifoliella (Chamb.),
  pine needle miner.
*Gnorimoschema operculella (Zell), L8, L16-17,
  potato tuberworm.
*Keiferia glochinella (Sell), L16,
  egg plant leaf miner.
*Keiferia lycopersicella (Busck), L16,
  tomato pinworm.
*Pectinophora gossypiella (Saund.), L16-17,
  pink bollworm.
*Recurvaria milleri Busck, L15,
  lodgepole needle miner.
Recurvaria nanella (Hbn.),
  lesser bud moth.
*Recurvaria variella Cham., L15,
  bald cypress needleworm.
*Sitotroga cerealella (Oliv.), L17,
  Angoumois grain moth.
Stegasta bosquella (Chamb.),
  red-necked peanutworm.

LEPIDOPTERA

GEOMETRIDAE

*Alsophila pometaria (Harr.), L18,
  fall cankerworm.
*Amphidasis cognataria Guen., L18,
  pepper and salt moth.
 Anavitrinella pampinaria (Guen.),
  cranberry spanworm.
*Cingilia catenaria (Drury), L18,
  chain-spotted geometer.
*Coryphista maedi Pack., L18,
  barberry leafworm.
 Ennomos subsignarius (Hbn.),
  elm spanworm.
 Erannis tiliaria (Harr.),
  linden looper.
*Itame riberia (Fitch), L56,
  currant spanworm.
 Lambdina fiscellaria (Guen.),
  hemlock looper.
 Lygris diversilineata (Hbn.),
  grapevine looper.
*Nematocampa limbata (Haw.), L56,
  filament bearer.
*Nemoria rubifrontaria Pack., L56,
  winged looper.
 Operophtera bruceata (Hulst),
  Bruce spanworm.
*Paleacrita vernata (Peck), L18,
  spring cankerworm.

GLYPHIPTERYGIDAE

 Anthophila pariana (Clerck),
  apple and thorn skeletonizer.

GRACILARIIDAE

 Cameraria cincinnatiella (Chamb.),
  gregarious oak leaf miner.
 Cameraria hamadryadella (Clem.),
  solitary oak leaf miner.
*Cameraria ostryarella (Chamb.), L19,
  an oak leaf miner.
 Cremastobombycia lantanella Busck,
  lantana leaf miner.
 Gracilaria azaleela Brants,
  azalea leaf miner.
 Gracilaria cuculipennella (Hbn.),
  privet leaf miner.
 Gracilaria negundella Chamb.,
  boxelder leaf roller.
 Gracilaria syringella (F.),
  lilac leaf miner.
*Lithocolletis crataegella Clem., L14,
  spotted tentiform leaf miner on apple.

 Marmara elotella (Busck),
  apple bark miner.
 Marmara pomonella Busck,
  apple fruit miner.
*Parectopa robiniella Clem., L19,
  locust digitate leaf miner.

HELIOZELIDAE

*Antispila nyssaefoliella Clem., L19,
  tupelo leaf miner.
*Coptodisca splendoriferella (Clem.), L19,
  resplendent shield bearer.

HESPERIIDAE

*Calpodes ethlius (Stoll), L20,
  larger canna leaf roller.
*Hylephila phylaeus Dru., L20,
  a bent grassworm.
*Lerodea tripunctus H. & S., L20,
  on bent grass.
*Proteides clarus (Cram.), L20,
  silver-spotted skipper.
 Urbanus proteus (L.),
  bean leaf roller.

INCURVARIIDAE

*Paraclemensia acerifoliella (Fitch), L57,
  maple leaf cutter.

LASIOCAMPIDAE

 Epicnaptera americana (Harr.),
  lappet moth.
*Malacosoma americanum (F.), L21,
  eastern tent caterpillar.
 Malacosoma californicum (Pack.),
  California tent caterpillar.
*Malacosoma disstria Hbn., L21,
  forest tent caterpillar.
 Malacosoma pluviale (Dyar),
  western tent caterpillar.
*Tolype velleda (Stoll), L21,
  velleda lappet moth.

LIMACODIDAE

 Cnidocampa flavescens (Wlkr.),
  oriental moth.
*Euclea delphinii Bdv., L22,
  on deciduous trees.

Parasa indetermina (Bdvl.),
  stinging rose caterpillar.
*Phobetron pithecium (A. & S.), L22,
  hag moth.
*Prolimacodes badia Hbn., L22,
  skiff caterpillar.
*Sibine stimulea (Clem.), L23,
  saddleback caterpillar.
*Tortricidia sp., L23,
  on woodland trees.

LIPARIDAE

*Hemerocampa leucostigma (A. & S.), L24,
  white-marked tussock moth.
Hemerocampa pseudotsugata McD.,
  Douglas-fir tussock moth.
Hemerocampa vetusta (Bdvl.),
  western tussock moth.
Notolophus antiqua (L.),
  rusty tussock moth.
*Nygmia phaeorrhoea (Donov.), L24,
  brown-tail moth.
*Porthetria dispar (L.), L24,
  gypsy moth.
*Stilpnotia salicis (L.), L24,
  satin moth

LYCAENIDAE

*Strymon melinus (Hbn.), L23,
  cotton square borer.

LYONETIIDAE

Bedellia orchilella Wlsm.,
  sweet potato leaf miner.
Bedellia somnulentella (Zell.),
  morning-glory leaf miner.
Bucculatrix ainsliella Murtf.,
  oak skeletonizer.
Bucculatrix canadensisella Chamb.,
  birch skeletonizer.
Bucculatrix thurberiella Busck.,
  cotton leaf perforator.

MEGATHYMIDAE

*Aegiale hesperiaris Wlk., L20,
  mageuyworm.

MEGALOPYGIDAE

Megalopyge crispata (Pack),
  crinkled flannel moth.

*Megalopyge opercularis (A. & S.), L23,
  puss caterpillar.
*Norape cretate Grt., L23,
  hackberry leaf slug.

NEPTICULIDAE

Nepticula gossypii F. & L.,
  cotton leaf miner.

NOLIDAE

Celama sorghiella (Riley),
  sorghum webworm.

NOTODONTIDAE

*Cerura borealis Bdv., L25,
  two-tailed cherry caterpillar
*Datana integerrima G. &. R., L25,
  walnut caterpillar.
*Datana major G. and R., L26,
  azalea caterpillar.
*Datana ministra (Drury), L26,
  yellow-necked caterpillar.
*Heterocampa guttivitta (Wlkr.), L25,
  saddled prominent.
*Heterocampa manteo (Dbldy.), L25,
  variable oak leaf caterpillar.
*Ichthyura inclusa Hbn., L26,
  poplar tent maker.
*Nerice bidentata Wlk., L25,
  serrate elm caterpillar.
*Schizura concinna (A. & S.), L8, L25,
  red-humped caterpillar.
*Schizura ipomoeae Dbldy., L25,
  false unicorn caterpillar.
*Schizura unicornis (A. & S.), L25,
  unicorn caterpillar.
*Symmerista albifrons N and D, L25,
  red-anal-humped notodontid.

NYMPHALIDAE

*Asterocampa clyton Bdv. and Lec., L27,
  a hackberry butterfly.
*Athena petreus Cram., L27,
  fig caterpillar.
*Basilarchia archippus (Cram.), L27,
  viceroy.
*Euptoieta claudia Cram., L27,
  pansyworm.
*Nymphalis antiopa (L.), L27,
  mourning-cloak butterfly.

**Nymphalis milberti Godt., L27,
  nettle caterpillar.
*Polygonia interrogationis Fabr., L27,
  violet tip.
 Vanessa atalanta (L.),
  red-admiral.
 Vanessa cardui (L),
  painted-lady.
 Vanessa virginiensis (Drury),
  painted beauty.

OECOPHORIDAE

*Depressaria heracliana (L.), L7, L28,
  parsnip webworm.

OLETHREUTIDAE

*Ancylis comptana fragariae (W. & R.), L30,
  strawberry leaf roller.
*Carpocapsa pomonella (L.), L29,
  codling moth.
*Carpocapsa saltitans Westwood, L31,
  Mexican jumping bean caterpillar.
*Ecdytolopha insiticiana Zell., L14,
  locust twig borer.
 Endothenia hebesana (Wlkr.),
  verbena bud moth.
 Epiblema otiosana (Clem.),
  bidens borer.
 Epiblema scudderiana (Clem.),
  from ragweed.
*Epiblema strenuana (Wlkr.), L31,
  ragweed borer.
 Epinotia aceriella (Clem.),
  maple trumpet skeletonizer.
*Eucosoma giganteana Riley, L31,
  Silphium crown borer.
 Exartema permundanum Clem.,
  raspberry leaf roller.
*Grapholitha interstinctana (Clem.),
  clover head caterpillar.
*Grapholitha molesta (Busck), L2, L6, L7, L8,
L17, L29,
  oriental fruit moth.
 Grapholitha packardi Zell.,
  cherry fruitworm.
 Grapholitha prunivora (Walsh),
  lesser appleworm.
 Gretchena bolliana (Sling.),
  pecan bud moth.
 Hedia variegana (Hbn.)
  green budworm.
 Laspeyresia caryana (Fitch),
  hickory shuckworm.
 Laspeyresia nigricana (Steph.),
  pea moth.

*Melissopus latiferreanus (Wlsm.), L30,
  filbertworm.
*Petrova albicapitana Busck, L14,
  pitch ball moth.
 Petrova comstockiana (Fern.),
  pitch twig moth.
*Polychrosis vitenna (Clem.), L30,
  grape berry moth.
 Proteoteras willingana (Kearf.),
  boxelder twig borer.
 Rhopobota naevana (Hbn.),
  black-headed fireworm.
*Rhyacionia buoliana (Schiff.), L31,
  European pine shoot moth.
*Rhyacionia frustrana (Comst.), L31,
  Nantucket pine moth.
*Spilonota ocellana (D. & S.), L31,
  eye-spotted bud moth.

PAPILIONIDAE

*Battus philenor (L.), L33,
  pipevine swallowtail.
*Papilio ajax L., L33,
  black swallowtail, celeryworm, parsleyworm.
*Papilio cresphontes Cram., L33,
  orange-dog.
*Papilio glaucus L., L33,
  tiger swallowtail.
*Papilio troilus (L.), L33,
  spice-bush swallowtail.

PHALAENIDAE

 Achatodes zeae (Harr.),
  elder shoot borer.
 Acronycta americana Harr.,
  American dagger moth.
*Acronycta funeralis G. & R., L37,
  paddle caterpillar.
 Acronycta lepusculina Guen.,
  cottonwood dagger moth.
*Acronycta oblinita (A. &.S.), L7, L8, L38,
  smeared dagger moth.
 Actebia fennica (Tausch.),
  black army cutworm.
 Agrotis malefida Guen.,
  pale-sided cutworm.
 Agrotis ypsilon (Rott.),
  black cutworm.
*Alabama argillacea (Hbn.), L7, L38,
  cotton leafworm.
 Amathes c-nigrum (L.)
  spotted cutworm.
 Anagrapha falcifera (Kny.),
  celery looper.

*Anticarsia gemmatilis (Hbn.), L38,
velvet bean caterpillar.

Autographs californica (Speyer),
alfalfa looper.

*Autographa oo Cram., L39,
flase cabbage looper.

Barathra configurata (Wlkr.),
bertha armyworm.

Caenurgina erechtea (Cram.),
forage looper.

Callopistria floridensis (Guen.),
Florida fern caterpillar.

*Catocala mira Grt., L39,
a catocala caterpillar.

*Ceramica picta (Harr.), L39,
zebra caterpillar.

*Chorizagrotis auxiliaris (Grote), L37,
army cutworm.

*Cirphis unipuncta (Haw.), L35,
armyworm.

Crymodes devastator (Brace),
glassy cutworm.

*Epizeuxis aemula Hbn., L40,
dry pea hay caterpillar.

*Epizeuxis americalis (Guen.), L40,
from bird nest.

Euxoa messoria (Harr.),
dark-sided cutworm.

*Euxoa ochrogaster (Guen.), L34,
red-backed cutworm.

Euxoa scandens (Riley),
white cutworm.

Euxoa tessellata (Harr.),
striped cutworm.

Feltia subgothica (Haw.),
dingy cutworm.

Feltia subterranea (F.),
granulate cutworm.

*Heliothis armigera (Hbn.), L6, L7, L36,
bollworm, corn earworm, tomato fruitworm.

*Heliothis ononis (Schiff.), L37,
flax bollworm.

*Heliothis virescens subflexa Gn., L36,
Physalis fruitworm.

*Heliothis virescens (F.), L36,
tobacco budworm.

Hydroecia micacea (Esp.),
potato stem borer.

Hypena humuli (Harr.),
hop looper.

Lacinipolia renigera (Steph.),
bristly cutworm.

Laphygma exempta (Wlkr.),
nutgrass armyworm.

*Laphygma exigua (Hbn.), L37,
beet armyworm.

*Laphygma frugiperda (A. & S.), L35,
fall armyworm.

Lithophane antennata (Wlkr.),
green fruitworm.

*Macronoctua onusta Grote, L38,
iris borer.

*Meropleon cosmion Dyar, L56,
pink sugar cane borer.

*Nephelodes emmedonia (Cram), L35,
bronzed cutworm.

Oligia fractilinea (Grote),
lined stalk borer.

*Papaipema nebris (Guen.), L40,
stalk borer.

*Papaipema purpurifascia (G. & R.), L40,
columbine borer.

*Peridroma margaritosa (Haw.), L34,
variegated cutworm.

*Plathypena scabra (F), L39,
green cloverworm.

Polia legitima (Grote),
striped garden caterpillar.

*Prodenia eridania (Cram.), L34,
southern armyworm.

*Prodenia ornithogalli Guen., L34,
yellow striped armyworm.

Protoleucania albilinea (Hbn.),
wheat head armyworm.

*Scolecampa liburna Geyer, L39,
decayed wood caterpillar.

Scotogramma trifolii (Rott.),
clover cutworm.

Septis artica (Freyer),
yellow-headed cutworm.

Spaelotis clandestina (Harr.),
w-marked cutworm.

*Sudariophora acutalis Wlk., L38,
single filament looper.

*Trichoplusia ni (Hbn.), L39,
cabbage looper.

PIERIDAE

*Colias philodice eurytheme Bdvl., L41,
alfalfa caterpillar.

Colias philodice philodice Latr.,
clouded sulphur.

Neophasia manapia (F. & F.),
pine butterfly.

*Pieris protodice B. & L., L41,
southern cabbageworm.

*Pieris rapae (L.), L41,
imported cabbageworm.

PLUTELLIDAE

Harpipteryz xylostella (L.),
European honeysuckle leaf roller.

*Plutella maculipennis (Curt.), L42,
diamondback moth.

PRODOXIDAE

*Prodoxus quinquepunctellus Cham., L58,
bogus yucca moth.
*Tegeticula yuccasella (Riley), L58,
yucca moth.

PSYCHIDAE

*Thyridopteryx ephemeraeformis (Haw.), L42,
bagworm.

PTEROPHORIDAE

*Oidaematophorus grandis Fish, L43,
on Baccharis pilularis.
*Platyptilia antirrhina Lange, L43,
snapdragon plume moth.
*Platyptilia carduidactyla (Riley), L43,
artichoke plume moth.
Platyptilia pusillodactyla (Wlkr.),
lantana plume moth.
*Pterophorus periscelidactylus Fitch, L43,
grape plume moth.

PYRALIDAE

Achatodes zeae Harr.,
elder shoot borer.
*Achroia grisella (F.), L45,
lesser wax moth.
*Acrobasis caryae Grote, L47,
pecan nut casebearer.
*Acrobasis juglandis (LeB), L47,
pecan leaf casebearer.
*Aglossa caprealis (Hbn.), L53,
murky meal caterpillar.
*Catoclysta fulicalis Clem., L46,
aquatic, under silk sheets on rocks.
*Chilo plejadellus Zinck., L53,
rice stalk borer.
Chilo simplex Butl.,
Asiatic rice borer.
*Crambus caliginosellus Clem., L47,
corn root webworm.
Crambus teterrellus (Zinck.),
bluegrass webworm.
Crambus topiarius Zell.,
cranberry girdler.
Crambus vulgivagellus Clem.,
vagabond crambus.

*Desmia funeralis (Hbn.), L51,
grape leaf folder.
*Diaphania hyalinata (L.), L51,
melonworm.
*Diaphania nitidalis (Stoll), L51,
pickleworm.
*Diatraea crambidoides (Grote), L44,
southern cornstalk borer.
*Diatraea grandiosella Dyar, L44,
southwestern corn borer.
*Diatraea saccharalis (E.), L44,
sugarcane borer.
Dioryctria reniculella (Grote),
spruce coneworm.
Dioryctria zimmermani (Grote),
Zimmerman pine moth.
*Elasmopalpus lignosellus (Zell), L47,
lesser cornstalk borer.
Ephestia cautella (Wlkr.),
almond moth.
*Ephestia elutella (Hbn.), L49,
tobacco moth.
*Ephestia figulilella Gregg, L49,
raisin moth.
*Ephestia kühniella Zell., L49,
Mediterranean flour moth.
*Etiella zinckenella (Treit), L48,
lima-bean pod borer.
*Euzophera semifuneralis Wlkr., L47,
American plum borer.
*Evergestis rimosalis Guen., L50,
cross-striped cabbageworm.
Fundella pellucens Zell.,
Caribbean pod borer.
*Galleria mellonella (L.), L45,
wax moth.
*Hellula undalis (F.), L50,
cabbage webworm.
Homoeosoma electellum (Hulst),
sunflower moth.
Hymenia perspectalis (Hbn.),
spotted beet webworm.
*Hymenia recurvalis (F.), L50,
Hawaiian beet webworm.
Hypsopygia costalis (F.),
clover hayworm.
*Lineodes integra (Zell.), L53,
nightshade leaf tier.
*Loxostege commixtalis (Walkr.), L50,
alfalfa webworm.
*Loxostege similalis (Guen.), L50,
garden webworm.
Loxostege sticticalis (L.),
beet webworm.
Melitara dentata (Grote),
blue cactus borer.
Mineola indigenella (Zell.),
leaf crumpler.

*Mineola vaccinii (Riley), L48,
  cranberry fruitworm.
*Monoptilota pergratialis (Hulst), L48,
  lima-bean vine borer.
Myelois venipars Dyar,
  navel orangeworm.
Nephopteryx rubrizonella Rag.,
  pear fruit borer.
Nymphula obliteralis (Wlkr.),
  waterlily leaf cutter.
*Nymphula gyralis Hlst., L46,
  on cattails.
Omiodes accepta (Butl.),
  sugar cane leaf roller.
Omiodes blackburni (Butl.),
  cocoanut leaf roller.
*Pachyzancla bipunctalis (F.), L51,
  southern beet webworm.
*Pantographa limata G. & R., L50,
  basswood leaf roller.
*Phlyctaenia rubigalis (Guen.), L51,
  celery leaf tier, greenhouse leaf tier.
Phlyctaenia tertialis, L53,
  elder leaf tier.
Pilocrocis tripunctata (F.),
  sweetpotato leaf roller.
*Plodia interpunctella (Hbn.), L49,
  Indian-meal moth.
*Psorosina hammondi (Riley), L48,
  apple leaf skeletonizer.
*Pyralis farinalis (L.), L49,
  meal moth.
*Pyrausta ainsliei Heir., L52,
  smartweed borer.
*Pyrausta futilalis Led., L51,
  Indian hempworm.
*Pyrausta nubilalis (Hbn.), L6, L7, L52,
  European corn borer.
*Pyrausta penitalis Grt., L52,
  lotus borer.
Salebria subcaesiella (Clem.),
  locust leaf roller.
*Tetralopha robustella Zell., L45,
  pine webworm.
Tetralopha scortealis (Led.),
  lespedeza webworm.
*Tlascala finitella Wlk., L48,
  Hill's fireworm.
Vitula serratilineella Rag.,
  dried-fruit moth.
*Zophodia convolutella (Hbn.), L48,
  gooseberry fruitworm.

SATURNIIDAE

*Automeris io (F.), L54,
  io moth.
*Callosamia promethea (Drury), L54,
  promethea moth.

Coloradia pandora Blake,
  pandora moth.
*Hemileuca maia (Drury), L54,
  buck moth.
Hemileuca oliviae Ckll.,
  range caterpillar.
Philosamia cynthia (Drury),
  cynthia moth.
*Samia cecropia (L.), L6, L7, L54,
  cecropia moth.
*Telea polyphemus (Cram.), L54,
  polyphemus moth.
*Tropaea luna (L.), L54,
  luna moth.

SPHINGIDAE

Ampeloeca myron (Cram.),
  Virginia-creeper sphinx.
*Celerio lineata (F.), L55, L56,
  white-lined sphinx.
*Ceratomia amyntor (Hbn.),
  five pronged sphinx.
*Ceratomia catalpae (Bdvl.), L55,
  catalpa sphinx.
Cressonia juglandis (A. & S.),
  walnut sphinx.
**Herse cingulata (F.), L56,
  sweetpotato hornworm.
*Lapara bombycoides Wlk., L55,
  pine needle sphinx.
*Pholus achemon (Drury), L55, L56,
  achemon sphinx.
Pholus satellitia pandorus Hbn., L56,
  pandorus sphinx on grapes.
*Protoparce quinquemaculata (Haw.), L55,
  tomato hornworm.
*Protoparce sexta (Johan.), L55,
  tobacco hornworm.

THYATIRIDAE

*Euthyatira sp., L8, L42,
  on dogwood (Cornus),

TINEIDAE

Nemapogon granella (L.),
  European grain moth.
*Tinea pellionella (L.), L57,
  casemaking clothes moth.
*Tineola bisselliella (Hum.), L57,
  webbing clothes moth.
Trichophaga tapetzella (L.),
  carpet moth.

LEPIDOPTERA

TISCHERIDAE

*Coptotriche zelleriella Clem., L19,
  an oak leaf miner.
Tischeria malifoliella Clem.,
  apple leaf trumpet miner.

TORTRICIDAE

Acleris minuta (Rob.),
  yellow-headed fireworm.
Acleris variana (Fern.),
  black-headed budworm.
*Archips argyrospila (Wlkr.), L32,
  fruit tree leaf roller.
*Archips cerasivorana (Fitch), L32,
  ugly-nest caterpillar.
Archips conflictana (Wlkr.),
  large aspen tortrix.
*Archips fervidana Clem., L31,
  scrub oak nest caterpillar.
*Archips fumiferana (Clem.), L31, L32,
  spruce budworm.
*Archips obsoletana Wlk., L17, L32,
  obsolete-banded strawberry leafroller.
*Archips rileyana Grt., L32,
  buckeye leafworm.
Archips rosaceana (Harr.),
  oblique-banded leaf roller.
Argyrotaenia citrana (Fern.),
  orange tortrix.
Argyrotaenia juglandana (Fern.),
  hickory leaf roller.
Argyrotaenia mariana (Fern.),
  gray-banded leaf roller.

Argyrotaenia pinatubana (Kearf.),
  pine tube moth.
Argyrotaenia velutinana (Wlkr.),
  red banded leaf roller.
Cnephasia langana (Haw.),
  omnivorous leaf tier.
*Platynota stultana Wlshm., L30,
  carnationworm.

YPONOMEUTIDAE

Argyresthia conjugella Zell.,
  apple fruit moth.
Argyresthia thuiella (Pack),
  arborvitae leaf miner.
*Atteva aurea (Fitch), L6, L7, L42,
  ailanthus webworm.
Hyponomeuta padella (L.),
  ermine moth.

ZANOLIDAE

*Apatelodes torrefacta A. and S., L26,
  tritufted zanolid.

ZYGAENIDAE

*Harrisina americana (Guer.), L8, L58,
  grape leaf skeletonizer.
*Harrisini brillians B. & McD., L58,
  western grape skeletonizer.

LEPIDOPTERA

EXPLANATION OF FIGURES L1, A-Z

HEAD AND OTHER PARTS

Figures A to F. Labra showing setae and notch types of several common larvae.

Figure A. Cephalic view of a typical labrum showing three pairs of median labial setae (m^1 to m^3), three pairs of lateral labral setae (la^1 to la^3) and one pair of labral punctures (p) according to Heinrich's nomenclature. Taken from Crumb, 1929.

Figure B. Cephalic view of a common labrum showing two methods of naming the setae; on the right half Heinrich's letter system of 3 median (m^1 to m^3) and 3 lateral (la^1 to la^3) setae and the left half lower case Roman numerals (i to vi) used by W. T. M. Forbes and others. Taken from Forbes, 1923.

Figure C. Ental surface of the labrum showing the epipharynx with three pairs of epipharyngeal setae. Taken from Crumb, 1929.

Figure D. Cephalic view of a notodontid labrum possessing an acute deep notch.

Figure E. Cephalic view of a sphingid labrum possessing a shallow notch with parallel sides and a groove extending dorsad of the notch.

Figure F. Cephalic view of a saturnid labrum possessing a deep notch with parallel sides.

Figures G to N. Various types of spinnerets among the Phalaenidae. Taken from Crumb, 1929.

Figures O and P. Lateral (ectal or outer) and mesal (ental, inner or oral) views of the right mandible of Agarastidae, Alypia octomaculata F, eight spotted forester. This mandible shows two common mandibular setae, dentation along the distal margin, a serrate destomesal cutting edge, presence of a prominent, unusual, tooth-like retinaculum on the inner or oral surface and one rounded condyle. See L28, J-K.

Figure Q. One labial palpus of a cutworm, Phalaenidae, possessing three segments and a small papilla. See Crumb, 1929.

Figures R to U. A typical antenna and parts. Drawings prepared by V. G. Dethier, 1941, Bul. Comp. Zool. Vol. 87:455.

Figure R. A typical three segmented (1, 2 and 3) antenna with sense organs mostly at the distal ends of the second and third segments. ACA = antacoria, LH = long hair (sensillum trichodeum), SB = sensillum basiconicum, SBS = small sensillum basiconicum, SC = sensillum campaniformium; SH = short hair (sensillum trichodium), SS = sensillum styloconicum.

Figures S, T, and U. Large sensilla basiconica showing three fundamental types of sculpturing; figure S shows a pitted surface common among Rhopalocera, figure T a longitudinally ridged surface characteristic of Sphingidae and Saturniidae and figure U a spiraled surface characteristic of most Heterocera.

Figure V. Lateral view of the caudal end of Drepana harpagula of Europe, Drepanidae, showing a dorsal anal process and anal prolegs absent. From Fracker, 1915.

Figure W. Dorsal view of a bifurcate anal plate of a European species of Satyridae. From Fracker, 1915.

Figure X. Lateral view of an elongated anal proleg of a notodontid called a stemapoda.

Figure Y. Mesal aspect of a ventral proleg of an arctiid showing uniordinal crochets arranged in a heteroideous mesoseries.

Figure Z. Lateral view of a thoracic leg of a sphingid larva showing the various parts.

Note. For explanation of all figures in part 1 see figure O1.

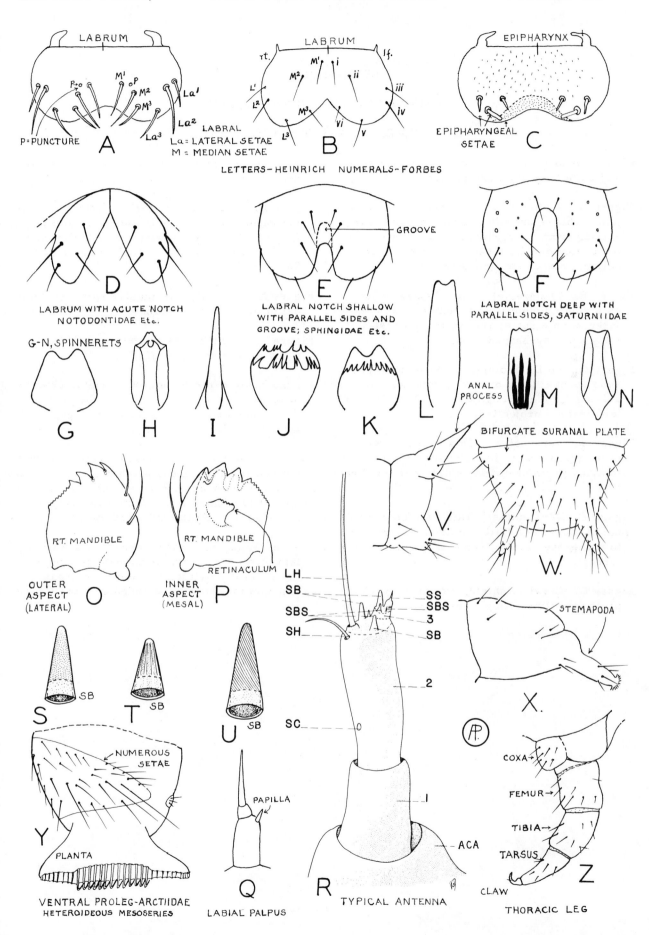

LEPIDOPTERA, HEAD AND OTHER PARTS FIGURE LI.

LABRUM

P₂o
M¹
oP
M²
M³
La¹
La²
La³
P=PUNCTURE
LABRAL
La=LATERAL SETAE
M=MEDIAN SETAE

A

LABRUM

rt.
M²
M¹
i
lf.
ii
L¹
L²
iii
iv
M³
vi
v
L³

B

LETTERS—HEINRICH NUMERALS—FORBES

EPIPHARYNX

EPIPHARYNGEAL
SETAE

C

D

LABRUM WITH ACUTE NOTCH
NOTODONTIDAE Etc.

E

GROOVE

LABRAL NOTCH SHALLOW
WITH PARALLEL SIDES AND
GROOVE; SPHINGIDAE Etc.

F

LABRAL NOTCH DEEP WITH
PARALLEL SIDES, SATURNIIDAE

G-N, SPINNERETS

G   H   I   J   K

L

ANAL
PROCESS

M   N

BIFURCATE SURANAL PLATE

V.

W.

RT. MANDIBLE

OUTER
ASPECT
(LATERAL)

O

RT. MANDIBLE

RETINACULUM

INNER
ASPECT
(MESAL)

P

LH
SB
SBS
SH

SS
SBS
3
SB

2

SC

STEMAPODA

X.

SB

S

SB

T

SB

U

NUMEROUS
SETAE

Y

PLANTA

VENTRAL PROLEG-ARCTIIDAE
HETEROIDEOUS MESOSERIES

PAPILLA

Q

LABIAL PALPUS

I

ACA

R

TYPICAL ANTENNA

COXA

FEMUR

TIBIA

TARSUS

CLAW

Z

THORACIC LEG

LEPIDOPTERA

EXPLANATION OF FIGURES L2, A-N

ARMATURE, GLANDS, SPIRACLES, ETC.

Figures A to F. Some common forms of setae and spines found on caterpillars.

Figure A. A simple primary seta and pinaculum. This figure illustrates a simple hair arising from a ring-like papilla located near the center of a flattened sclerotized area called a pinaculum, (pl. pinacula).

Figure B. Chalaza(ae). This chalaza possesses a single plumose seta (may possess one to three simple setae) arising from a distinctly elevated cone-shaped area.

Figure C. and D. Scolus(e). These scoli possess several (four or more) setae or spines arising from an elongated smooth or irregular elevated projection.

Figure E. Verruca(ae). This verruca, typical of many, is a wart-like elevation giving rise to many prominent setae pointing many directions.

Figure F. Verricule(s). This verricule, typical of many, is a flattened area giving rise to numerous parallel setae all pointing one direction.

Figure G. Cervical shield. Dorsal view of a prothorax illustrating a sclerotized pronotum or cervical shield and its six pairs of setae, see L5, B.

Figure H. Anal comb or fork. Ventral view of the caudal end of an oriental fruit moth larva, Grapholitha molesta Busck, illustrating the position and shape of an anal comb or fork. See L29, G-L.

Figure I. A circular or annular spiracle, typical of many microlepidoptera.

Figure J. An elliptical spiracle, typical of many macrolepidoptera.

Figure K. An osmeterium or eversible (V or Y shaped) gland located caudad of the head on the dorsomeson of the prothorax of papilionid larvae.

Figure L. A ventral, eversible gland located on the ventromeson of the prothorax between the legs and the head. Found among various species of the Agaristidae, Danaidae, Hesperiidae, Nymphalidae, Phalaenidae, Pieridae, etc.

Figures M and N. Lateral and dorsal views of larvae showing some of the names given to the several longitudinal coloration areas found on the thorax and abdomen. See Crumb, 1929.

LEPIDOPTERA, ARMATURE-GLANDS-SPIRACLES &. FIGURE L2

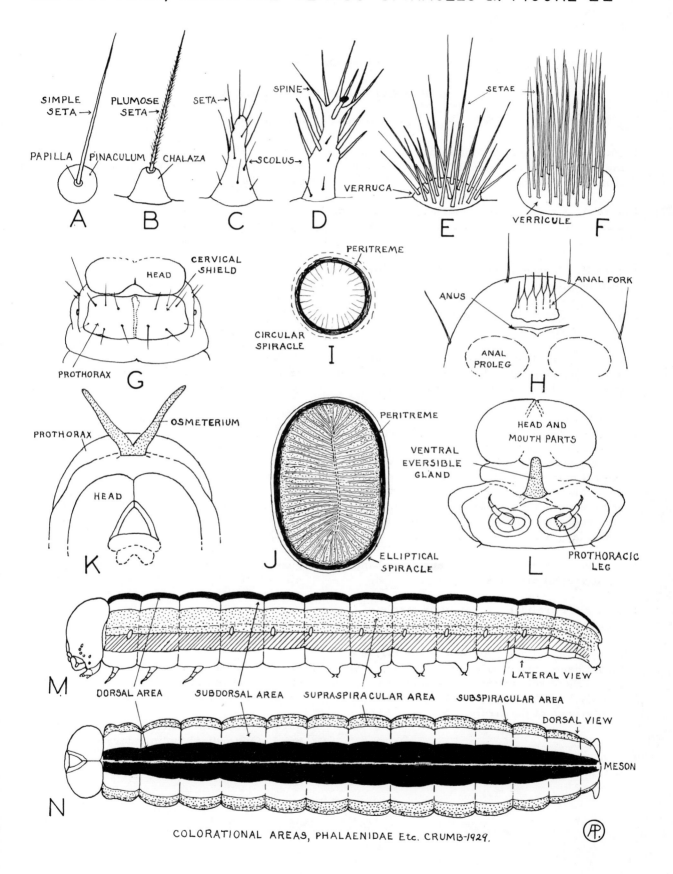

COLORATIONAL AREAS, PHALAENIDAE Etc. CRUMB-1929.

EXPLANATION OF FIGURES L3, A-P

CROCHETS ON PROLEGS

Figures A to D. Diagrammatic drawings showing detailed arrangement of the crochets in small sections of given bands.

Figure A. Crochets are uniserial (arising from a given line) and uniordinal (all of the same length).

Figure B. Crochets are uniserial and biordinal (two lengths).

Figure C. Crochets are uniserial and triordinal (three lengths).

Figure D. Crochets or rudiments are multiserial (arising from three or more lines) and uniordinal (same length in a given line).

Figures E to P. Diagrammatic drawings of the entire arrangement of the crochets on the ventral prolegs of various larvae. Each figure represents a left ventral proleg with the lateral margin toward the top, the mesal margin near the bottom side adjacent to the meson and the cephalic margin toward the left. All the crochets in figures E to K and O to P are uniserial (arising from a given line).

Figure E. Aegeriidae. Two transverse bands of uniordinal crochets.

Figure F. Pyralidae. A complete circle of biordinal crochets.

Figure G. Pyralidae. An incomplete circle or mesal penellipse of triordinal crochets. The gap in the circle on the lateral aspect is usually less than one-third the projected circumference of the circle.

Figure H. Psychidae. An incomplete circle or lateral penellipse of uniordinal crochets. The gap in the circle is adjacent to the meson.

Figure I. Saturniidae. One band of biordinal crochets located on the mesal aspect of the proleg and called a mesoseries which is homoideous.

Figure J. Arctiidae. A mesoseries of crochets with all the crochets near the two ends greatly reduced in size while those in the center are well developed and functional. Such an arrangement is said to be heteroideous. If all the crochets were uniordinal and all more or less alike in size (typical of many Phalaenidae) they would be designated as homoideous.

Figure K. Drepanidae. A proleg with crochets on the lateral and mesal aspects. The lateroseries is uniordinal while the mesoseries is biordinal. Fracker calls this arrangement a pseudocircle.

Figure L. Gracilariidae. Uniordinal crochets in a lateral penellipse with a few scattered crochets within the penellipse.

Figure M. Acrolophidae. Several complete circles of uniordinal crochets producing a regular multiserial arrangement.

Figure N. Yponomeutidae. An irregular multiserial arrangement of crochets.

Figure O. Lycaenidae. A triordinal mesoseries of crochets interrupted near the center by the presence of a fleshy lobe or spatula.

Figure P. Incurvariidae. A single transverse band of uniordinal rudimentary crochets.

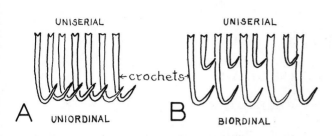

A — UNISERIAL / crochets / UNIORDINAL

B — UNISERIAL / BIORDINAL

C — UNISERIAL / TRIORDINAL

D — MULTISERIAL / UNIORDINAL

FIGURES E to P,—LEFT VENTRAL PROLEGS

← CEPHALAD   ── LATERAL MARGIN ──   CAUDAD →

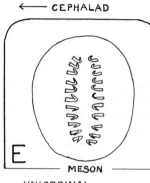

E — MESON

UNIORDINAL,
TRANSVERSE BANDS,
AEGERIIDAE.

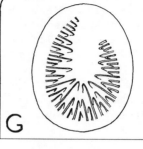

F —

BIORDINAL,
CIRCLE,
PYRALIDAE

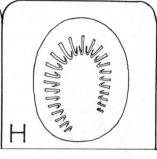

G —

TRIORDINAL,
MESAL PENELLIPSE
PYRALIDAE

H —

UNIORDINAL,
LATERAL PENELLIPSE,
PSYCHIDAE.

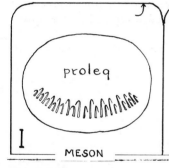

── LATERAL MARGIN ──

I — proleg / MESON

BIORDINAL,
HOMOIDEOUS MESOSERIES,
SATURNIIDAE

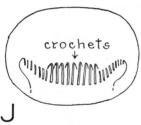

J — crochets

HETEROIDEOUS
MESOSERIES,
ARCTIIDAE

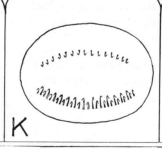

K —

UNIORDINAL LATEROSERIES,
PLUS BIORDINAL MESOSERIES
= PSEUDOCIRCLE, DREPANIDAE

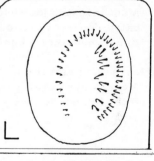

L —

LATERAL PENELLIPSE
PLUS SCATTERED CROCHETS,
GRACILARIIDAE

── LATERAL MARGIN ──

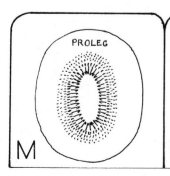

M — PROLEG

MULTISERIAL
CIRCLE,
ACROLOPHIDAE

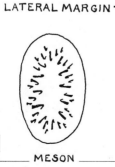

N — MESON

MULTISERIAL
CIRCLE,
YPONOMEUTIDAE

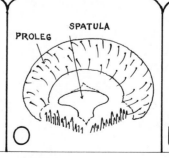

O — PROLEG / SPATULA

TRIORDINAL
INTERRUPTED MESOSERIES,
LYCAENIDAE

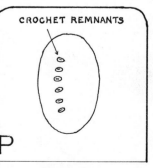

P — CROCHET REMNANTS

UNIORDINAL, SINGLE,
TRANSVERSE BAND,
INCURVARIIDAE.

LEPIDOPTERA

EXPLANATION OF FIGURES L4, A-H

HEAD AND MOUTH PARTS, CHAETOTAXY

Figure A. Cephalic view of a head capsule illustrating the distribution of the primary setae with the names or numbers used by various investigators. The names (see key at bottom of plate) are those used by Heinrich and others. The numbers are those used by Dyar. Taken from W. T. M. Forbes, 1923 (with corrections).

Figure B. Cephalic view of the head of a common full grown cutworm, Phalaenidae. Heinrich's system of names used for the setae shown.

Figure C. Lateral view of the head of a common full grown cutworm, Phalaenidae. Heinrich's system of names used for the setae shown. The ocelli are numbered. Most investigators use the numbers as indicated; however, Fracker, reverses the position of numbers 5 and 6.

Figure D. Lateral view of the head capsule of Meskea dyspteraria Grt. Thyrididae. Taken from Heinrich, 1921.

Figure E. Ventral view of the head of a common full grown cutworm, Phalaenidae, showing the distribution of the setae and the mouth parts.

Figure F. An open front. A portion of the head capsule showing the absence of a coronal suture, also the arms of the epicranial suture do not meet on the meson. This creates a so-called open front, see Gracilariidae.

Figure G. A caudal or ventral view of the labium and maxillae of a cutworm, Phalaenidae, showing the distribution of the setae, spinneret and other details. Also see Crumb, 1929.

Figure H. Detailed structure of the surface of the hypopharynx of a cutworm. See Crumb, 1929.

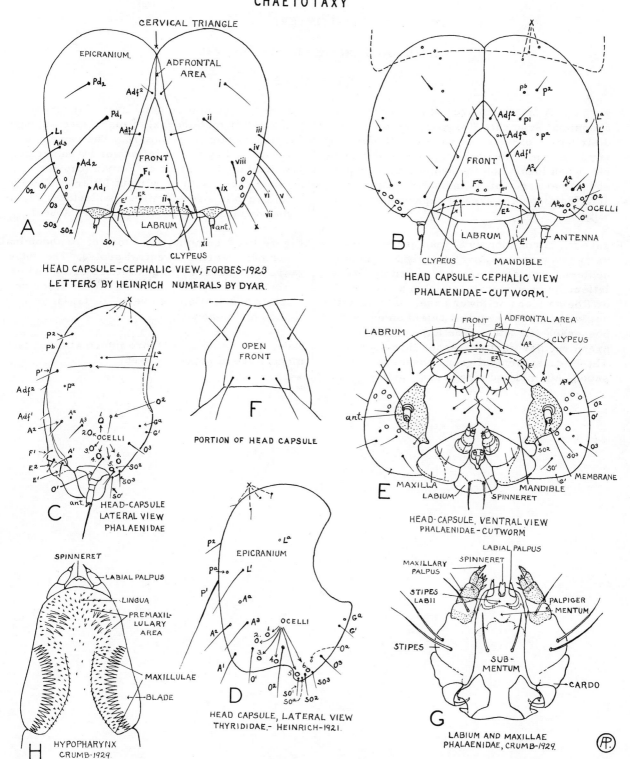

A — HEAD CAPSULE–CEPHALIC VIEW, FORBES–1923
LETTERS BY HEINRICH NUMERALS BY DYAR.

B — HEAD CAPSULE–CEPHALIC VIEW
PHALAENIDAE–CUTWORM.

C — HEAD-CAPSULE LATERAL VIEW PHALAENIDAE

F — PORTION OF HEAD CAPSULE

E — HEAD-CAPSULE, VENTRAL VIEW PHALAENIDAE–CUTWORM

H — HYPOPHARYNX CRUMB–1929

D — HEAD CAPSULE, LATERAL VIEW THYRIDIDAE.– HEINRICH–1921.

G — LABIUM AND MAXILLAE PHALAENIDAE, CRUMB–1929.

Key to setae and punctures:– A (Ad)-anterior; Adf-adfrontal; E-epistomal; F-frontal; G-genal; L-lateral; O-ocellar; P (Pd)-posterior; SO-subocellar; X-ultraposterior. See Crumb, 1929; Forbes, 1923.

LEPIDOPTERA

EXPLANATION OF FIGURES L5, A-D

SETAL MAPS

Figure A. A setal map area of any thoracic or abdominal segment. This area records the distribution of the setae on one, left half of any segment. The usual position of the spiracle, when located on the prothorax or on any abdominal segment, is indicated. The thoracic leg or proleg area is represented by an ellipse.

Figure B. A common setal map of the prothorax of many species, particularly Microlepidoptera. The setae are designated by Greek letters or by numerals, which may be Arabic or Roman (caps or lower case), with or without letters. The cervical shield on one side possesses six setae. The Kappa group or prespiracular wart possesses three setae. The Pi or subventral group possesses two setae. Mu, phi and omega are wanting.

Figure C. A common setal map of the mesothorax (or metathorax) of many species, particularly Microlepidoptera. The setae are designated by Greek letters or by numerals, which may be Arabic or Roman (caps or lower case), with or without letters. The Pi (6) group in a few families is bisetose. Gamma, delta, mu, lambda and phi are absent.

Figure D. A common setal map of an abdominal segment bearing a ventral proleg. The setae are designated by Greek letters or by numerals which may be Arabic or Roman (caps or lower case). Gamma, delta, theta, lambda and phi are absent.

Note. See Table 2 for more information on nomenclature of setae, page 65.

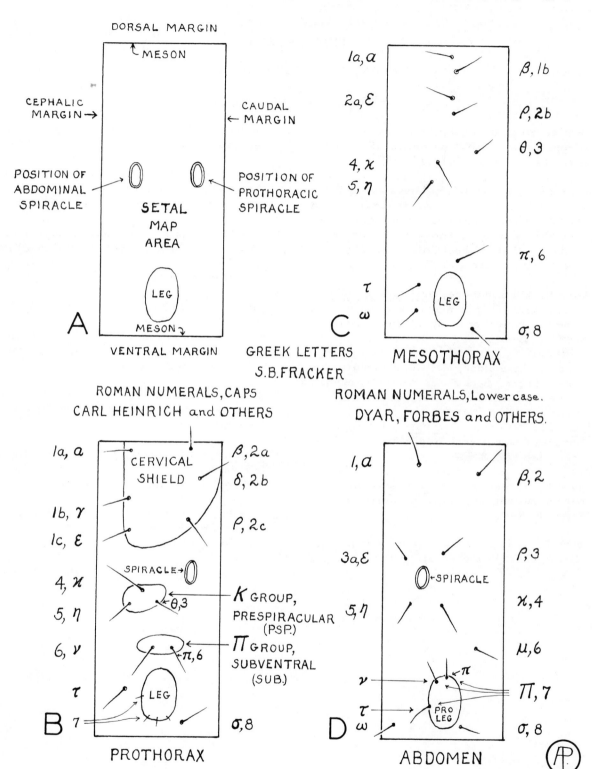

LEPIDOPTERA   SETAL MAPS   FIGURE L5

LEPIDOPTERA

EXPLANATION OF FIGURES L6, A-L

SETAL MAPS, PROTHORAX

CER = cervical shield, PSP = prespiracular (Kappa group), SUB = subventral (Pi group). Also see key below figures.

Figure A. Yponomeutidae, Atteva aurea Fitch, on Ailanthus. Seta beta (2a) is further from the meson than alpha (1a). This figure also records the numerals (may be Roman or Arabic) with or without letters used by many investigators. See L42, G-I.

Figure B. Olethreutidae, Grapholitha molesta Busck, oriental fruit moth, Kappa group is trisetose typical of many Microlepidoptera. See L29, G-L.

Figure C. Aegeriidae, Melittia cucurbitae Harr. squash borer. Seta rho is distinctly cephalad on the cervical shield. See L9, A-C.

Figure D. Pyralidae, Pyrausta nubilalis Hbn., European corn borer. Kappa group is bisetose. See L52, A-I.

Figure E. Phalaenidae, Heliothis armigera Hbn. corn earworm. Kappa group is bisetose. See L36, K-P.

Figure F. Coleophoridae, Coleophora pruniella Clem., cherry casebearer. Some species of Coleophora have a unisetose Kappa group. See L13, K-M.

Figure G. Pyralidae, Nymphula sp. Kappa unisetose and spiracle vestigial, an aquatic species found on cattails. See L46, E-I.

Figure H. Hepialidae, Hepialus humuli (see Fracker - 1915). On most hepialids all nine dorsal setae and the spiracles are located on one sclerotized area.

Figure I. Psychidae, Thyridopteryx ephemeraeformis Haw., bagworm. Long axis of the spiracle is horizontal. It and the nine dorsal setae are located on one continuous sclerotized area. See L42, A.

Figure J. Acrolophidae, Acrolophus sp. Kappa group is adjacent to but partially separated from the cervical shield. See L11, K-N.

Figure K. Arctiidae, Hyphantria cunea Drury, fall webworm. The location of the verrucae (with setae omitted) is shown. See L10, F-G.

Figure L. Saturniidae, Samia cecropia L., cecropia moth. Setal groups, Kappa and Pi, represented by distinct scoli. L54, A.

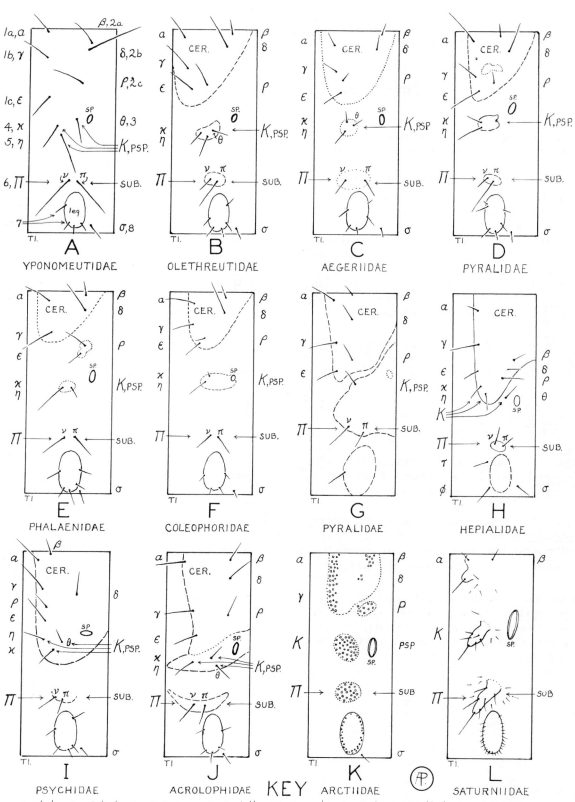

A — YPONOMEUTIDAE
B — OLETHREUTIDAE
C — AEGERIIDAE
D — PYRALIDAE
E — PHALAENIDAE
F — COLEOPHORIDAE
G — PYRALIDAE
H — HEPIALIDAE
I — PSYCHIDAE
J — ACROLOPHIDAE
K — ARCTIIDAE
L — SATURNIIDAE

KEY

a-alpha-1a, β-beta-2a, γ-gamma 1b, δ-delta-2b, ε-epsilon-1c, ρ-rho-2c, θ-theta-3, κ-kappa-4,
η-eta-5, ν-nu-6, π-pi-6, τ-tau, φ-phi, σ-sigma-8, 7(on coxa), Κ-kappa=θ(3)+κ(4)+η(5), Π-pi=ν+π(6).

LEPIDOPTERA

EXPLANATION OF FIGURES L7, A-L

SETAL MAPS, MESOTHORAX, ABDOMEN

Figures A to H. Setal maps of the mesothorax, T2. Among most species the setal map of the metathorax resembles the mesothorax.

Figure A. Mesothorax, Pyralidae, Pyrausta nubilalis Hbn., European corn borer. Pi group unisetose, setae arise from pinacula. This figure also records the numerals (may be Roman or Arabic) with or without letters used by many investigators. See L52, A-I.

Figure B. Mesothorax, Pyralidae, Galleria mellonella L. wax moth. Pi group bisetose, typical of Galleriinae. See L45, I-M.

Figure C. Mesothorax, Phalaenidae, Alabama argillacea Hbn., cotton leafworm. Most setae arise from chalazae. See L38, G-J.

Figure D. Mesothorax, Oecophoridae, Depressaria heracliania L., parsnip webworm. Most setae arise from pinacula. See L28, A-E.

Figure E. Mesothorax, Arctiidae, Hyphantria cunea Drury, fall webworm. Distribution of verrucae (setae omitted) shown. See L10, F.

Figure F. Mesothorax, Phalaenidae, Acronicta oblinita A and S, smeared daggar moth. Shows distribution of verrucae (setae omitted) and theta (3) as a simple seta. See L38, K.

Figure G. Mesothorax, Saturniidae, Samia cecropia L., cecropia moth. All primary setae in form of scoli or cornicula. A number of short secondary setae are present. See L54, A.

Figure H. Mesothorax, Citheroniidae, Anisota senatoria A and S., orange-striped oak worm. All primary setae in form of scoli with alpha very prominent and much longer than similar scoli on the abdomen. Secondary setae small and numerous. See L12, A-D.

Figures I to L. Setal maps of mid-abdominal segments, especially A4.

Figure I. Abdomen (A4), Olethreutidae, Grapholitha molesta Buscke, oriental fruit moth. Typical of many Olethreutidae and Tortricidae. Kappa (4) and eta (5) adjacent and on the same pinaculum. This figure also records the numerals (may be Roman or Arabic) with or without letters used by many investigators. See L29, G-L.

Figure J. Abdomen (A4), Aegeriidae, Sanninoidae exitiosa Say, peach tree borer. Epsilon wanting. Kappa (4) and eta (5) adjacent. See L9, P-V.

Figure K. Abdomen (A4), Phalaenidae, Heliothis armigera Hbn., bollworm, corn earworm or tomato fruit worm. Kappa (4) caudad of spiracle and remote from eta (5). See L36, K-P.

Figure L. Abdomen (A4), Yponomeutidae, Atteva aurea Fitch, on Ailanthus. Typical of most Yponomeutidae and many Plutellidae. Kappa (4) and eta (5) remote. See L42, G-I.

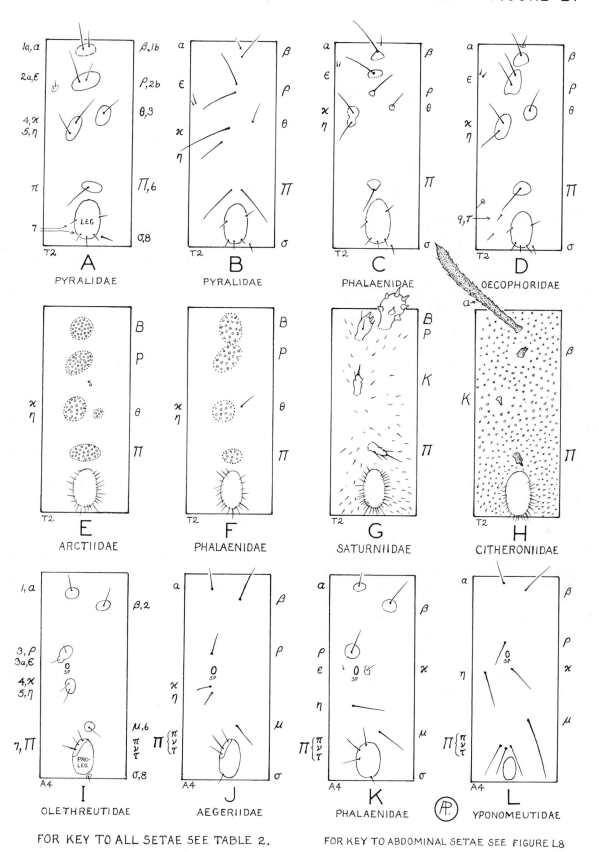

FOR KEY TO ALL SETAE SEE TABLE 2.   FOR KEY TO ABDOMINAL SETAE SEE FIGURE L8

LEPIDOPTERA

EXPLANATION OF FIGURES L8, A-P

SETAL MAPS, ABDOMEN

Figure A. Abdomen (A4), Thyatiridae, Euthyatira sp., probably pudens Guen. Note presence of two extra setae between the spiracle and the proleg. Forbes designates these as X (10) while Fracker appears to call one of them lambda. This figure also records the numerals (may be Roman or Arabic) used by many investigators. See L42, J-K.

Figure B. Abdomen (A4), Phalaenidae, Acronicta oblinita A. & S., smeared dagger moth. The distribution of the verrucae (setae omitted) are shown. See L38, K-M.

Figure C. Abdomen (A4), Zygaenidae, Harrisina americana Guer., grape leaf skeletonizer. The distribution of the verrucae (setae omitted) are shown, alpha (1) and beta (2) combined. See L58, C-D.

Figure D. Abdomen (A4), Arctiidae, Utetheisa bella (L.), bella moth. Most of the setae arise from chalazae; kappa (4) and eta (5) are re-remote; also mu (6) is bisetose. See L10, J-M.

Figures E and F. Abdomen (A6 and A7), Notodontidae, Schizura concinna A. and S., red-humped caterpillar. Note that the distance (usually ventrad) between seta kappa (4) and the spiracle is greater on the seventh abdominal segment, figure F, than on the sixth segment (or the eighth segment), figure E. See L25, H-I.

Figures G and H. Abdomen (A6 and A7), Arctiidae, Hyphantria cunea Drury, fall webworm.

Note that the distances between verrucae kappa (4) and the spiracles on the sixth and seventh abdominal segments are subequal. See L10, F-G.

Figures I and J. Abdomen (A7 and A8), Aegeriidae, Sanninoidae exitiosa Say, peach tree borer. The spiracle on the eighth segment is distinctly larger than the spiracle on the seventh segment and also located more dorsad. See L9, P-U.

Figure K. Abdomen (A8), Gelechiidae, Gnorimoschema operculella Zell, potato tuber worm. Seta rho (3) is dorsad (not distinctly cephalad) of the spiracle. See L16, A-E.

Figures L and M. Abdomen (A8 and A9), Olethreutidae, Grapholitha molesta Busck, oriental fruit moth. Seta rho (3) on the eighth segment is distinctly cephalad of the spiracle, typical of most Olethreutidae and Tortricidae. Also seta alpha (1) on the ninth segment is located ventrad of beta (2). See L29, G-L.

Figures N and O. Abdomen (A8 and A9), Yponomeutidae, Atteva aurea Fitch, Ailanthus webworm. The setal map of this species typifies many larvae of this family and the Plutellidae. The setae are long; kappa (4) and eta (5) are remote on the eighth segment, also alpha (4) on the ninth segment is located distinctly cephalad of beta (2). See L42, G-I.

Figure P. Abdomen (A9), Aegeriidae, Sanninoidae exitiosa Say, peach tree borer. All the setae on ninth segment are located in a more or less straight line. See L9, P-U.

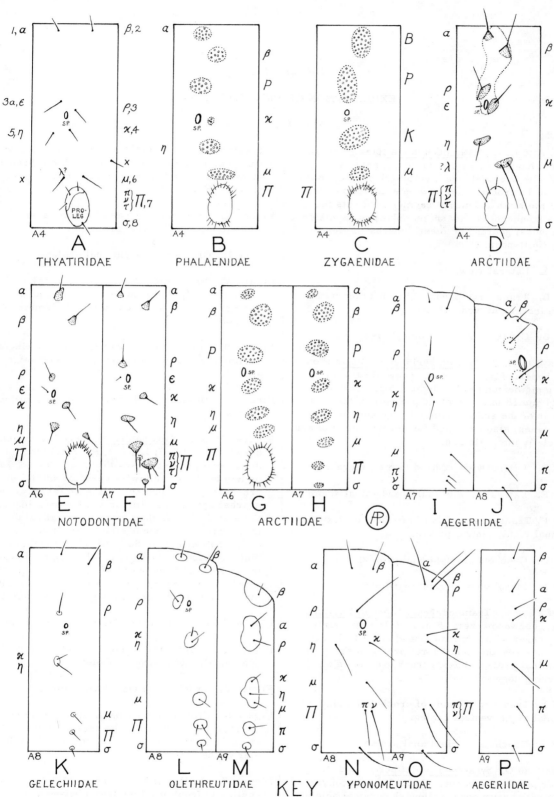

KEY

α-alpha-1, β-beta-2, ε-epsilon-3a, ρ-rho-3, ϰ-kappa-4, η-eta-5, μ-mu-6, π-pi-7, ν-nu-7, τ-tau-7, σ-sigma-8, ω-omega-9, λ-lambda, θ-theta; B-Beta=α+β, P-Rho=ε+ρ, K-Kappa=θ+ϰ+η, Π-Pi = π+ν+τ.

EXPLANATION OF FIGURES L9, A-U.

AEGERIIDAE

Figures A to C. Melittia cucurbitae Harr., squash
borer, also L6, C. F.g.1., $35^{\pm}$ mm., near-white
borer with brownish head, yellowish cervical plate
and 6 to 10 crochets per row on each ventral proleg of the sixth abdominal segment. Infests the
stems (runners) of squash, pumpkins, muskmelons,
cucumbers, gourds and other cucurbs. Friend,
1931, Chittenden, 1908.

Figure A. Lateral view.

Figure B. Transverse bands of crochets on sixth
abdominal, right, ventral proleg.

Figure C. Crochets on right anal proleg.

Figures D to H. Podosesia syringae syringae Harr.,
lilac borer. F.g.1. $18^{\pm}$ mm., near-white with
brown pigmented head, a light colored cervical
shield and 18 to 20 crochets per row on the ventral
prolegs of the sixth abdominal segment. Infests
lilac canes, also recorded for several kinds of ash,
especially mountain ash.

Figure D. Lateral view of head to mesothorax.

Figure E. Lateral view of fourth abdominal segment.

Figure F. Transverse bands of crochets on sixth abdominal right, ventral proleg.

Figure G. Crochets on right anal proleg.

Figure H. Mesal view of right mandible.

Figures I and J. Thamnosphecia (Conopia) scitula
Harr., dogwood borer. F.g.1. 13-15 mm., dirty
white borer with pigmented head and 9 to 12 crochets per row on each ventral proleg of the sixth
abdominal proleg. Infests trunk and crown of
flowering dogwood.

Figure I. Transverse bands of crochets on sixth abdominal right, ventral proleg.

Figure J. Crochets on right anal proleg.

Figures K to O. Synanthedon pictipes G. and R.,
lesser peach tree borer. F.g.1. $20^{\pm}$ mm., dirty
white with brown head, yellowish cervical shield,
nine $^{\pm}$ crochets on anal prolegs, distance (y) between the nearest seta of the prothoracic Kappa
group and the spiracle at least three times the diameter of the spiracle, sixth ocellus on a line be-

tween setae SO^2 and O^3 and right mandible with
five dentes. Infests the trunk and large branches
of various stone fruits especially peach, plum and
cherry. King, 1917.

Figure K. Transverse bands of crochets on sixth
abdominal, right ventral proleg.

Figure L. Crochets on right anal proleg.

Figure M. Prothoracic Kappa group of setae showing distance (y) between nearest seta and spiracle
to be at least three times smallest diameter of the
spiracle.

Figure N. Portion of the head capsule showing sixth
ocellus located in a line drawn between setae SO^2
and O^3.

Figure O. Mesal view of right mandible showing five
dentes.

Figures P to U. Sanninoidea exitiosa Say, peach tree
borer. Also L7, J; L8, I, J, P. F.g.1. $30^{\pm}$ mm.,
dirty white, sometimes with a reddish cast, brown
pigmented head, yellowish cervical shield, six $^{\pm}$
crochets on anal prolegs, distance (x) between the
nearest seta of the prothoracic Kappa group and
the spirable less than twice the smallest diameter
of the spiracle, sixth ocellus in front of a line
drawn between setae SO^2 and O^3 and right mandible with four dentes on distal margin. Infests
the crown and large roots of stone fruits especially
peach, plum, cherry, prune, nectarine, apricot and
other plants of the genus Prunus. Peterson, 1923.

Figure P. Lateral view of fourth abdominal segment.

Figure Q. Transverse bands of crochets on the sixth
abdominal, right, ventral proleg.

Figure R. Crochets on right anal proleg.

Figure S. Prothoracic kappa group of setae showing
the distance (x) between the nearest setae and the
spiracle to be less than twice the smallest diameter of the spiracle.

Figure T. Portion of head capsule showing the sixth
ocellus in front of a line drawn between setae SO^2
and O^3.

Figure U. Mesal view of right mandible showing
four dentes.

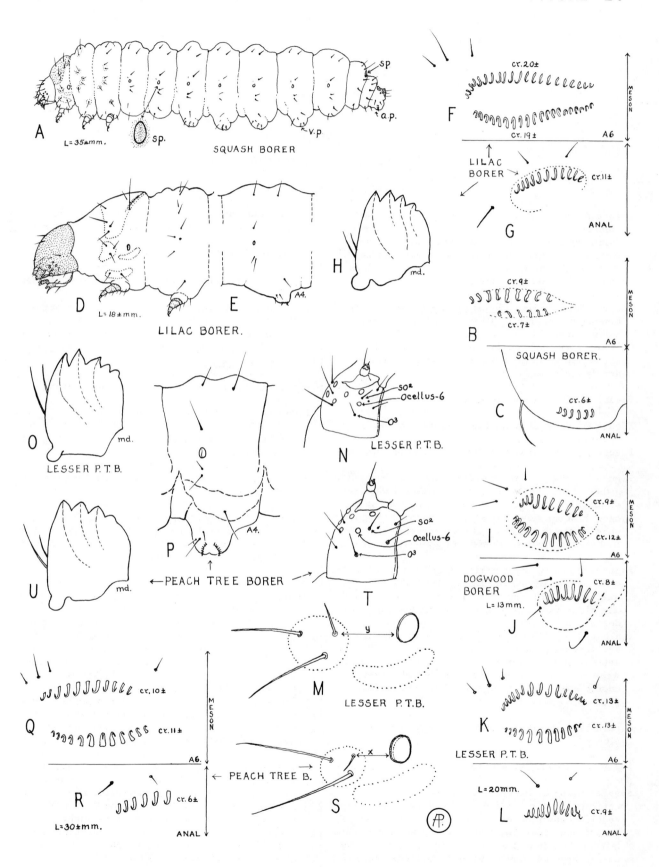

SQUASH BORER

L=35±mm.

LILAC BORER.

L=18±mm.

LESSER P.T.B.

LESSER P.T.B.

PEACH TREE BORER

LESSER P.T.B.

PEACH TREE B.

LILAC BORER

SQUASH BORER.

DOGWOOD BORER

L=13mm.

LESSER P.T.B.

L=20mm.

LEPIDOPTERA

EXPLANATION OF FIGURES L10, A-N

AMATIDAE A, ARCTIIDAE B-N

Figure A. Syntomeida epilais jucundissima Dyar. An oleander caterpillar. F.g.l. 30± mm., possesses a small, yellow head and prominent, laterally projecting tufts (verrucae rho, 3) of dark plumose setae on abdominal segments one to eight. Occurs on oleander trees in Florida.

Figures B to D. Halisidota harrisii Walsh, sycamore tussock moth. F.g.l. 30-40 mm., light colored, hairy caterpillar with prominent white to orange (some dark) tufts on the mesothorax, metathorax and eighth abdominal segment. Head moderate to deeply pigmented.

Figure B. Dorsal view of larva.

Figure C. Lateral view of head to metathorax.

Figure D. Lateral view of fourth abdominal segment.

Figure E. Estigmene acrea Drury, salt-marsh caterpillar. F.g.l. 45± mm., reddish brown, hairy (setae plumose), with a brown head and numerous verrucae. Lateral view of the fourth abdominal segment showing the distribution of the verrucae and mottled pigment areas. Found on many garden crops.

Figures F and G. Hyphantria cunea Drury, fall webworm. Also L6, K; L7, E; L8, G-H. F.g.l. 30-35 mm., hairy with many long setae and a dark head. The pigmentation, especially on the head, legs and dorsal aspect, varies from a deep or near black to a light buff. Almost all of the long plumose setae are very long and light in color except a few dark setae on beta (2) verrucae. Produces conspicuous webs on more than 100 fruit, shade and forest trees during late summer and early fall. See Baerg, 1928.

Figure F. Lateral view of head to mesothorax inclusive.

Figure G. Lateral view of fourth abdominal segment.

Figures H and I. Hypoprepia fucosa Hbn., a lichen caterpillar. F.g.l. 32± mm. Preserved specimens reddish-brown on dorsum and light on the venter; conspicuous near-black pinacula on the dorsum and lateral aspects of most segments each possessing one to three prominent, barbed, dark colored, primary setae; head near black; crochets on prolegs a

uniordinal, uniserial, homoideous mesoseries. Larvae recorded on mosses and lichens on trees.

Figure H. Lateral view of head to mesothorax.

Figure I. Lateral view of fourth abdominal segment.

Figures J to M. Utetheisa bella L., bella moth. Also L8, D. F.g.l. 20-25 mm., with primary setae prominent and plumose, no verrucae and head yellow. Found on cherry, elm, Myrica, Crotalaria and Lespedeza.

Figure J. Lateral view of head to mesothorax.

Figure K. Lateral view of fourth abdominal segment.

Figure L. Tarsus of mesothoracic leg showing spatulate setae.

Figure M. Mesal view of fourth ventral proleg with 6 to 9 crochets.

Figure N. Utetheisa bella prob. venusta Dal.. F.g.l. 25± mm. Lateral view of a fourth ventral proleg with 10-14 crochets. This form, except the head, more deeply and extensively pigmented than U. bella.

**Halisidota caryae Harr., hickory tussock moth. F.g.l. 32-38 mm. A striking, greyish-white, hairy caterpillar with a dorsal row of contiguous black tufts producing a velvety crest along the dorsomeson. Also slender, paired, black pencil tufts of setae may arise from the first and seventh abdominal segments. Head and legs black, concealed by thoracic setae. The side tufts of setae make the larva appear depressed. The larva feeds on 50 or more deciduous woodland and fruit trees. Some of these are hickory, maple, birch, ash, walnut, sycamore, elm, oak, pear and apple. Isely, 1918.

*Isia isabella, A. and S. banded woollybear. F.g.l. 45± mm., densely covered with plumose setae of more or less uniform length arising from verrucae on all segments. Setae on the thorax and frequently the first abdominal segment and also on abdominal segments 8 to 10 black, all others a light reddish brown. Food a wide range of vegetables, flowers, grasses and weeds.

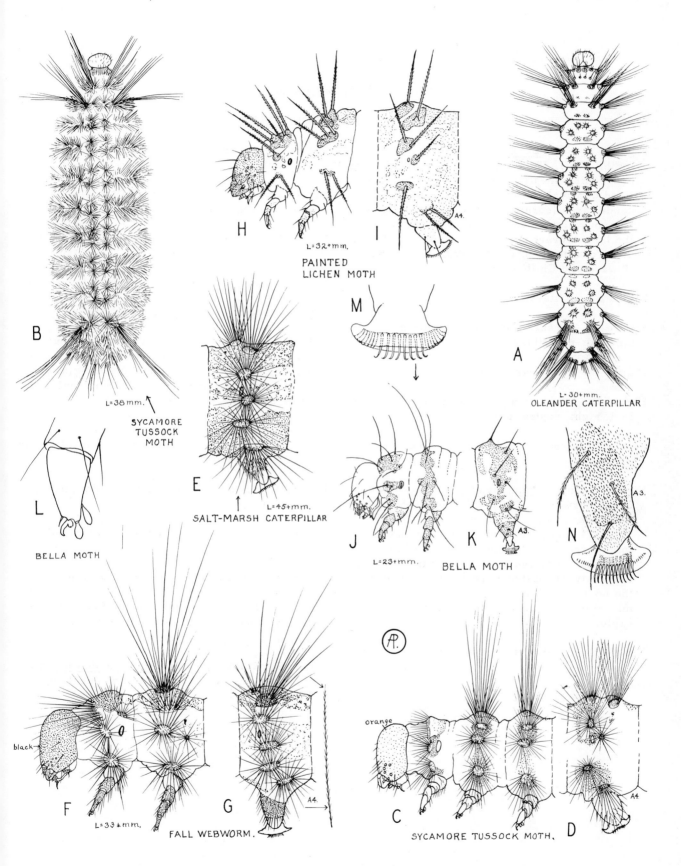

B

L=38mm.

SYCAMORE
TUSSOCK
MOTH

H

L=32+mm.

PAINTED
LICHEN MOTH

I

A4.

M

A

L=30+mm.
OLEANDER CATERPILLAR

E

L=45+mm.
SALT-MARSH CATERPILLAR

L

BELLA MOTH

J

K

A3.

A3.

N

L=23+mm.   BELLA MOTH

black

F

L=33±mm.

FALL WEBWORM.

G

A4.

orange

C

SYCAMORE TUSSOCK MOTH,

D

A4.

LEPIDOPTERA

EXPLANATION OF FIGURES L11, A-N

COSSIDAE A-J, ACROLOPHIDAE K-N

Figures A to E. Zeuzera pyrina L., leopard moth. F.g.l. 25-30 mm., pinkish-white borer possessing deeply pigmented head, sclerotized cervical shield bearing a roughened caudal area (cornicula), anal plate and conspicuous pigmented pinacula. Found within the larger branches of elm, maple, apple and other deciduous shade and fruit trees. See Howard and Chittenden, 1909.

Figures A. Lateral view of larva.

Figure B. Dorsal view of head showing the conspicuous mandibles.

Figure C. Prothoracic spiracle.

Figure D. Crochets and setae on sixth abdominal, right, ventral proleg.

Figure E. Crochets and setae on right anal proleg.

Figures F to J. Prionoxystus robiniae Peck, carpenterworm. F.g.l. 75± mm., robust, near-white with a brown head and smooth cervical shield. Pinacula inconspicuous. Infests trunks and large branches of many woodland trees and occasionally fruit trees, especially if located near woods. Some of the hosts are ash, black and red oaks, chestnut, elm, locust, poplar, willow, peach and apple.

Figure F. Lateral view of head and mesothorax.

Figure G. Lateral view of fourth abdominal segment.

Figure H. Crochets and setae of the sixth abdominal, right ventral proleg.

Figure I. Crochets and setae on right anal proleg.

Figure J. Mesal view of right mandible.

Figures K to N. Acrolophus prob. arcanellus Clem., acrolophid borer. Also L6, J. F.g.l. 25-30 mm., near white larva with a brown head, a united sclerotized cervical shield and prothoracic Kappa group and multiserial crochets on the ventral prolegs. Found within aster stems.

Figure K. Lateral view of head to mesothorax showing continuous sclerotized cervical shield and Kappa group.

Figure L. Lateral view of fourth abdominal segment.

Figure M. Lateral view of eighth abdominal segment.

Figure N. An ellipse arrangement of multiserial crochets on the sixth abdominal, right, ventral proleg, with one ellipse of large functional uniordinal crochets and several rows of rudimentary sclerotized projections.

Note. For information on Prionoxystus macmurtrei Guer., lesser carpenter worm, see Hutchings, 1924.

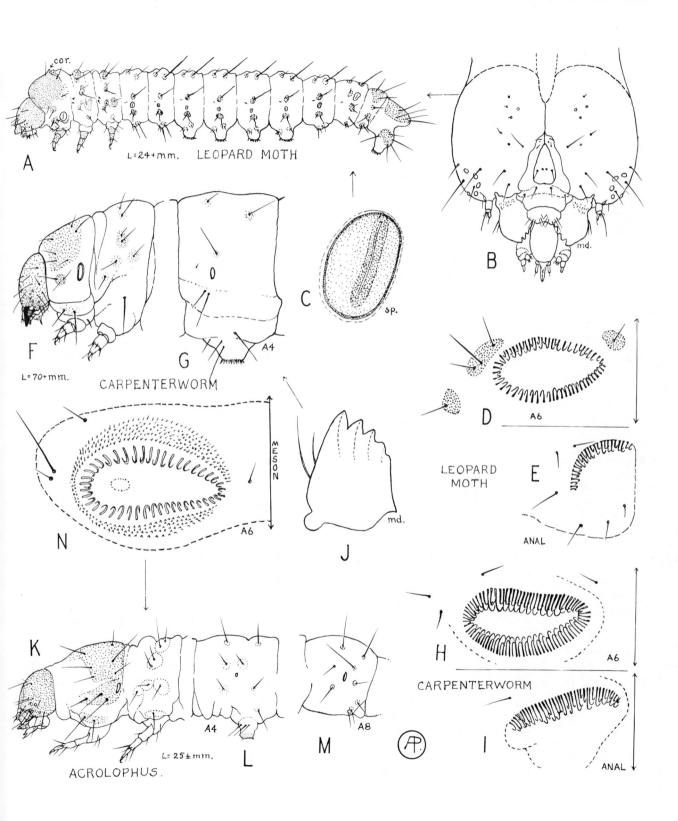

cor.

A   L=24+mm.   LEOPARD MOTH

B   md.

C   sp.

F   G   A4

L=70+mm.
CARPENTERWORM

D   A6

LEOPARD
MOTH   E

ANAL

N   MESON   A6

J   md.

H   A6

CARPENTERWORM

I   ANAL

K   L   A4   M   A8   Ⓐ.

L=25±mm.

ACROLOPHUS.

EXPLANATION OF FIGURES L12, A-K

CITHERONIIDAE

Figures A to D. Anisota senatoria A. and S., orange-striped oakworm. Also L8, H. F.g.l. 45± mm., brown to black with four narrow, yellow to orange, longitudinal stripes on each side, three above the spiracles and one below. Feeds primarily on oak foliage, rarely on birch and raspberry in the eastern half of North America.

Figure A. Lateral view of head (black) to mesothorax showing one of the prominent club-shaped mesothoracic scoli.

Figure B. Lateral view of fourth abdominal segment.

Figure C. Dorsal view of three caudal segments of the abdomen.

Figure D. Mesal view of homoideous mesoseries of crochets on the fourth abdominal, right, ventral proleg.

Figures E and F. Anisota rubicunda F., green-striped mapleworm. F.g.l. 40± mm., yellowish and green with alternating dark green stripes and yellowish to near-white ones dorsad of the spiracles. Head dull green and anal plate yellow. Yellowish to pink blotches may occur ventrad of the spiracles on the seventh and eigth abdominal segments. Feeds primarily on maples, especially red or swamp maple, rarely on oak in the eastern half of the United States. Howard and Chittenden, 1909.

Figure E. Lateral view of fourth abdominal segment.

Figure F. Dorsal view of caudal segments of the abdomen.

Figures G and H. Anisota stigma F., spiny oakworm. F.g.l. 45± mm., pale, tawny-red caterpillar with entire surface covered with bright yellow to almost white papillae (speckled) and bears prominent, black, frequently branched scoli marked with white papillae. The head, cervical shield and anal plate are yellow. Feeds on oak and hazel nut foliage in the eastern half of the United States and Canada.

Figure G. Lateral view of fourth abdominal segment.

Figure H. Dorsal view of caudal segments.

Figure I. Citheronia regalis F., hickory horned devil or regal moth. F.g.l. 130-140 mm., lateral view. This very large caterpillar when half grown has a reddish brown color. During the last instar it changes to a pea green and when full grown to a deep, blueish green (not granulated). The prominent scoli on the thorax are yellow to orange tipped with black. Feeds on the foliage of many deciduous trees, chiefly hickory, walnut, butternut, ash, persimmon, sweet gum and sassafrass, rarely on pine.

Figure J. Eacles imperialis Drury., imperial moth. F.g.l. 80± mm., lateral view. This deep yellow to greenish caterpillar is covered with long, scattered, slender, white setae and bears large, conspicuous, oval spiracles. It feeds on a wide varity of deciduous trees and also many conifers in the eastern and southern United States.

Figure K. Citheronia sepulchralis G and R., pine needle citheronid. F.g.l. 90± mm., lateral view. This reddish to deep-brown caterpillar bears conspicuous, paired, orange colored scoli on the thoracic segments and one on the dorsomeson of the eighth segment. It feeds on the needles of several pines (not white pine) in eastern United States.

Note. For descriptions and colored figures of above species see Packard, 1905.

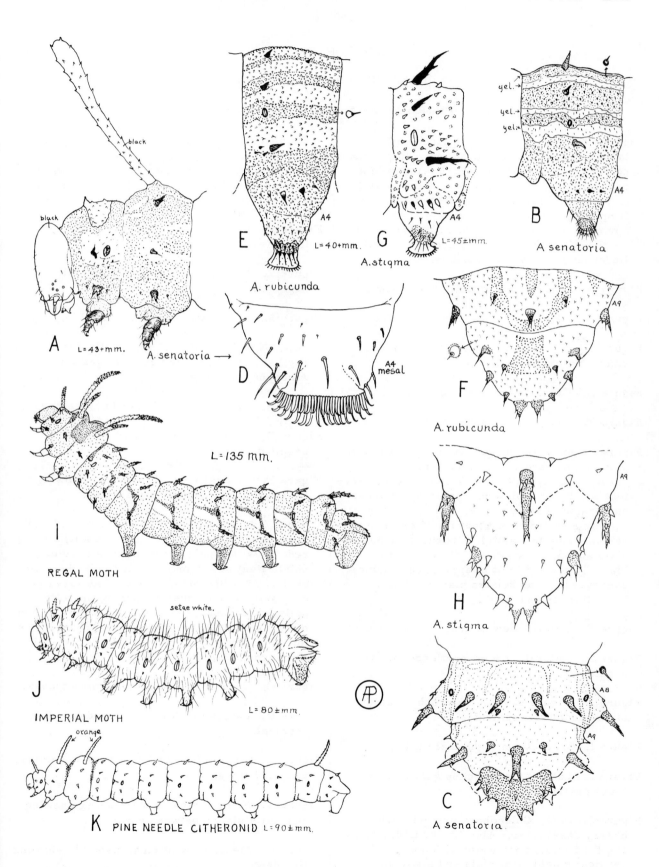

black

black

A   L=43+mm.

E   L=40+mm.   A4

A. rubicunda

G   A4   L=45±mm.

A. stigma

yel.→
yel.→
yel.→   A4

B   A senatoria

A. senatoria →   D   A4 mesal

F   Aq

A. rubicunda

L=135 mm.

I

REGAL MOTH

H   Aq

A. stigma

setae white.

J   L=80±mm.

IMPERIAL MOTH

orange

K   PINE NEEDLE CITHERONID   L=90±mm.

A8   Aq

C   A senatoria

EXPLANATION OF FIGURES L13, A-U

COLEOPHORIDAE A-M, COSMOPTERYGIDAE N-U

Figures A to E. Coleophora laricella Hbn., larch casebearer. F.g.l. 5$\pm$ mm., tiny, cream colored to somewhat brownish larva with a brown head, cervical shield and anal plate, and a case about its body. Hibernating cases frequently located in the axils of buds. In the spring it increases the size of the case and continuous to feed on larch needles of both European or American species.

Figure A. Lateral view of full grown larva.

Figure B. Lateral view of head and prothorax.

Figure C. Crochets on the sixth abdominal, right, ventral proleg.

Figure D. Crochets on right anal proleg.

Figure E. Case of full grown larva.

Figures F to J. Coleophora malivorella Riley, pistol casebearer. F.g.l. 5$\pm$ mm., tiny, cream to dirty white with a brown head, cervical shield, anal plate and sclerotized areas on dorsum of mesothorax. The larva constructs a coiled case about itself which bears resemblance to a pistol. Crochets absent on sixth abdominal segment. Feeds on the leaves, buds and fruit of apple, pear, quince, cherry, plum and related plants including haw. Slingerland, 1897.

Figure F. Lateral view of head to mesothorax.

Figure G. Lateral view of fourth abdominal segment.

Figure H. Figure showing no crochets on the sixth abdominal segment.

Figure I. Crochets on right anal proleg.

Figure J. Lateral view of case with head of larva protruding.

Figures K to M. Coleophora pruniella Clem., cherry casebearer. Also L6, F; L14, I to K. F.g.l. 5$\pm$ mm., dirty white with a brown head, cervical shield, anal plate and pigmented spots on dorsum of mesothorax. Crochets on

6th abdominal prolegs. Its case (L14, I) resembles that of C. fletcherella. Feeds primarily on foliage of apple, cherry, plum and other plants but may attack buds, stems and young fruit.

Figure K. Lateral view of head to mesothorax inclusive.

Figure L. Lateral view of fourth abdominal segment.

Figure M. Mesal view of right mandible.

Figures N to P. Walshia amorphella Clem. F.g.l. 12$\pm$ mm., reared on stem galls on Amorpha fruticosa.

Figure N. Lateral view of head to mesothorax.

Figure O. Lateral view of fourth abdominal segment.

Figure P. Ventral view of methorax showing the unusual distance between coxae.

Figures Q to V. Pyroderces rileyi Wlsn., pink scavenger caterpillar. F.g.l. 8$\pm$ mm., pink or reddish with a pale brown head, a cervical shield light brown on dorsum and darker laterally and a brown anal plate. The larva is primarily a scavenger occurring in cotton bolls, corn husks, dried and decayed fruit and other plants where other insects produced the initial injury. Chittenden, 1916; Busck, 1917; Heinrich, 1921; Hinton, 1943.

Figure Q. Lateral view of head to mesothorax.

Figure R. Lateral view of fourth abdominal segment.

Figure S. Circle of crochets on sixth abdominal, ventral proleg.

Figure T. Ventral view of metathorax showing unusual distance between coxae.

Figure U. Mesal view of right mandible showing five dentes.

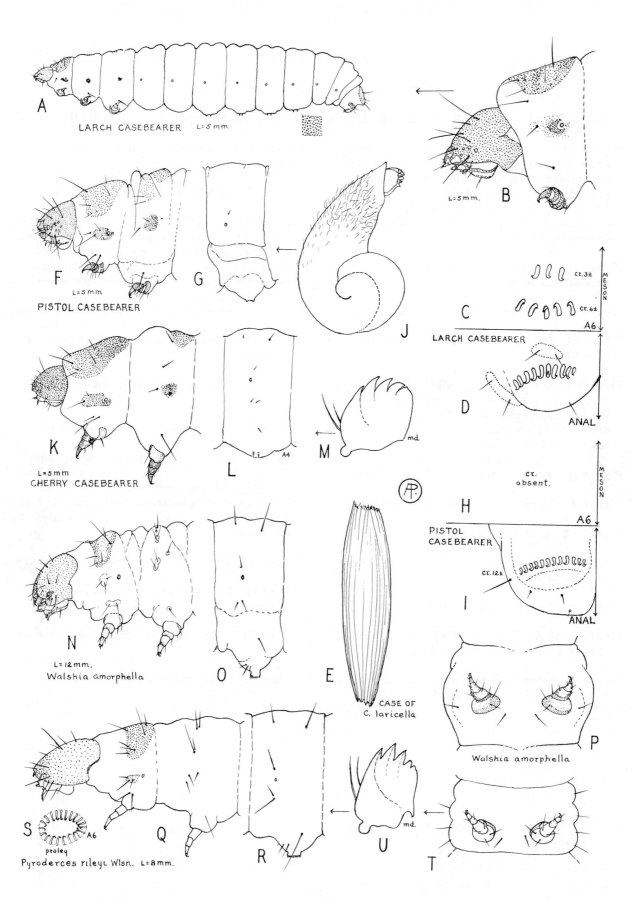

A   LARCH CASEBEARER   L=5mm.

B   L=5mm.

C   cr.3±   cr.6±   MESON   A6
LARCH CASEBEARER

D   ANAL

F   L=5mm   PISTOL CASEBEARER

G

J

K   L=5mm   CHERRY CASEBEARER

L   A4

M   md.

H   cr. absent.   MESON   A6
PISTOL CASEBEARER

I   cr.12±   ANAL

N   L=12mm.   Walshia amorphella

O

E   CASE OF C. laricella

P   Walshia amorphella

S   A6   proleg   Pyroderces rileyi Wlsn.   L=8mm.

Q

R

U   md.

T

LEPIDOPTERA

EXPLANATION OF FIGURES L14, A-S

GRACILARIIDAE A-C, ELACHISTIDAE D-H, COLEOPHORIDAE I-K, OLETHREUTIDAE L-S

Figures A to C. Lithocolletis (Phyllonorycter) prob. crataegella Clem. spotted tentiform leaf miner. F.g.l. 3.5 mm., near white to greenish. Prolegs without crochets on abdominal segments 3 to 5. Infests the foliage of apple, crataegus and related plants. Beckman, 1947.

Figure A. Lateral view of a late instar larva, an external feeder.

Figure B. Dorsal view of a late instar head.

Figure C. Dorsal view of an early instar larva, a leaf miner.

Figures D to H. Elachista albicapitella Engd. F.g.l. $6^{\pm}$ mm., greenish yellow with a yellowish head and sclerotized cervical shield and prothoracic sternal plate. A leaf miner in basal leaves of grass, Poa sylvestris.

Figure D. Ventral view of last instar larva.

Figure E. Dorsal view of head and prothorax.

Figure F. An enlarged prothoracic leg.

Figure G. Crochets on sixth abdominal, right, ventral proleg.

Figure H. Crochets on right anal proleg.

Figures I to K. Coleophora pruniella Clem., cherry casebearer. See L13, K to M.

Figure I. Lateral view of a case produced by a full grown larva with head protruding.

Figure J. Crochets on sixth abdominal, right, ventral proleg.

Figure K. Crochets on right anal proleg.

Figures L to O. Ecdytolopha insiticiana Zell., locust twig borer. F.g.l. $17^{\pm}$ mm., pink to red, younger larvae dirty white with brown pinacula. Produces gall-like swellings in twigs and young shoots of common locust.

Figure L. Lateral view of head to mesothorax.

Figure M. Lateral view of fourth abdominal segment.

Figure N. Setal map of ninth abdominal segment.

Figure O. Mesal view of right mandible.

Figures P to S. Petrova prob. albicapitana Busck. F.g.l. $15^{\pm}$ mm., closely resembles P. comstockiana Fern. pitch twig moth. It has a yellowish to brown head, cervical shield and light yellow pinacula. Found in pitch balls on pines.

Figure P. Lateral view of head to mesothorax.

Figure Q. Lateral view of fourth abdominal segment.

Figure R. Setal map of ninth abdominal segment.

Figure S. Mesal view of right mandible.

138

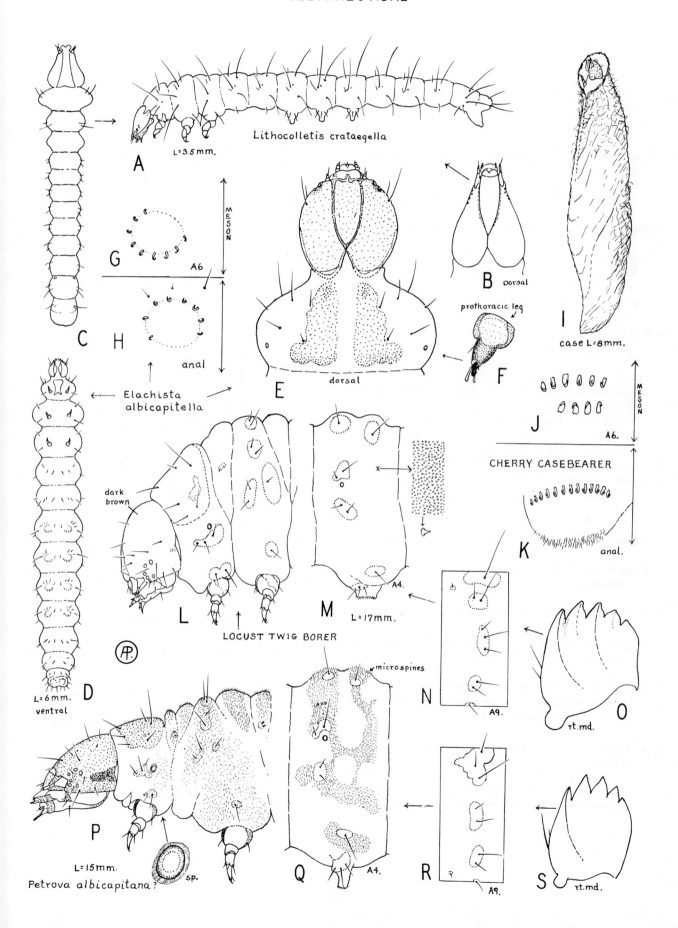

A
Lithocolletis crataegella
L=3.5 mm.

B dorsal

I case L=8mm.

C

G MESON A6

H anal

Elachista albicapitella

E dorsal

prothoracic leg

F

J MESON A6.

CHERRY CASEBEARER

K anal.

D L=6mm. ventral

dark brown

L

M L=17mm.

LOCUST TWIG BORER

N A9.

O rt.md.

P L=15mm. *Petrova albicapitana?* sp.

microspines

Q A4.

R A9.

S rt.md.

LEPIDOPTERA

EXPLANATION OF FIGURES L15, A-S

GELECHIIDAE

Figures A to D. <u>Recurvaria</u> <u>variella</u> Cham.,
bald cypress needleworm. F.g.l. 7± mm.
Entire larva near white to cream colored.
Feeds on the needles of bald cypress.

Figure A. Lateral view of head to mesothorax.

Figure B. Lateral view of fourth abdominal
segment.

Figure C. Mesal view of right mandible.

Figure D. Crochets and setae on sixth abdominal, right, ventral proleg.

Figures E to I. <u>Recurvaria</u> <u>milleri</u> Busck,
lodgepole needle miner. F.g.l. 7± mm. lemon
yellow to deep orange with a darker red line
along the dorsomeson. Head and cervical
shield brown to black, anal plate and lateral
plates on anal proleg light brown. Anal comb
consists of two prominent curved spines and
several small ones. A needle-miner of lodgepole pines, <u>Pinus</u> <u>murrayana.</u> Patterson,
1921.

Figure E. Lateral view of head to mesothorax.

Figure F. Lateral view of fourth abdominal
segment

Figure G. Mesal view of right mandible.

Figure H. Crochets and setae on sixth abdominal, right, ventral proleg.

Figure I. Ventral view of caudal segment showing distribution of setae and crochets on anal
prolegs and the anal comb.

Figures J to N. <u>Dichomeris</u> <u>marginella</u> F.,
juniper webworm. Also see L17, A. F.g.l.
14± mm. possesses a light brown brown body
with a median reddish-brown line paralleled
by two wider dark brown stripes. Most setae

are near white and arise from pigmented
pinacula. Head, cervical shield, anal plate
and legs are brown to near black. Anal comb
6± prongs. Larvae feed on and web together
terminal shoots of <u>Juniperus</u> <u>communis</u> and
varieties.

Figure J. Lateral view of head to mesothorax.

Figure K. Lateral view of fourth abdominal
segment.

Figure L. Mesal view of right mandible.

Figure M. Crochets and setae on sixth abdominal, right, ventral proleg.

Figure N. Ventral view of caudal segment showing distribution of setae and crochets on anal
prolegs and the anal comb.

Figures O to S. <u>Anarsia</u> <u>lineatella</u> Zell., peach
twig borer. Also L17, C. F.g.l. 10± mm., light
to reddish brown with near black head, cervical shield, anal plate and true legs, also distinct pigmented pinacula from which light colored moderately long setae arise. Anal comb
6± prongs. Single band of crochets on each
anal proleg broken into two groups. Infests
tender twigs or late in the season the fruit of
the peach, plum, apricot or almond.

Figure O. Lateral view of head to mesothorax.

Figure P. Lateral view of fourth abdominal segment.

Figure Q. Mesal view of right mandible.

Figure R. Crochets and setae on sixth abdominal, right, ventral proleg.

Figure S. Ventral view of caudal end showing
distribution of setae and crochets on anal prolegs and the anal comb.

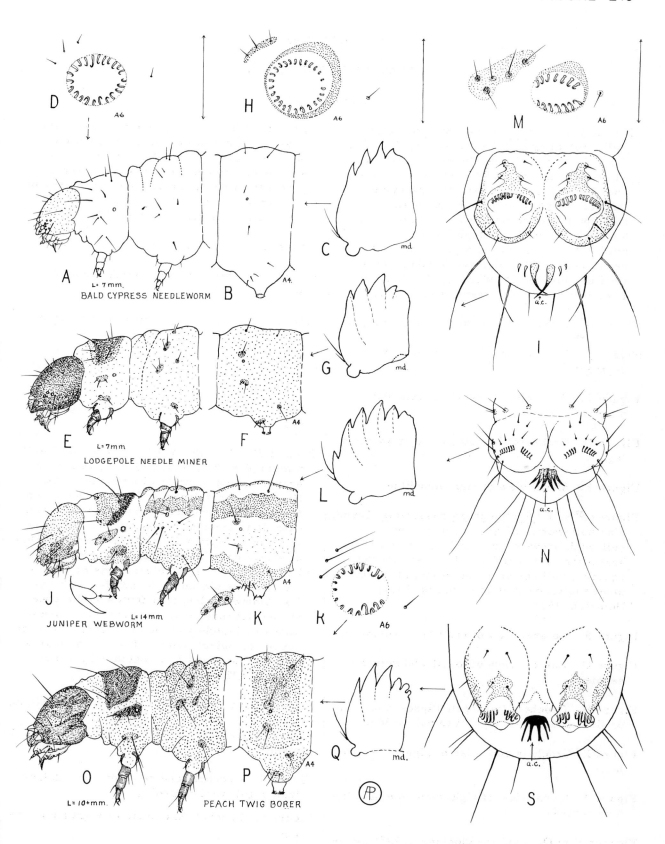

D A6

H A6

M A6

C md

A
L=7mm.
BALD CYPRESS NEEDLEWORM
B A4.

I
a.c.

G md

E
L=7mm
LODGEPOLE NEEDLE MINER
F A4

L md

N
a.c.

J
JUNIPER WEBWORM
L=14mm
K

K A6

Q md.

O
L=10+mm.
P A4
PEACH TWIG BORER

S
a.c.

LEPIDOPTERA

EXPLANATION OF FIGURES L16, A-T

GELECHIIDAE

Figures A to E. Gnorimoschema operculella Zell., potato tuberworm. Also L8, K; L17, B. F.g.l. 12± mm., slightly fusiform, creamy white, greenish or pinkish-white with a fuscous head, near black cervical shield and thoracic legs and yellowish anal plate. No anal comb. In the field it attacks plants by burrowing in the leaves, petioles or stems of potato, tobacco, tomato, eggplant and solanceous weeds. May also riddle tubers in the field or storage with slender, silk-lined burrows filled with excrement. Graf, 1917.

Figure A. Lateral view of head to mesothorax.

Figure B. Lateral view of fourth abdominal segment.

Figure C. Crochets and setae of sixth abdominal, right, ventral proleg.

Figure D. Crochets and setae of right anal proleg.

Figure E. Mesal view of right mandible.

Figures F to J. Pectinophora gossypiella Saund., pink bolloworm. F.g.l. 11± mm. pink with a yellowish brown head, cervical shield and anal plate. No anal fork. It bores into the squares, bolls or seeds of cotton, also attacks other malvaceous plants. Busck, 1917; Heinrich, 1921.

Figure F. Lateral view of head to mesothorax.

Figure G. Lateral view of fourth abdominal segment.

Figure H. Crochets (mesopenellipse) and setae of sixth abdominal, right, ventral proleg.

Figure I. Crochets and setae of right, anal proleg.

Figure J. Mesal view of right mandible showing four dentes.

Figures K to O. Keiferia glochinella Zell., eggplant leaf miner. F.g.l. 9± mm. brownish or greenish white turning to dark blue or green before pupation with a depressed yellowish head and cervical shield. Mandibles nearly square with five dentes on distal margin. It produces mines along the edges of leaves of eggplants and related species. See Gapps, 1946, Key to species; Jones, 1923.

Figure K. Lateral view of head to mesothorax.

Figure L. Lateral view of fourth abdominal segment.

Figure M. Crochets and setae of sixth abdominal, right, ventral proleg.

Figure N. Crochets and setae of right anal proleg.

Figure O. Mesal view of an eroded right mandible.

Figures P to T. Keiferia lycopersicella Busck, tomato pinworm. F.g.l. 8± mm. yellowish, gray or green, usually with purple spots. Head somewhat depressed, yellowish with a conspicuous dark area about the ocelli which extends to the caudal margin. Yellowish cervical shield with a dark caudal margin. Thoracic legs dark brown. Anal plate yellowish. Primary setae light colored arising from inconspicuous pinacula. Mandibles with five to six somewhat elongated dentes with a cone shaped arrangement. It produces serpentine mines or blotches in tomato leaves in greenhouses or out-of-doors. The leaf or leaves may be folded and held together by silken threads. Thomas, 1936.

Figures P. Lateral view of head to mesothorax.

Figure Q. Lateral view of fourth abdominal segment.

Figure R. Crochets and setae of sixth abdominal, right, ventral proleg.

Figure S. Crochets and setae of right anal proleg.

Figure T. Mesal view of right mandible.

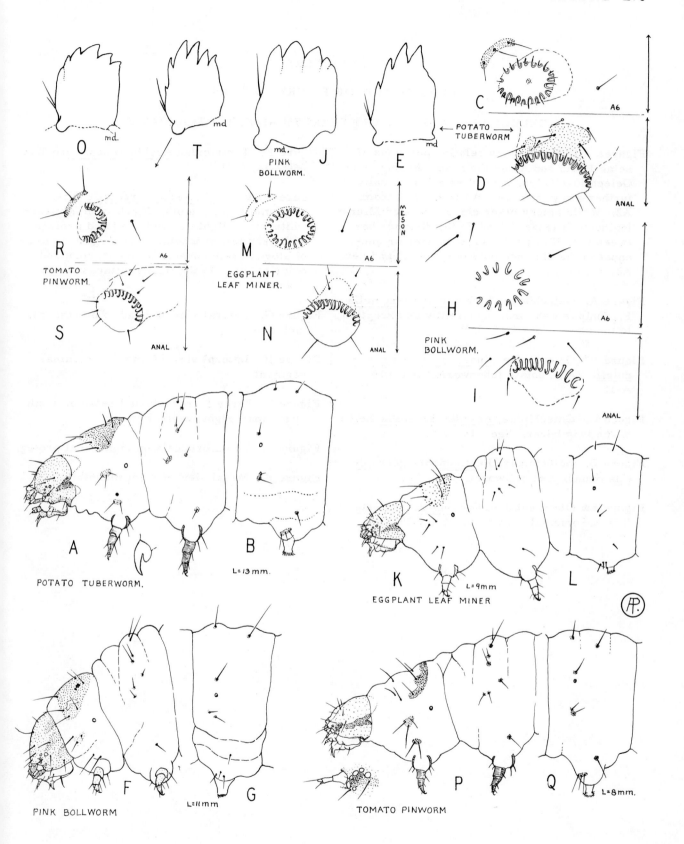

O

T

md.

PINK
BOLLWORM.

J

md

E

md

POTATO
TUBERWORM

C

A6

D

ANAL

R

A6

TOMATO
PINWORM.

S

ANAL

M

A6

EGGPLANT
LEAF MINER.

N

ANAL

MESON

H

A6

PINK
BOLLWORM.

I

ANAL

A

B

L=13mm.

POTATO TUBERWORM.

K

L

L=9mm

EGGPLANT LEAF MINER

F

G

L=11mm

PINK BOLLWORM

P

Q

L=8mm.

TOMATO PINWORM

LEPIDOPTERA

EXPLANATION OF FIGURES L17, A-K

GELECHIIDAE A-D, G-K, OLETHREUTIDAE E, TORTRICIDAE F

Figures A to F. Showing relative positions of setae L, A3 and A2 on the head. Among most Gelechiidae (Figs. A to D) seta L is usually further away from seta A3 than A3 is from A2. While among other closely related Micro-lepidoptera (Figs. E and F) the distance between seta L and seta A3 is shorter or sub-equal to the distance between seta A3 and seta A2.

Figure A. Gelechiidae, Dichomeris marginella F., juniper webworm, apparently an exception to the above. See L15, J-N.

Figure B. Gelechiidae, Gnorimoschema oper-culella Zell., potato tuberworm. See L16, A-E.

Figure C. Gelechiidae, Anarsia lineatella Zell., peach twig borer. See L15, O-S.

Figure D. Gelechiidae, Pectinophora gossypi-ella Saund., pink bollworm. See L16, F-J.

Figure E. Olethreutidae, Grapholitha molesta Busck., oriental fruit moth. See L29, G-L.

Figure F. Tortricidae, Archips obsoletana Wlk. See L32, A-D.

Figures G to K. Sitotroga cerealella Oliv., Angoumois grain moth. F.g.l. 6$\pm$ mm. near-white with a light colored head and prolegs with very few crochets. It is largely a pest of stored grain especially wheat, corn and other grains. In the field it attacks wheat heads.

Figure G. Lateral view of head to mesothorax inclusive.

Figure H. Lateral view of fourth abdominal segment.

Figure I. Three $\pm$ crochets and setae on sixth abdominal, right, ventral proleg.

Figure J. Two $\pm$ crochets on right, anal proleg.

Figure K. Mesal view of right mandible.

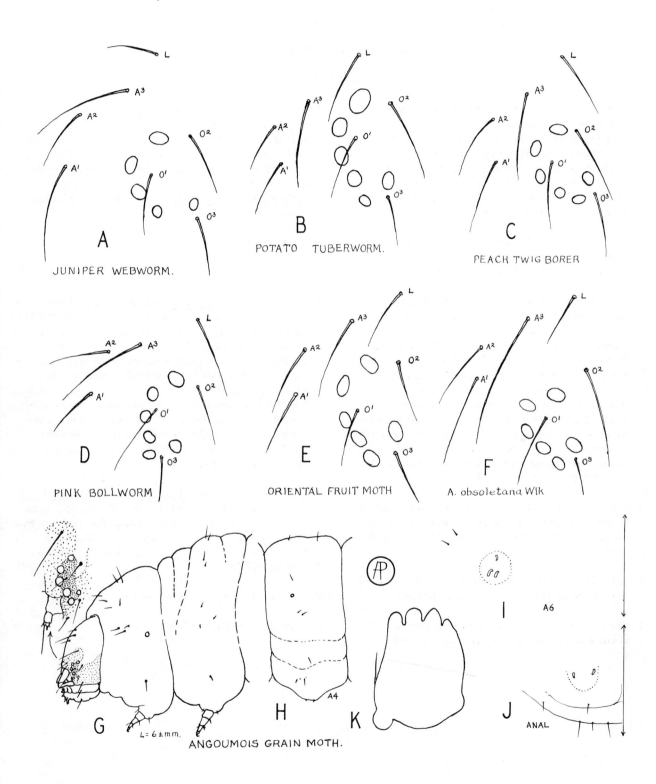

A
JUNIPER WEBWORM.

B
POTATO TUBERWORM.

C
PEACH TWIG BORER

D
PINK BOLLWORM

E
ORIENTAL FRUIT MOTH

F
A. obsoletana Wlk

G   L=6±mm.
ANGOUMOIS GRAIN MOTH.

H

K

I   A6

J   ANAL

LEPIDOPTERA

EXPLANATION OF FIGURES L18, A-J

GEOMETRIDAE

Figures A to B. Paleacrita vernata Peck, spring canker worm. F.g.l. 22 ± mm., usually light brown to nearly black with a yellowish subspiracular stripe and one pair of ventral prolegs on the sixth segment. This measuring worm feeds on the foliage of many shade and fruit trees, especially elm and apple. Porter, 1924.

Figure A. Lateral view of caudal segments five to ten showing presence of one pair of ventral prolegs on the sixth segment.

Figure B. Ventral view of sixth abdominal, ventral proleg.

Figures C to E. Alsophila pometaria Harr., fall cankerworm. F.g.l. 22± mm., green to brown with three narrow, whitish, longitudinal stripes above the spiracles and a yellow one below. In addition to the well developed ventral prolegs on the sixth abdominal segment a rudimentary pair exists on the fifth. This measuring worm feeds on foliage of many shade and fruit trees, especially elm and apple. Porter, 1924.

Figure C. Lateral view of caudal segments five to ten showing rudimentary, ventral prolegs on fifth segment and normal prolegs on the sixth.

Figure D. Crochets and setae on rudimentary fifth abdominal, right, ventral proleg.

Figure E. Crochets and setae on normal, sixth abdominal, right, ventral proleg.

Figures F and G. Cingilia caternaris Drury, chain-spotted geometer. F.g.l. 35± mm., f faintly striped, yellow, measuring worm with white spots about the spiracles each flanked with two, conspicuous, black marks. Feeds on species of Genista, Myrica, Quercus, Rubus, Rhus toxicodendron, Spirea and other shrubs.

Figure F. Lateral view of entire larva.

Figure G. Cephalic view of the head.

Figure H. Coryphista meadi Pack., barberry leafworm. F.g.l. 25± mm. Lateral view shows an overall dark brown color and an orange head. A broad, light colored, spiracular stripe exists on each side of the body. Located within this stripe are brown areas and black spiracles surrounded by orange blotches. On the dorsum four, narrow, white lines extend the entire length of the body. This species feeds at night on the foliage of several varieties of barberry and a species of Mahonia. Neiswander, 1941.

Figures I and J. Amphidasis (Lycia) cognataria Guen., pepper and salt moth. F.g.l. 35± mm. light colored and without conspicuous pigment lines or marks. Feeds on the foliage of a great variety of orchard and woodland trees and small fruits.

Figure I. Lateral view of entire larva.

Figure J. Cephalic view of head.

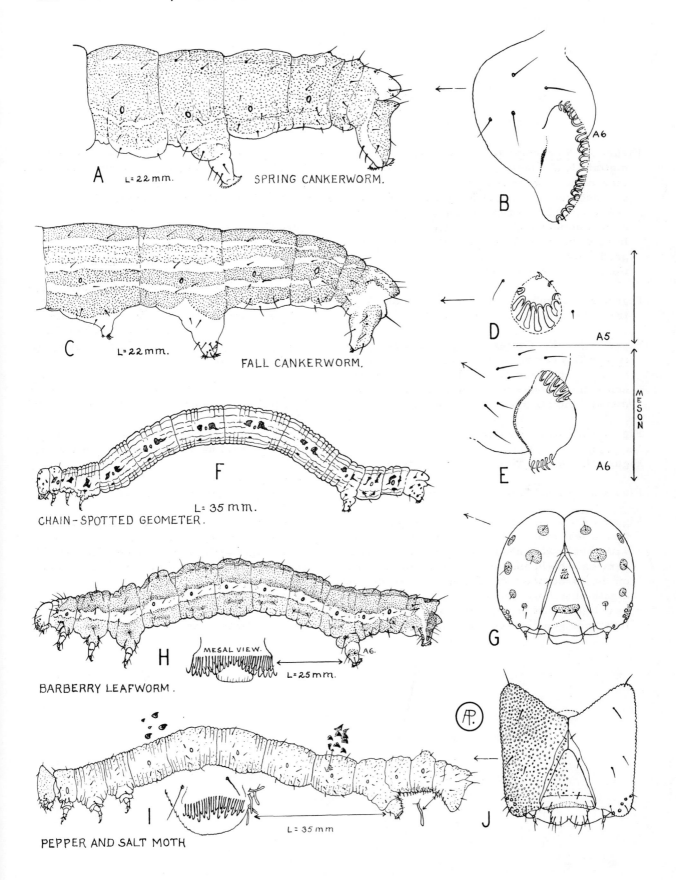

A   L = 22 mm.   SPRING CANKERWORM.

B

C   L = 22 mm.   FALL CANKERWORM.

D   A5

E   A6   MESON

F   L = 35 mm.

CHAIN-SPOTTED GEOMETER.

G

H   MESAL VIEW.   A6.   L = 25 mm.

BARBERRY LEAFWORM.

I   L = 35 mm.

PEPPER AND SALT MOTH

J

LEPIDOPTERA

EXPLANATION OF FIGURES L19, A-L

GRACILLARIIDAE A-E, HELIOZELIDAE F-J, TISCHERIIDAE K-L

Figure A. Parectopa robiniella Clem., locust digitate leaf miner. F.g.l. 5± mm. Ventral view of near-white leaf miner with a depressed yellow head, inconspicuous true legs and single bands of small uniserial, uniordinal crochets on abdominal segments 3 to 5. Infests foliage of locust and other legumes producing blotches with finger-like projections on the upper surface.

Figure B. Cameraria sp. F.g.l. 5.5 mm. Ventral view of a leaf miner on white oak.

Figures C to E. Cameraria (Lithocolletis) ostryarella Chamb., an oak leaf miner. F.g.l. 5 mm., depressed, near-white, with yellowish sclerotized plates on the dorsum of all segments. Infests oak and horn bean.

Figure C. Dorsal view of larva.

Figure D. Dorsal view of head enlarged.

Figure E. Mesal view of mandible.

Figures F and G. Antispila nyssaefoliella Clem., tupelo leaf miner. F.g.l. 5 mm., depressed with a yellowish head, a conspicuous fuscous cervical shield and smaller pigmented areas on the dorsomeson of all segments except the eighth abdominal segment; on venter single oval light spots on segments 3 to 6. This legless sour gun case-cutter at first makes a linear mine which eventually results in a blotch that may obscure the early linear mine.

Figure F. Dorsal view of larva.

Figure G. Mesal view of mandible.

Figures H and J. Coptodisca splendoriferella Clem., resplendent shield bearer or case cutter. F.g.l. 2.5-3 mm., legless feeding stages brownish and hibernating stage near white. A leaf miner in its early stages on apple, quince, pear, crataegus, Cydonia, Populus alba, Prunnus serotina and Pyrus carolina. Snodgrass, 1922.

Figure H. Ventral view of a pigmented (brownish) full grown feeding stage (summer form).

Figure I. Ventral view of a near-white, hibernating or resting stage found within a case.

Figure J. Side view of a flattened disc-shaped case showing position of larva within.

Figures K and L. Coptotriche zelleriella Clem., an oak leaf miner. F.g.l. 5.5 mm., near white with a light yellowish head, cervical shield and anal plate. A leaf miner of several oaks.

Figure K. Dorsal view of larva.

Figure L. Ventral view of larva.

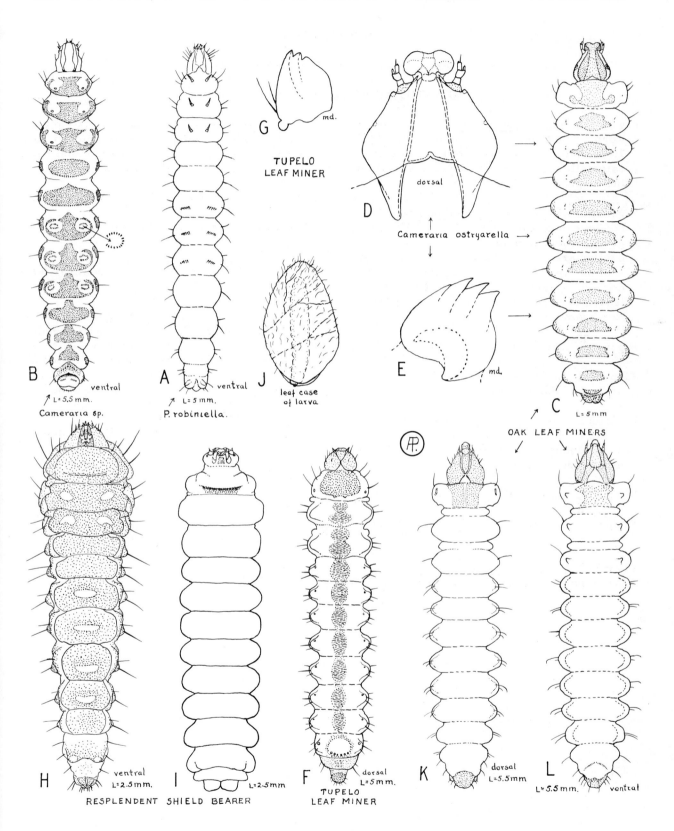

G   TUPELO
LEAF MINER

md.

D   dorsal

Cameraria ostryarella

E   md.

B   ventral
L= 5.5 mm.
Cameraria sp.

A   ventral
L= 5 mm.
P. robiniella.

J   leaf case
of larva

C   L= 5 mm

OAK LEAF MINERS

H   ventral
L= 2.5 mm.
RESPLENDENT SHIELD BEARER

I   L= 2.5 mm

F   dorsal
L= 5 mm.
TUPELO
LEAF MINER

K   dorsal
L= 5.5 mm.

L   L= 5.5 mm.   ventral

LEPIDOPTERA

EXPLANATION OF FIGURES L20, A-M

MEGATHYMIDAE A, HESPERIIDAE B-M

Figure A. <u>Aegiale hesperiaris</u> Wlk., maguey-worm, an edible delicacy in Mexico. F.g.l. 70-75 mm. Lateral view of a near-white caterpillar living in the leaves and heart of the maguey or century plant.

Figures B and C. <u>Calpodes ethlius</u> Stoll., larger canna leaf roller. F.g.l. $60^{\pm}$ mm., greenish and spindle-shaped with a dark ocellar area on a yellowish head and a dark spot on the extreme lateral portions of the cervical shield. Feeds on and rolls the leaves of canna in the southeastern part of North America.

Figure B. Lateral view of head to mesothorax.

Figure C. Lateral view of fourth abdominal segment. Same scale as fig. B.

Figures D and E. <u>Lerodea</u> <u>tripunctus</u> H.-S., a grass feeder. F.g.l. 20 mm., greenish with conspicuous pigment areas on the head. Food plants are grasses.

Figure D. Lateral view of head to mesothorax.

Figure E. Lateral view of fourth abdominal segment.

Figures F to H. <u>Hylephila phylaeus</u> Drury, fiery skipper. F.g.l. 20 mm., greenish brown with a dark brown head, cervical shield and thoracic legs. Numerous, dark colored, secondary setae arise from small pigment spots on all segments. A pest of bent grass.

Figure F. Lateral view of head to mesothorax.

Figure G. Lateral view of fourth abdominal segment.

Figure H. Crochets on fourth, abdominal, ventral proleg.

Figures I to L. <u>Proteides</u> <u>clarus</u> Cram., silver-spotted skipper. F.g.l. 35-40 mm., green with a conspicuous reddish-brown head possessing yellow or orange spots adjacent to the ocelli. Feeds on the foliage of legumes especially <u>Wisteria</u> and the common locust (<u>Robinia</u> <u>pseudacacia</u>) in the United States and Canada.

Figure I. Lateral view of head to mesothorax.

Figure J. Lateral view of fourth abdominal segment.

Figure K. Dorsal view of entire larva.

Figure L. Mesal view of right mandible.

Figure M. Anal comb located dorsad of anus.

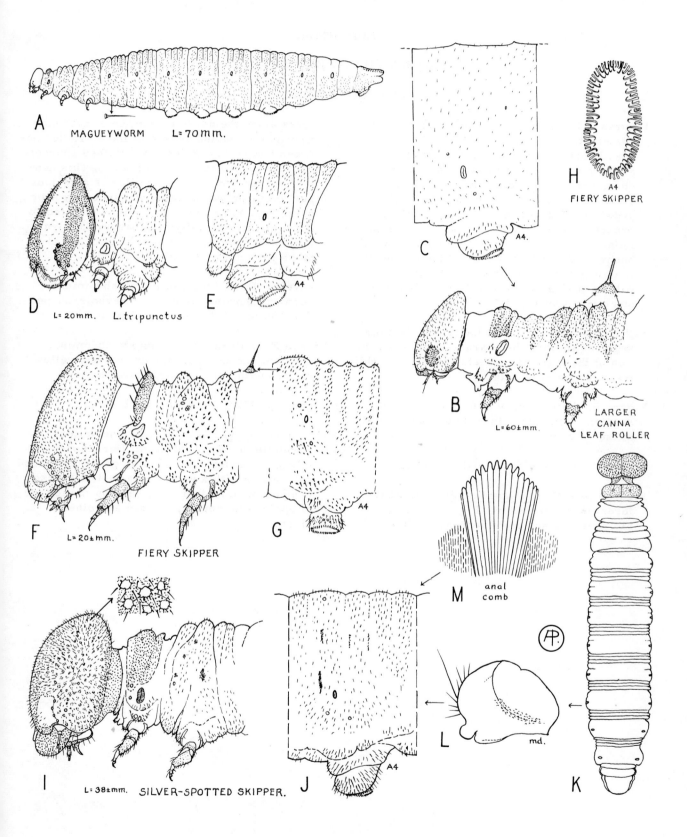

A   MAGUEYWORM   L=70mm.

C   A4.

H   A4   FIERY SKIPPER

D   L=20mm.   L. tripunctus

E   A4

B   L=60±mm.   LARGER CANNA LEAF ROLLER

F   L=20±mm.   FIERY SKIPPER

G   A4

M   anal comb

L   md.

I   L=38±mm.   SILVER-SPOTTED SKIPPER.

J   A4

K

LEPIDOPTERA

EXPLANATION OF FIGURES L21, A-G

LASIOCAMPIDAE

Figures A to C. Malacosoma americanum F., eastern tent caterpillar. F.g.l. 55± mm., near black with a near white continuous stripe along the dorsomeson, bluish dots dorsad of the spiracles and clothed with fine yellowish setae. This web forming caterpillar constructs nests in the crotches or branches of trees and shrubs and feeds on the foliage. It is common on wild cherry but also occurs frequently on apple, plum and peach. It also is recorded for beech, birch, oak, willow, poplar, witch hazel, rose, barberry and other plants.

Figure A. Dorsal view of the fourth abdominal segment showing the characteristic distribution of the pigment, especially the near-white mesal stripe, and setae.

Figure B. Lateral view of fourth abdominal segment with a prominent blue spot dorsad of the spiracle.

Figure C. Mesal view of right mandible.

Figures D to F. Malacosoma disstria Hbn., forest tent caterpillar. F.g.l. 45± mm., bluish with a series of near-white diamond spots along the dorso meson, an almost continuous blue stripe dorsad of the spiracles between two yellow stripes and clothed sparsely with long soft setae. Head bluish. This nontent or web forming, caterpillar is a serious pest on many woodland trees especially aspen, oaks, poplar, and maples. It may also feed on other trees especially ash, basswood, birch, elm and conifers. .During migrations it attacks field and vegetable crops.

Figure D. Dorsal view of fourth abdominal segment showing diamond or keyhole-shaped distribution of the near white pigment.

Figure E. Lateral view of fourth abdominal segment showing position of two pale yellow stripes with blue pigment between them.

Figure F. Mesal view of right mandible.

Figure G. Tolype velleda Stoll, the velleda lappet moth. F.g.l. 55± mm. Dorsal view of a large, inconspicuous, bluish gray, depressed caterpillar with a velvety-black, transverse band on the metathorax. Feeds on the foliage of apple, ash, poplar, syringa and other plants.

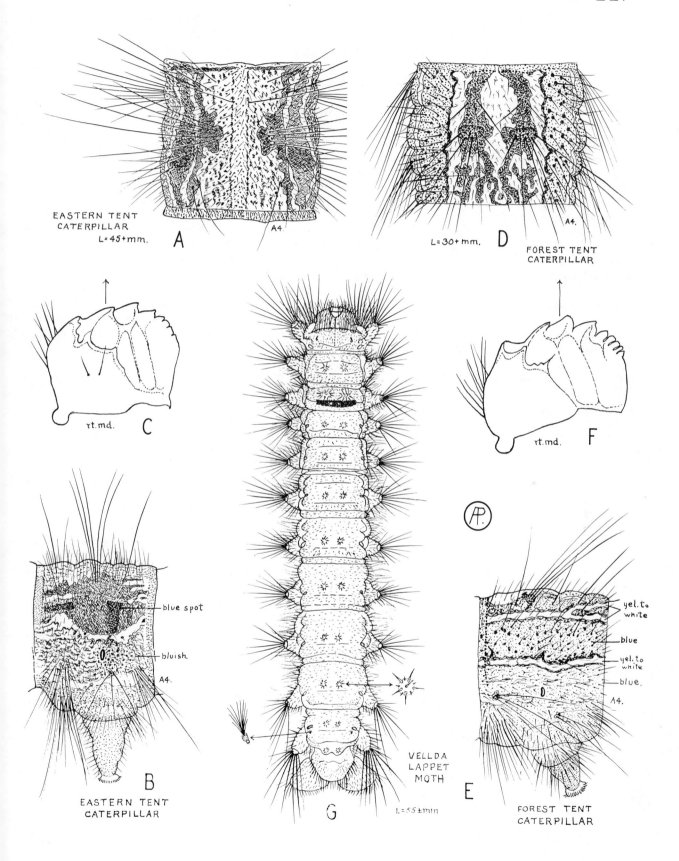

EASTERN TENT
CATERPILLAR
L=45+mm.

A4

A

L=30+mm.

D

FOREST TENT
CATERPILLAR

A4

rt.md.

C

rt.md.

F

blue spot

bluish

A4.

B

EASTERN TENT
CATERPILLAR

VELLDA
LAPPET
MOTH

G

L=55±mm

yel.to
white

blue

yel.to
white

blue.

A4.

E

FOREST TENT
CATERPILLAR

LEPIDOPTERA

EXPLANATION OF FIGURES L22, A-D

LIMACODIDAE

Figures A and B. Prolimacodes badia. Skiff caterpillar. F.g.l. 13$\pm$ mm. pale green, smooth, hairless, pear-shaped, firmly sclerotized slug with a brown patch on its back in the last instar. Feeds on foliage of ash and other woodland trees.

Figure A. Lateral view of a partially grown larva with head withdrawn into prothorax, minute thoracic legs present and no prolegs.

Figure B. Dorsal view of some larva.

Figures C and D. Euclea delphinii Bdv., F.g.l. 18$\pm$ mm., pale, yellowish green, spiny, venomous slug with four patches of dark colored spines at bases of caudal scoli. Feeds on the the folliage of oak, chestnut, pear, willow, wild cherry and other trees. Dyar 1896, 4: 125; 1897, 5:57.

Figure C. Dorsal view of larva showing the scoli possessing venomous setae.

Figure D. Ventral view of larva showing retracted head, very small thoracic legs and sucker-like structures on the abdominal segments.

Figure E. Phobetron pithecium A. and S., hag moth. F.g.l. 16$\pm$ mm. Dorsal view of a dark brown, hairy caterpillar with nine pairs of fleshy, lateral appendages, three of which are long, pointed and twisted. It feeds on many shrubs and the low branches of deciduous trees.

Note. These and other slug caterpillars see Dyar, 1895-99.

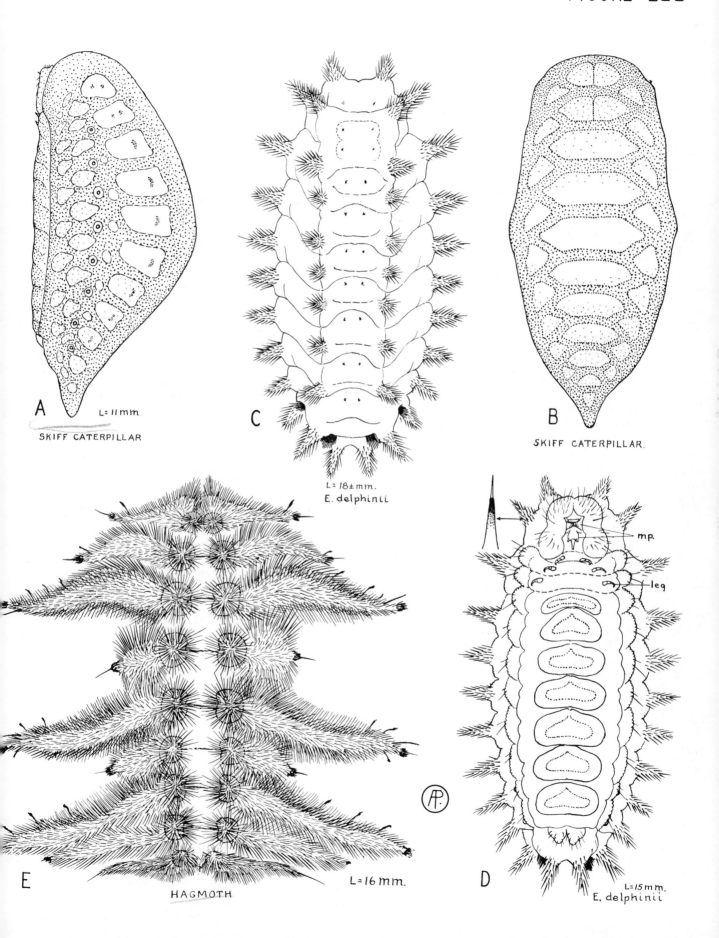

A

L=11mm.

SKIFF CATERPILLAR

C

L=18±mm.
E. delphinii

B

SKIFF CATERPILLAR.

E

HAGMOTH

L=16mm.

D

mp.

leg

L=15mm.
E. delphinii

LEPIDOPTERA

EXPLANATION OF FIGURES L23, A-I

LIMACODIDAE A-B, MEGALOPYGIDAE C-F, LYCAENIDAE G-I

Figure A. Tortricidia sp. F.g.l. 8 + mm. Dorsal view of a pale, green, late instar slug found on woodland trees.

Figure B. Sibine stimulae Clem., saddleback caterpillar. F.g.l. 25 ± mm. Dorsal view of a venomous, barbed, slug-like caterpillar which has a bright, purplish brown spot on the dorsomeson located on the center of a green area which extends between the bases of prominent, reddish-brown scoli on the thorax and caudal segments. Except for very small thoracic legs the larva is legless. Feeds on foliage of basswood, chestnut, cherry, oak, plum and other trees. It also occurs on corn foliage. See Dyar 1896, 4:1.

Figure C. Norape cretata Grt., hackberry leaf slug. F.g.l. 24 ± mm. Lateral view of an ornate venomous slug. Earlier instars possess a few very long plumose setae on most verrucae. A short heavy spine adjacent to each spiracle. Food plant hackberry.

Figures D to F. Megalopyge opercularis A. and S., puss caterpillar. F.g.l. 25 ± mm. This distinctly, venomous, somewhat pear shaped caterpillar has a short thick body covered with many pale yellow, gray, reddish-brown or mouse colored, long setae which project dorsad and caudad and possess little curled tufts on each side of the tail of setae. Feeds on many shade trees and is common in the south on citrus, hackberry, elm, wild and cultivated plum, sycamore, oak and rose bushes. Bishopp, 1923.

Figure D. Lateral view of larva.

Figure E. Ventral view of a proleg without crochets on second abdominal segment.

Figure F. Ventral view of a proleg bearing crochets on third abdominal segment.

Figures G and H. F.g.l. 12 + mm. An unknown genus and species of a lycaenid collected from foliage of woodland trees with the head completely extended.

Figure G. Lateral view with head protracted.

Figure H. Lateral view of fourth abdominal, ventral proleg showing a median lobe.

Figure I. Strymon melinus Hbn., cotton square borer or gray hair streak. F.g.l. 13-16 mm. Lateral view of a stout larva somewhat depressed and tapering toward the rounded ends. It may be bright or pale green with a darker stripe along the dorso meson. Venter is light green including the legs. The velvety appearance is due to the many setae of varying lengths on all parts of the body. Head usually retracted. In the south it is a pest on cotton. cowpeas, beans and okra. It also attacks hops, hawthorn, bush cloves, Lespedeza, wild aster, pepper-vine, trumpet weed, mistletoe, goatweed and many other flowering plants. Reinhard, 1929.

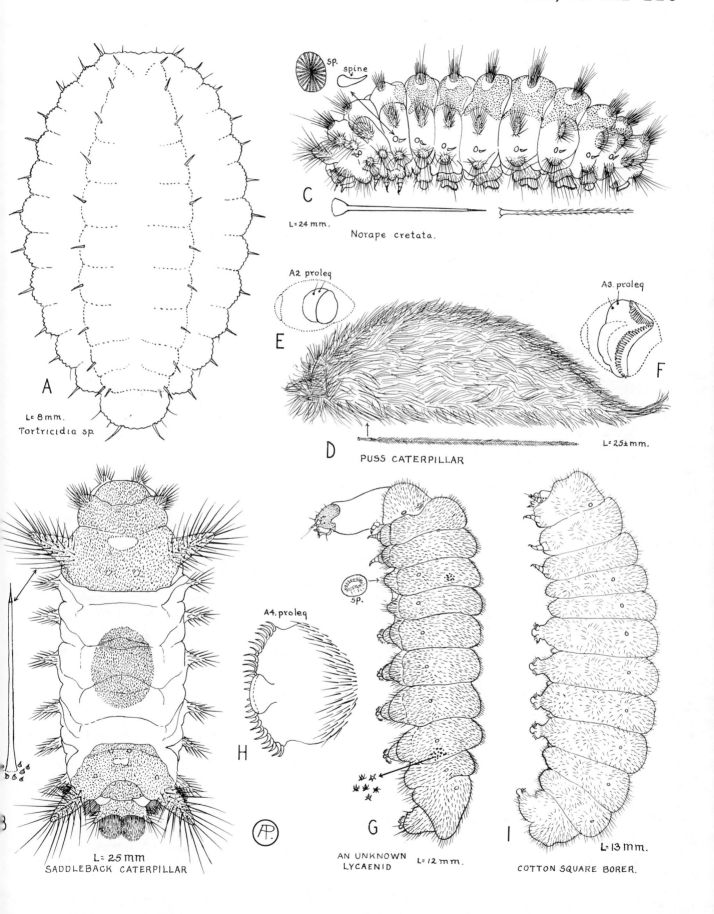

sp. spine

C
L=24 mm.
Norape cretata.

A
L=8 mm.
Tortricidia sp.

A2 proleg

E

A3 proleg

F

D
PUSS CATERPILLAR
L=25± mm.

A4 proleg

H

sp.

B
L=25 mm
SADDLEBACK CATERPILLAR

G
AN UNKNOWN
LYCAENID   L=12 mm.

I
L=13 mm.
COTTON SQUARE BORER.

LEPIDOPTERA

EXPLANATION OF FIGURES L24, A-K

LIPARIDAE

Figures A and B. Stilpnotia salicis L., satin moth. F.g.l. 30-35 mm., has a bluish, black head, conspicuous irregular white areas without setae on the dorsum of most segments, paired cone shaped glands adjacent to the dorsomeson of the first and second abdominal segments and single eversible glands on the dorsomeson of the sixth and seventh segments. On most of the abdominal segments seta alpha (1) consists of one or two setae while beta (2) and rho (3) are conspicuous, orange to brown verrucae covered with yellowish-brown setae. Food plants chiefly poplars and willows. Burgess and Crossman, 1927.

Figure A. Dorsal view of the sixth abdominal segment showing the distribution of the pigment, the orange or brown verrucae with numerous lighter brown setae surrounded by pigmented or mottled areas and the gland opening on the meson, also a pair of cone-shaped glands adjacent to the meson on the first or second abdominal segments.

Figure B. Mesal view of a mandible.

Figures C to E. Porthetria dispar L., gypsy moth. F.g.l. 55 ± mm., dusky brown to gray, finely marked with darker spots, possessing a yellow head densely covered with black, pigment blotches and spots, a light brown stripe on the dorsomeson of the body with prominent, paired, pigmented verrucae (beta) on each side. The verrucae on the thorax and first two abdominal segments are blue while those on abdominal segments three to eight are brick red. Feeds on foliage of more than 600 deciduous and coniferous plants, chiefly woodland, shade and fruit trees in New England and adjacent states.

Figure C. Dorsal view of abdominal segments six to ten showing distribution of the pigment, prominent verrucae and glands on the meson of segments six and seven.

Figure D. Lateral view of sixth abdominal segment.

Figure E. Mesal view of right mandible.

Figures F to H. Nygmia phaeorrhoea Donov., brown-tail moth. F.g.l. 35 ± mm., reddish brown due to a dark brown splashed with light brown and bearing reddish brown setae. On most of the abdominal segments the dorsal verrucae possess numerous, short, white, plumose setae which produce the effect of two white broken lines. Prominent, reddish, gland openings occur on the dorsomeson of the sixth and seventh abdominal segments. The caterpillars feed on more than 80 plants, mostly deciduous shade and fruit trees, shrubs, vines and herbs in New England.

Figure F. Lateral view of sixth abdominal segment showing the verrucae and gland.

Figure G. An enlarged view of a rho verrucae possessing short, white, plumose setae.

Figure H. Mesal view of a mandible.

Figures I to K. Hemerocampa leucostigma A. and L., white marked tussock moth. F.g.l. 32 ± mm., strikingly colored, yellow, black, red and white, with the following distinctive characteristics, a bright red head and pronotum, two long, black, plumose, setae tufts projecting cephalad from the prothorax, a medium dorsal tuft on the eighth abdominal segment, four conspicuous near-white verricules on the dorsomeson of abdominal segments one to four and two, bright red, knob-like glands on the dorsomeson of abdominal segments six and seven. It is a common leaf feeder on many shade trees and a few fruit trees chiefly apple, pear, quince and plum. It may also scar the surface of fruits.

Figure I. Head and a portion of the thorax showing the position and structure of the black plumose setal tuft.

Figure J. Lateral view of sixth abdominal segment showing position of the red gland.

Figure K. Lateral view of fourth abdominal segment showing position of the near-white verricule on the dorsomeson.

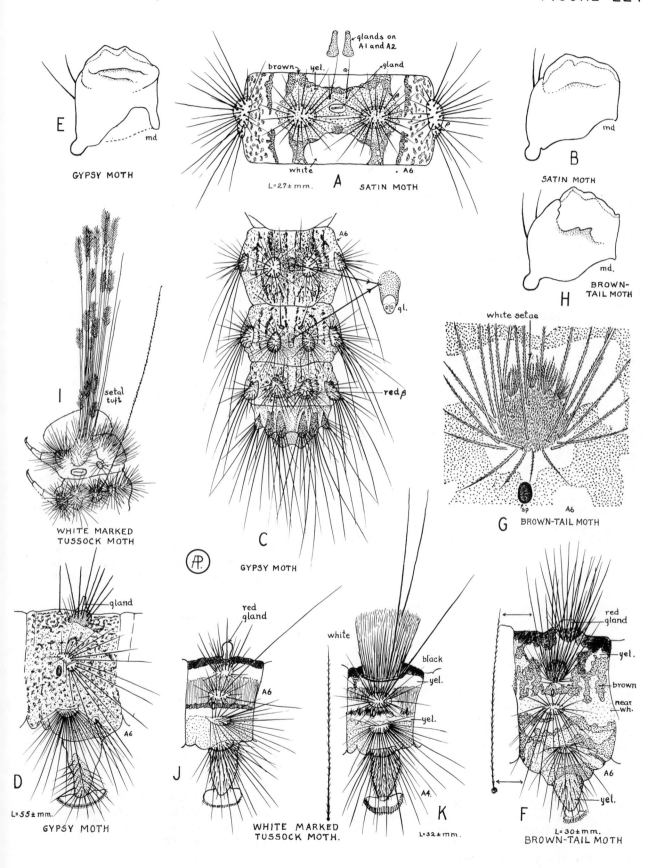

E
md
GYPSY MOTH

glands on
A1 and A2
brown   yel.   a   gland
white   · A6
L=27±mm.   A   SATIN MOTH

B
md
SATIN MOTH

md.
BROWN-
TAIL MOTH
H

I
setal
tuft
WHITE MARKED
TUSSOCK MOTH

A6
gl.
red β
C
℗
GYPSY MOTH

white setae
A6
sp   G   BROWN-TAIL MOTH

D
gland
A6
L=55±mm.
GYPSY MOTH

J
red
gland
A6
WHITE MARKED
TUSSOCK MOTH.

white
black
yel.
yel.
A4.
L=32±mm.   K

F
red
gland
yel.
brown
near
wh.
A6
yel.
L=30±mm.
BROWN-TAIL MOTH

EXPLANATION OF FIGURES L25, A-J

NOTODONTIDAE

Figure A. <u>Nerice</u> <u>bidentata</u> Wlk., serrate elm caterpillar. F.g.l. 32 ± mm., entirely bluish-green to near white possessing prominent, anteriorly directed projections on the dorsomeson of abdominal segments one to nine inclusive. Light green to near white areas occur on the dorsal half of each segment. Food plant elm.

Figure B. <u>Heterocampa</u> <u>guttivitta</u> Wlk., saddled prominent. F.g.l. 33 ± mm. Lateral view of a late stage greenish caterpillar which may or may not show a bright red saddle-like mark on the meson of abdominal segments three to five. The lower half of most segments are usually flecked with red spots. Feeds on foliage of maples and oak chiefly, also recorded for beech, chestnut and viburnum.

Figures C and D. <u>Heterocampa</u> <u>manteo</u> Dbld., variable oak leaf caterpillar or red streaked prominent. F.g.l. 40 ± mm., usually possessing between the subdorsal yellowish-white lines a medium red area varying in width from the head to the caudal segment. The sides of the body may be flecked with red. Food plants are chiefly woodland and fruit trees, namely oak, black birch, basswood, walnut, hawthorn, persimmon, and apple.

Figure C. Lateral view of head to mesothorax.

Figure D. Lateral view of sixth to tenth abdominal segments.

Figure E. <u>Cerura</u> <u>borealis</u> Bdvl., two tailed cherry caterpillar. F.g.l. 40 ± mm. Lateral view of a long, two-tailed pale, yellowish-green larva with a dorsal median reddish-brown band extending from the prothorax to the eighth abdominal segment being widest on the third and fourth abdominal segments. Head reddish-brown, tails brown and thoracic legs deep red. Food chiefly wild species of cherry, however, it may feed on aspen and willow.

Figure F. <u>Symmerista</u> <u>albifrons</u> A. and S., a red-anal-humped notodontid. F.g.l. 35 ± mm., Dorsal view of a longitudinally lined, deeply pigmented, caudal humped oakworm possessing five black lines against a near blue-black ground which extend from the head to the enlarged, red, dorsal hump (gibbose area) on the eighth abdominal segment. On each side laterad and caudad of the five black lines is a pair of red, longitudinal lines and more black and near blue stripes. Feeds on oak and beech foliage.

Figure G. <u>Schizura</u> <u>unicornis</u> A. and S., unicorn caterpillar. F.g.l. 35 ± mm. Lateral view of last instar, with a prominent, dorsal, pointed projection on the first abdominal segment. Variegated in color, mostly shades of brown to orange with a prominent pea green area on the lateral aspects of the mesothorax and metathorax. It has a wide variety of food plants, some of these are apple, plumb, cherry, hawthorn, elm, locust, dogwood, alder, oak and hazel.

Figures H and I. <u>Schizura</u> <u>concinna</u> A. and S., red-humped caterpillar. Also L8, E-F. F.g.l. 30 ± mm., deeply pigmented with orange, red, black and brown. The head and the enlarged dorsal gibbose area on the first abdominal segment are distinctly red. Prominent, black scoli occur on the dorsal portions of most segments. Several narrow, longitudinal stripes occur dorsad of the spiracles on the thorax and abdominal segments two to eight. The larva feeds on apple, cherry, plum, pear, willow, aspen, blackberry, rose, hawthorn, huckleberry, and other deciduous plants.

Figure H. Lateral view of head to first abdominal segment.

Figure I. Lateral view of abdominal segments 6 to 10.

Figure J. <u>Schizura</u> <u>ipomeae</u> Dbldy., false unicorn caterpillar. F.g.l. 35 ± mm., resembles <u>S.</u> <u>unicornis</u> in color. When full grown it may be larger and has a purple head with four dark lines extending from the mandibles to the vertex. The larger, pointed, dorsal projection on the first abdominal segment is bifurcate, each point bearing a stiff truncated spine. The meso- and metathorax are green, the body a brick-red slashed with pale lines. Food plants are oak, maple, birch, blackberry and honey locust.

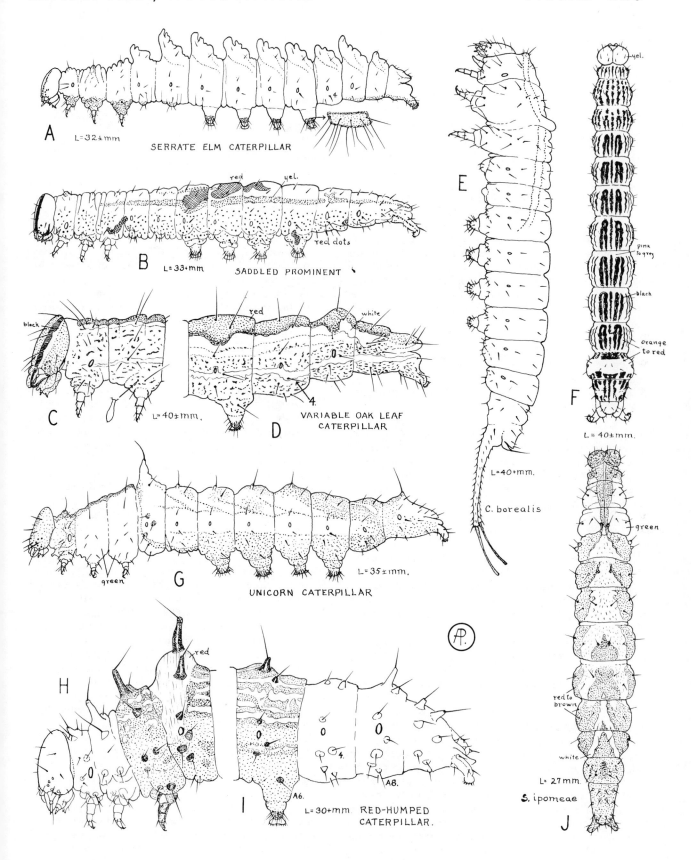

A   L=32±mm.

SERRATE ELM CATERPILLAR

B   L=33+mm.   red   yel.   red dots

SADDLED PROMINENT

C   black   L=40±mm.

D   red   white   4.

VARIABLE OAK LEAF
CATERPILLAR

E   L=40+mm.   C. borealis

F   yel.   pink to grey   black   orange to red   L= 40±mm.

G   green   L=35±mm.

UNICORN CATERPILLAR

H   red

I   A6.   4.   A8.   L=30+mm.   RED-HUMPED
CATERPILLAR.

J   yel.   green   red to brown   white   L= 27mm.   S. ipomeae

EXPLANATION OF FIGURES L26, A-J

NOTODONTIDAE A-H, ZANOLIDAE I-J

Figures A and B. Ichthyura inclusa Hbn., poplar tent maker. F.g.l. 40 ± mm., has a black head and a few setae scattered over the body. Prominent black tubercles are present on the dorsomeson of abdominal segments 1 and 8. Also on the dorsum four narrow yellow lines alternating with narrow black ones occur. Above the spiracular line an irregular alternation of black and white lines occur and below the spiracles a narrow yellow line. Host plants chiefly poplar and willow.

Figure A. Lateral view of head to first abdominal segment.

Figure B. Lateral view of sixth to tenth abdominal segments.

Figures C and D. Datana ministra Drury, yellow-necked caterpillar. F.g.l. 45 ± mm. Typical of several species of Datana this caterpillar in its early stages is reddish to chestnut brown with numerous yellow to orange longitudinal stripes. In the last stage it is black with four continuous light yellow to near white stripes on each side, also the dorsal aspect of the prothorax is yellow. Numerous, very long, white, scattered setae occur on the various segments. The ventral prolegs are reddish-yellow with black sclerotized plates above the planta. Its food plants are apple, pear, cherry, quince, linden, walnut, oak, chestnut, beach, hazel, hornbean, birch, locust, etc.

Figure C. Lateral view of head to mesothorax inclusive.

Figure D. Lateral view of fourth abdominal segment.

Figure E. Lateral view of a fourth abdominal, ventral proleg.

Figure F. Datana major G. and R. azalea caterpillar. F.g.l. 45 mm. This Datana caterpillar in the early instars has a black head, brown cervical shield and anal plate and many longitudinal continuous narrow red and greenish-yellow lines. In the last instar it is black with the longitudinal, near-white or yellow lines broken one or more places on each segment, producing a spotted condition. Its head, pronotum, anal plate and bases of the legs are orange-brown or mahogany-red. The primary hairs are long and white and the secondary ones short and black. Food plants are Azalea, Andromeda ligustrinia and A. marina. Lateral view of fourth abdominal segment.

Figures G and H. Datana integerrima G. & R., walnut caterpillar. F.g.l. 33 ± mm. Earlier instars have a black head and pronotum and are red to dark reddish-brown with narrow yellowish to grayish lines that extend the entire length of the thorax and abdomen. In the last instar the larvae is near black with only two grayish lines on the dorsal aspect and two on the sides. Numerous soft, fine, long, gray plumose setae cover the entire body. Food plants are walnut, butternut, hickory, beech and ash, rarely on willow, honey locust, hawthorn and apple. Baerg, 1928.

Figure G. Lateral view of fourth abdominal segment.

Figure H. Lateral view of last three caudal segments.

Figures I and J. Apatelodes torrefacta A. and S., tritufted zanolid. F.g.l. 50 ± mm. very densely clothed with numerous, long, soft, yellowish to pure white setae. Three prominent, single, black tufts of setae occur on the dorsomeson, two on the thorax and one on the eighth abdominal segment. Head near black. Body cuticle with dark pigment spots dorsad of the spiracles as indicated. Food plants alder, ash, azalea, blackberry, bayberry, hazel, ironwood, sassafrass, viburnum, willow and other deciduous plants.

Figure I. Lateral view of head to metathorax.

Figure J. Lateral view of fourth (setae omitted) and fifth abdominal segments.

Note. For detailed descriptions and colored figures of species shown on L25 and L26 see Packard, 1895.

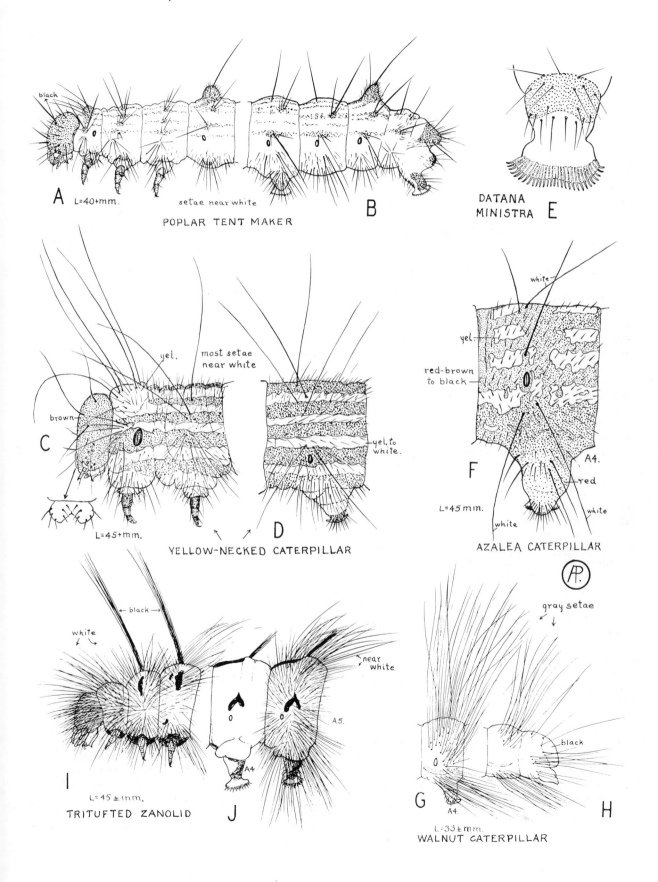

black

A   L=40+mm.   setae near white   B

POPLAR TENT MAKER

DATANA
MINISTRA   E

yel.   most setae
near white

brown

C   D

L=45+mm.   YELLOW-NECKED CATERPILLAR   yel.to white.

white

yel.

red-brown
to black

F   A4.

L=45mm.   white   red

white

AZALEA CATERPILLAR

black

white   near
white

gray setae

A5.

A4   black

I   L=45±1mm.   J   G   A4.   H

TRITUFTED ZANOLID   L=33±mm.
WALNUT CATERPILLAR

LEPIDOPTERA

EXPLANATION OF FIGURES L27, A-N

NYMPHALIDAE

Figures A to C. Asterocampa clyton B. and L., a hackberry butterfly. F.g.l. 35 ± mm., light colored without prominent scoli on the thorax or abdomen. Dorsal aspect of head with several small scoli and two large branched scoli. Food hackberry (Celtis) foliage.

Figure A. Lateral view of head to mesothorax.

Figure B. Lateral view of fourth abdominal segment.

Figure C. Dorsal view of caudal segment.

Figure D. Athena petreus Cram. A fig caterpillar. F.g.l. 30-35 mm. Lateral view. Living specimen have a general brick red color with four, black tipped, dorsal spines on the first, fourth, sixth and eighth abdominal segments. Three pink areas lie between the spines also diagonal deeply pigmented, near black marks occur ventrad of the dorsal spines. Food plant is figs. See Strohecker, 1938.

Figure E. Basilarchia archippus Cram., viceroy. F.g.l. 40-50 mm. Lateral view (pigmented omitted). This caterpillar differs decidedly from Danaus plexippus L. (Fig. L33, I) even though the adults resemble each other. General color dark, yellowish-brown or olive-green with a buff or white patch near the center of the abdomen. One prominent pair of scoli on the dorsum of the mesothorax. Feeds on the foliage of willow, poplar, aspen, cottonwood and balm of gilead.

Figures F and G. Polygonia prob. interrogationis Fabr., the violet tip. F.g.l. 35 ± mm., reddish, to orange with conspicuous scoli or chalazae on the head and all segments. Feeds on foliage of elm, basswood, hackberry and other trees.

Figure F. Lateral view of head to mesothorax inclusive.

Figure G. Lateral view of the fourth abdominal segment.

Figures H and J. Euptoita claudia Cram., pansyworm or variegated fritillary. F.g.l. 30-35 mm., orange-red to dull brown with whitish longitudinal stripes on the body also dark brown scoli tipped with black. Head black with dorsal portion light brown. Spiracles, thoracic legs and lateral aspects of prolegs near black. Feeds on pansies, passion flower, violets, Portulacca, Sedum and Desmodum.

Figure H. Lateral view of head to mesothorax.

Figure I. Lateral view of fourth abdominal segment.

Figure J. Dorsal view of caudal segments.

Figures K to N. Nymphalis antiopa L., mourning-cloak butterfly. F.g.l. 45-50 mm., near black gregarious, spiny caterpillar with seven yellowish-orange to red spots on the dorsomeson of abdominal segments one to seven. Feeds on foliage of willow, poplar, elm, hackberry and other plants.

Figure K. Lateral view of head to mesothorax inclusive.

Figure L. Lateral view of fourth abdominal segment.

Figure M. Dorsal view of caudal segments.

Figure N. Mesal view of fourth abdominal, ventral proleg.

**Nymphalis milberti Godt., nettle caterpillar. F.g.l. 30 ± mm. Head black with setae arising from near white chalazae. Area dorsad of spiracles reddish purple to brown flecked with near-white spots from which secondary setae may arise. Distribution and size of scoli resembles that of Polygonia. All scoli dorsad of spiracles prominent, brown to near-black, those ventrad of spiracles light in color resembling the light colored venter. Spiracles black located between two irregular light lines. Younger larvae decidedly reddish brown to purple. Food plant nettles, Urtica gracilis.

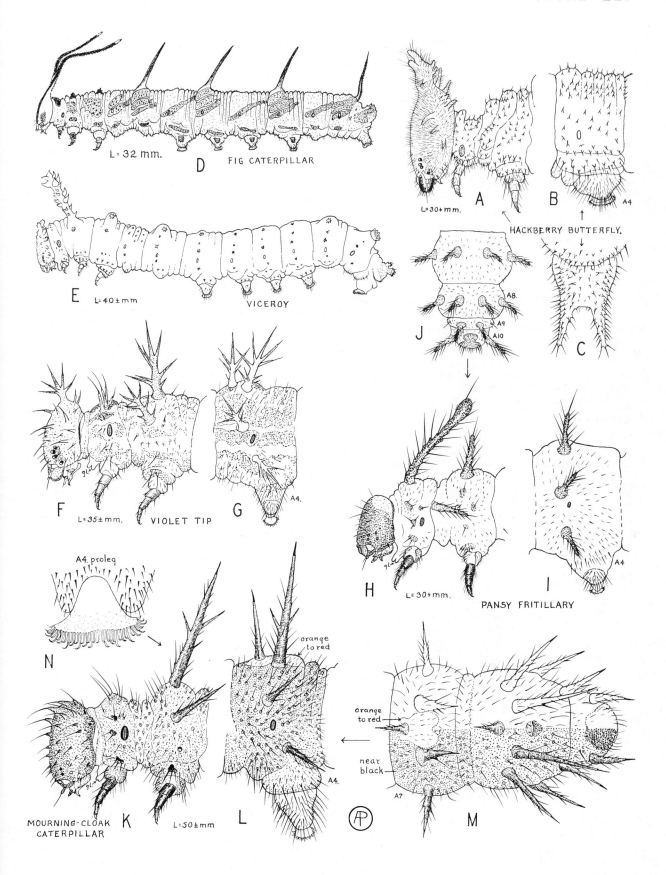

L=32 mm. D FIG CATERPILLAR

L=30+mm. A B A4

HACKBERRY BUTTERFLY.

C

E L=40±mm VICEROY

J A8. A9 A10

F L=35±mm. VIOLET TIP G gl. A4.

H L=30+mm. PANSY FRITILLARY I A4

N A4. proleg

orange to red

K MOURNING-CLOAK CATERPILLAR L=50±mm L A4.

M A7 orange to red near black

LEPIDOPTERA

EXPLANATION OF FIGURES L28, A-K

OECOPHORIDAE A-E, ETHMIIDAE F-H. AGARISTIDAE J-K

Figures A to E. <u>Depressaria heracliana</u> DeG., parsnip webworm. Also L7, D. F.g.l. 15 $\pm$ mm., brown to black spotted, yellowish-green larva with a grayish blue dorsum. Food plants parsnip, celery, wild parsnip, wild carrot and related weeds. Webs together and feeds on the leaves and flower portions of the plant. Pupae occur within stems of the host plant.

Figure A. Lateral view of head to mesothorax.

Figure B. Lateral view of fourth abdominal segment.

Figure C. Crochets and setae of sixth abdominal, right, ventral proleg.

Figure D. Crochets and setae of right anal proleg.

Figure E. Mesal view of right mandible.

Figures F to H. <u>Ethmia fuscipedella</u> Wlsm., F.g.l. 20 $\pm$ mm., with two, conspicuous, wide, supraspiracular, near black bands and prominent black pinacula. Food plant <u>Lithospermum</u> <u>Gmelini</u> (Michx), Col. A. F. Braun.

Figure F. Lateral view of the head to mesothorax inclusive.

Figure G. Lateral view of the fourth abdominal segment.

Figure H. Crochets of the fourth abdominal, right, ventral proleg.

Figure I. Mesal view of the right mandible.

Figures J and K. <u>Alypia</u> <u>octomaculata</u> F., eight-spotted forester. Also L1, O-P. F.g.l. 35 $\pm$ mm., transversely striped and blotched with yellow, white and reddish brown bands and spotted with numerous conspicuous near-black pinacula. Head a deep yellow and with a few black dots. Mandible with a distinct tooth-like retinaculum on the oral surface, L1, O-P. Food plants (foliage) are species of <u>Ampelopsis</u> including Virginia creeper and grapes, wild and domestic.

Figure J. Lateral view of head to mesothorax.

Figure K. Lateral view of sixth to tenth abdominal segments.

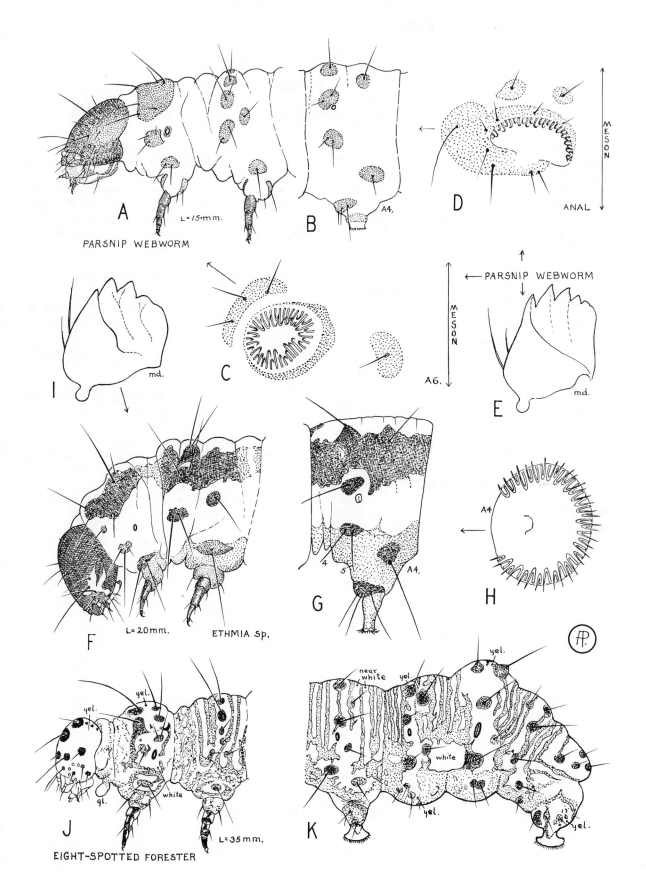

PARSNIP WEBWORM

L=15·mm.

A4.

MESON

ANAL

md.

C

PARSNIP WEBWORM

MESON

A6.

md.

E

I

L=20mm.

ETHMIA Sp.

F

4 5

A4.

G

A4

H

yel.

near white

yel.

yel.

yel.

yel.

white

white

yel.

yel.

yel.

gl.

J

EIGHT-SPOTTED FORESTER

L=35mm.

K

LEPIDOPTERA

EXPLANATION OF FIGURES L29, A-L

OLETHREUTIDAE

Figures A to F. Carpocapsa pomonella L., codling moth. F.g.l. 14-16 mm., moderately plump, cream colored, dirty white or pinkish with a mottled, deep brown head, inconspicuous pinacula about the setae and no anal comb. Infests the fruit of apple, pear, quince, crab, wild haw, English walnut and other plants. See Simpson, 1903; Symons and Peairs, 1910, Lopez, 1929.

Figure A. Lateral view of head to mesothorax.

Figure B. Lateral view of fourth abdominal segment.

Figure C. Lateral view of ninth and tenth abdominal segments.

Figure D. Caudal view of caudal segments.

Figure E. Crochets and setae of sixth abdominal, right, ventral proleg.

Figure F. Mesal view of right mandible.

Figures G to L. Grapholitha molesta Busck, oriental fruit moth. Also L2, H; L6, B; L7, I; L8, L-M. F.g.l. 10-11 mm., moderately slender, usually pinkish to near white with a light brown head, faintly sclerotized cervical shield and anal plate, inconspicuous pinacula about most of the primary setae and an anal comb with five to seven prongs. Infests the twigs and fruit of peaches, nectarines and apricots and primarily the fruit of quince, plums and apple, especially fall varieties of apples when grown near peach orchards. P. Garman, 1917, 1918; Wood and Selkregg, 1918.

Figure G. Lateral view of head to mesothorax inclusive.

Figure H. Lateral view of fourth abdominal segment.

Figure I. Lateral view of ninth and tenth abdominal segments showing position of anal comb.

Figure J. Ventral view of ninth and tenth abdominal segments showing distribution of setae, crochets on anal prolegs and anal comb.

Figure K. Crochets and setae of sixth abdominal, right ventral proleg.

Figure L. Mesal view of right mandible.

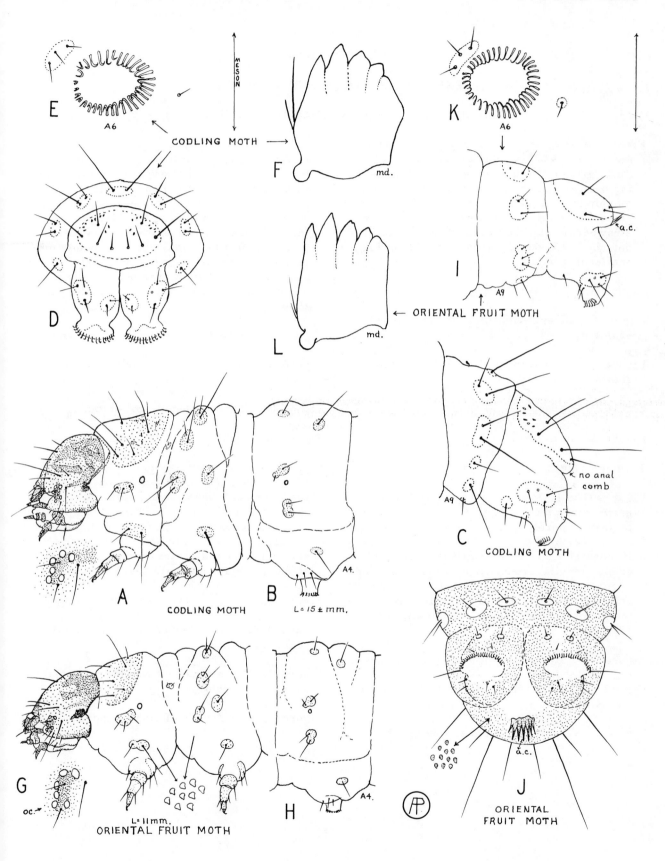

MESON

E
A6

CODLING MOTH

F
md.

L
md.

K
A6

ORIENTAL FRUIT MOTH

I
A9
a.c.

D

A
CODLING MOTH

B
A4.
L=15±mm.

C
A9
no anal comb
CODLING MOTH

G
oc.
L=11mm.
ORIENTAL FRUIT MOTH

H
A4.

J
a.c.
ORIENTAL
FRUIT MOTH

EXPLANATION OF FIGURES L30, A-Q

OLETHREUTIDAE A-I AND N-Q, TORTRICIDAE J-M

Figures A to F. <u>Ancylis</u> <u>comptana</u> <u>fragariae</u> W.. and R., strawberry leaf roller. F.g.l. 12 $\pm$ mm., greenish to bronze colored with a shining brown head and cervical shield. Caudal margin of anal plate deeply pigmented. Anal comb 6 $\pm$ prongs. Feeds on the leaves of strawberry, blackberry, dewberry and raspberry. Folds the leaf longitudinally, living and feeding within.

Figure A. Lateral view of head to mesothorax.

Figure B. Lateral view of fourth abdominal segment.

Figure C. Lateral view of ninth and tenth abdominal segments.

Figure D. Dorsal view of caudal segment.

Figure E. Anal fork.

Figure F. Mesal view of right mandible.

Figures G to I. <u>Polychrosis</u> <u>viteana</u> Clem. grape berry moth. F.g.l. 9-10 mm., greenish to gray to purple with a light brown head and a dark cervical shield. Anal comb, 5 $\pm$ prongs, inconspicuous. Infests cultivated and wild grapes feeding externally on young fruit and bores within mature berries. On foliage it cuts out and folds over a small flap and within spins a cocoon. Johnson and Hammer, 1912.

Figure G. Lateral view of head and prothorax.

Figure H. Lateral view of ninth and tenth segments.

Figure I. Ventral view of anal comb.

Figures J to M. <u>Platynota</u> <u>stultana</u> Wlsn., a leaf roller, tyer and fruit scarring worm. F.g.l. 13-18 mm., yellowish to brownish green with a light brown head and cervical shield. Earlier instars have black heads. A median dark stripe occurs along the dorsomeson. Pinacula about most setae chalky white. Anal comb 6 $\pm$ prongs, conspicuous. Food plants carnations, roses, peppers, tomatoes, grapefruit, oranges, cotton, walnut, avacado and other field and greenhouse plants. Nelson, 1936.

Figure J. Lateral view of head to mesothorax.

Figure K. Lateral view of fourth abdominal segment.

Figure L. Ventral view of anal comb.

Figure M. Mesal view of the right mandible.

Figures N to Q. <u>Melissopus</u> <u>latiferreanus</u> Wlsm., filbertworm. F.g.l. 15 $\pm$ mm., dirty white with a reddish brown head, yellowish to light brown cervical shield, anal plate and pinacula at bases of all primary setae. Cuticule covered with microscopic dots (stippled). No anal comb. Infests various nuts, especially acorns, filberts and wild hazel nuts.

Figure N. Lateral view of head to mesothorax.

Figure O. Lateral view of fourth abdominal segment.

Figure P. Lateral view of ninth and tenth abdominal segments.

Figure Q. Mesal view of right mandible.

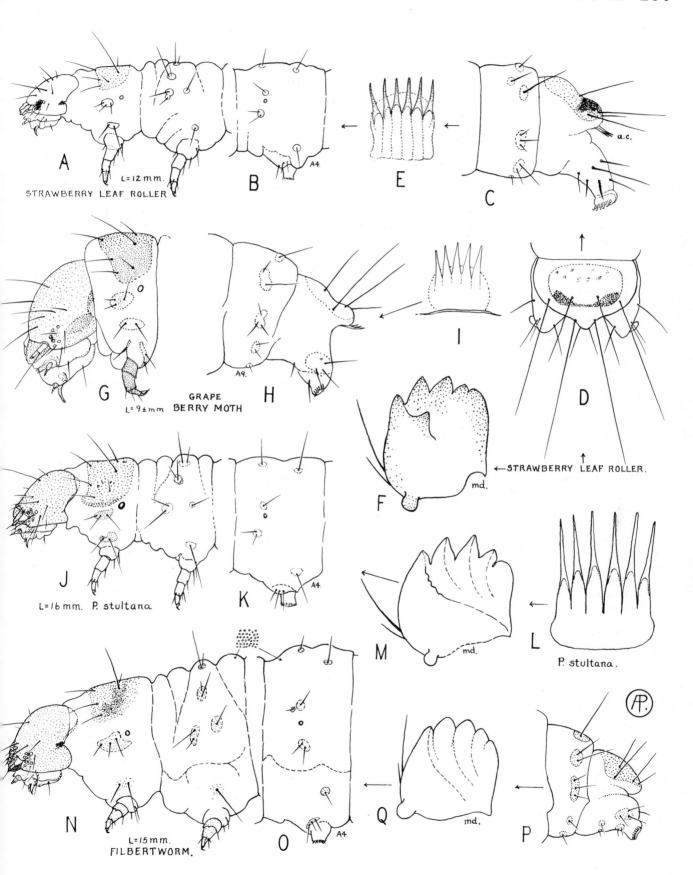

A
L=12 mm.
STRAWBERRY LEAF ROLLER

B
A4.

E

C
a.c.

I

D
←STRAWBERRY LEAF ROLLER.

G
L=9±mm
GRAPE BERRY MOTH

H
A9.

F
md.

J
L=16 mm. P. stultana

K
A4.

M
md.

L
P. stultana.

N
L=15 mm.
FILBERTWORM.

O
A4.

Q
md.

P

AP.

EXPLANATION OF FIGURES L31, A-Q

OLETHREUTIDAE A-D and G-P, TORTRICIDAE E, F and Q

Figures A to D. Rhyacionia buoliana Schiff. European pine shoot moth. F.g.l. 14 ± mm., dark brown with head, cervical shield and thoracic legs near black and a yellowish brown speckled anal plate. Cuticle finely stippled with tiny microspines. Infests the terminal shoots of several species of pines, especially Scotch pine, also red pine, white pine and Mugo pines. See Busck, 1915.

Figure A. Lateral view of eighth to tenth abdominal segments.

Figure B. Area about fourth abdominal spiracle greatly magnified.

Figure C. Crochets of sixth abdominal, right ventral proleg.

Figure D. Crochets and setae of right anal proleg.

Figures E and F. Archips fumiferana Clem., spruce budworm. F.g.l. 17 ± mm. See L32, O to R for more details.

Figure E. Crochets and setae of sixth abdominal, right, ventral proleg.

Figure F. Crochets and setae of right anal proleg.

Figures G and H. Rhyacionia frustrana Comst., Nantucket pine tip moth. F.g.l. 9 ± mm., yellowish with a light brown head and cervical shield. Larva spins a web about the terminal bud and mines the twig and bases of the leaves. Food plants pitch pine, Virginia pine and scrub pine.

Figure G. Crochets and setae of sixth abdominal, right, ventral proleg.

Figure H. Crochets and setae of right anal proleg.

Figures I and J. Eucosoma giganteana Riley, silphium crown borer. F.g.l. 24-27 mm., stout, near white to cream colored with a brown head and yellow cervical shield. Infests the main stalk and crown portion of Silphium sp. weeds.

Figure I. Crochets and setae of sixth abdominal, right, ventral proleg.

Figure J. Crochets and setae of right anal proleg.

Figures K and L. Spilonota ocellana D. and S., eyespotted bud moth. F.g.l. 12 ± mm., dull brown with dark brown shiny head, cervical shield, anal plate and thoracic legs. Cuticle of body finely granulate. Pinacula about setae conspicuous and darker than surrounding surface, especially on thorax. Beta (2) setae on ninth abdominal on same pinaculum, also alpha (1) and rho (3) on same pinaculum. Anal comb short with 2 to 5 prongs. In the spring the small caterpillar feeds on buds, cuts off leaf stems, folds leaf edges together and pulls leaves together near the tip of twig. They also may make small holes in the fruit. Food plants are apple, blackberry, cherry, crataegus, peach, pear, Japanese quince, oak, raspberry, wild plum, and other plants. Frost, 1927; Porter, 1924.

Figure K. Crochets and setae of the sixth abdominal right ventral proleg.

Figure L. Crochets and setae of the right anal proleg.

Figure M.. Carpocapsa saltitans Westwood, Mexican jumping bean larva. F.g.l. 8 + mm. Lateral view of the full grown, near-white caterpillar with a brown head which lives within the fruit (seeds) of Sebastiana pavoniana.

Figures N to P. Epiblema strenuana Wlkr., ragweed borer. F.g.l. 20 ± mm., dirty white to yellowish. Head, cervical shield and suranal plate are deep brown. Sclerotized, brown pinacula associated with the setae are conspicuous. Produces stem galls or enlargements on ragweed.

Figure N. Lateral view of head to mesothorax.

Figure O. Lateral view of fourth abdominal segment.

Figure P. Mesal view of right mandible.

Figure Q. Archips fervidana Clem., scrub oak nest caterpillar. F.g.l. 12 ± mm., dirty brown with a near-black head, brown cervical shield, anal plate and thoracic legs. All setae appear to arise from small brown pinacula. Cuticle densely covered with tiny pigmented microspines. Mandible with prominent, sharp, fluted ridge on oral surface (L31, Q). Constructs and lives within thick webbed nests on scrub oak in June. Mesal view of right mandible.

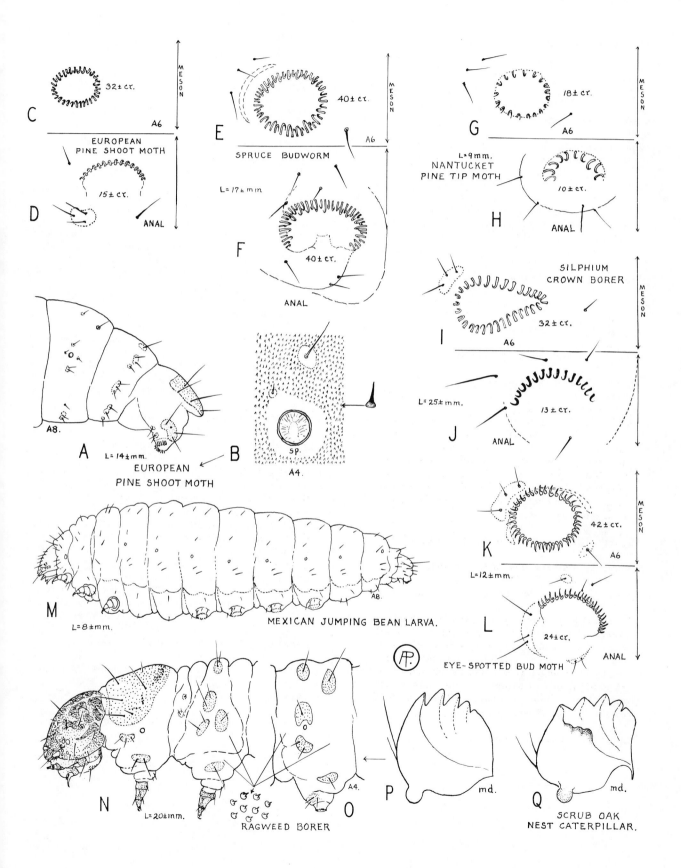

C   32±cr.   A6

EUROPEAN
PINE SHOOT MOTH

D   15±cr.   ANAL

E   40±cr.   A6

SPRUCE BUDWORM

L=17±mm.

F   40±cr.   ANAL

G   18±cr.   A6

L=9mm.
NANTUCKET
PINE TIP MOTH

H   10±cr.   ANAL

SILPHIUM
CROWN BORER

I   32±cr.   A6

L=25±mm.

J   13±cr.   ANAL

A8.

A   L=14±mm.
EUROPEAN
PINE SHOOT MOTH

B   sp.   A4.

K   42±cr.   A6

L=12±mm.

L   24±cr.   ANAL

EYE-SPOTTED BUD MOTH

M   L=8±mm.   MEXICAN JUMPING BEAN LARVA.   A8.

N   L=20±mm.
RAGWEED BORER   O   A4.

P   md.

Q   md.
SCRUB OAK
NEST CATERPILLAR.

LEPIDOPTERA

EXPLANATION OF FIGURES L32, A-R

TORTRICIDAE

Figures A to D. Archips obsoletana Walker, obsolete-banded strawberry leaf roller. F.g.l. 22-25 mm., olive-green with a yellow to light brown head. Cervical shield lightly pigmented except for a narrow brown band about the caudal and ventral margin. Thoracic legs brown. Anal plate yellow. Anal comb conspicuous with 8 ± prongs. This strawberry pest folds the leaves or webs them together with the young fruits and feeds upon them.

Figure A. Lateral view of head to mesothorax.

Figure B. Lateral view of fourth abdominal segment.

Figure C. Ventral view of anal comb.

Figure D. Mesal view of right mandibles.

Figures E to G. Archips cerasivorana Fitch, uglynest caterpillar. F.g.l. 15 ± mm., yellowish with a black head and a near black or dark brown cervical shield, anal plate, lateral areas on anal legs and pinacula Kappa and Pi on the prothorax. No anal comb. Mandible with one small tooth on oral surface immediately below first lateral tooth (L32, G). Microspines on cuticle inconspicuous and light colored. Produces thick dingy nests at times of great size on choke cherry and occasionally on cultivated cherries.

Figure E. Lateral view of head to mesothorax.

Figure F. Lateral view of fourth abdominal segment.

Figure G. Mesal view of right mandible.

Figures H to J. Archips rileyana Grt., buckeye leafworm. F.g.l. 23 ± mm., greenish-yellow with a near black head, a deep brown to black cervical shield, deep brown to black anal plate, thoracic legs and prolegs, also conspicuous brown to black pinacula about all setae. Microspines numerous, pigmented in folds of cuticle. Feeds in clusters on the foliage of buckeye trees.

Figure H. Lateral view of head to mesothorax.

Figure I. Lateral view of fourth abdominal segment.

Figure J. Mesal view of right mandible.

Figures K to N. Archips argyrospila Wlkr., fruit tree leaf roller. F.g.l. 15-18 mm., green to greenish-brown with a light to dark brown head and a light yellowish cervical shield. Most specimens without a pigmented anal plate or pinacula. Feeds on buds, leaves and small fruits. The leaves may be rolled and drawn together by silken threads. Omnivorous in its hosts attacking fruit trees, especially apple, pear, cherry, plum, apricot and quince; small fruits, namely, currant, raspberry and gooseberry, several woodland trees, roses, and other herbaceous plants. Hawley, 1926.

Figure K. Lateral view of head to mesothorax.

Figure L. Lateral view of fourth abdominal segment.

Figure M. Ventral view of anal comb.

Figure N. Mesal view of right mandible.

Figures O to R. Archips fumiferana Clem., spruce budworm. Also L31, E. and F. F.g.l. 20-22 mm., thick, dark brown except a lighter subspiracular area. Possesses a mottled, brown head, a near black cervical shield and brown anal plate. Light, yellowish pinacula about the setae dorsad of the spiracles, and on the extreme venter are conspicuous against a dark cuticle. Covered with pigmented microprojections. Feeds on the leaves (needles) of the terminal shoots of first and second year's growth. Balsam appears to be the preferred food, however, spruce may be seriously injured.

Figure O. Lateral view of head to mesothorax.

Figure P. Lateral view of fourth abdominal segment.

Figure Q. Ventral view of anal comb.

Figure R. Mesal view of right mandible.

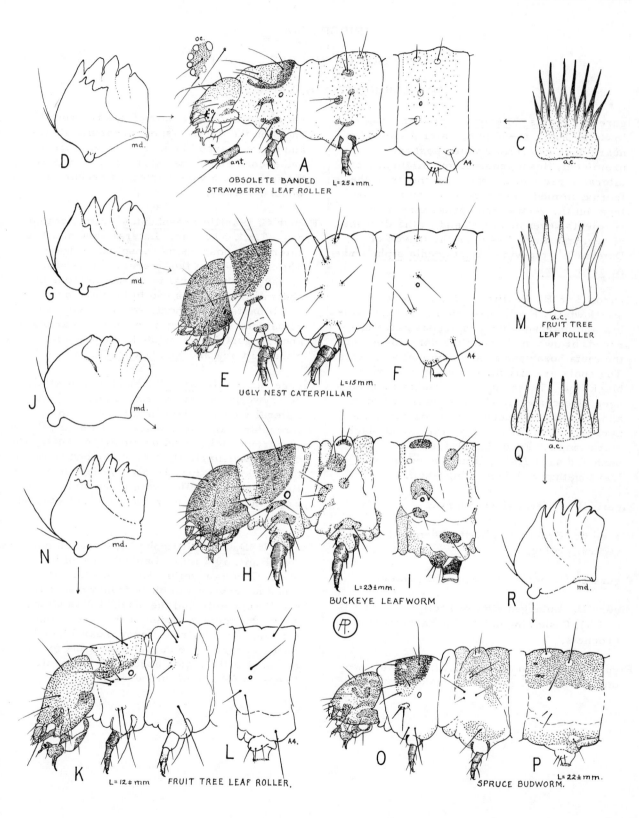

D

oc.

ant.

md.

A

OBSOLETE BANDED
STRAWBERRY LEAF ROLLER

L=25±mm.

B

A4.

C

a.c.

G

md.

E

UGLY NEST CATERPILLAR

L=15mm.

F

A4

M

a.c.
FRUIT TREE
LEAF ROLLER

J

md.

N

md.

H

I

BUCKEYE LEAFWORM

L=23±mm.

Q

a.c.

R

md.

K

L=12±mm

L

A4.

FRUIT TREE LEAF ROLLER.

O

P

SPRUCE BUDWORM.

L=22±mm.

LEPIDOPTERA

EXPLANATION OF FIGURES L33, A-I

PAPILIONIDAE A-H, DANAIDAE I

Figure A. Battus philenor L., pipevine swallowtail. F.g.l. 45-50 mm., lateral view of a near-black caterpillar which possesses prominent, fleshy, conspicuous filaments on lateral aspects of the three segments of the thorax, immediately dorsad of ventral prolegs, on the ventral and dorsal aspects of segments seven and eight and on the dorsum of segment nine. Feeds on the leaves of Dutchman's pipevine, Aristolochia sipho and A. serpentaria.

Figures B to E. Papilio troilus L., spice bush swallowtail. F.g.l. 40-45 mm., greenish yellow and marked with conspicuous pairs of round, orange spots near the dorsomeson on the metathorax and first abdominal segments. The spots are circumscribed by a narrow black line. Those on the metathorax possess deep blue centers. The head is light brown and immediately caudad of the osmeteria a narrow, short, transverse orange and black mark exists. Feeds on the foliage of spice bush and sassafras, pulling the edges of a leaf together and concealing itself.

Figure B. Lateral view of larva.

Figure C. Crochets of sixth abdominal, right, ventral proleg.

Figure D. Crochets of right anal proleg.

Figure E. Enlarged view of sections A' and B' of L33, C showing detailed arrangement of crochets.

Figure F. Papilio glaucus L., tiger swallowtail. F.g.l. 40 ± mm., last instars greenish-yellow possessing a pair of colored round spots on the dorsal aspect of the metathorax and a transverse black band between first and second abdominal segments. Feeds on the foliage of a wide variety of orchard and woodland trees.

Figure G. Papilio cresphontes Cram., orange-dog. F.g.l. 50 ± mm. Lateral view of a brown caterpillar possessing conspicuous near-white blotches on the lateral aspects of the thorax, on the lateral to dorsal portions of abdominal segments two to four and on most or all parts of segments seven to ten. The remainder of the body is brown to near black and irregularly distributed. Food plants citrus, Ptelea and Xanthoxylon.

Figure H. Papilio ajax L., black swallowtail, celeryworm, parsleyworm. F.g.l. 40 ± mm. Lateral view of a last instar larva showing irregular transverse black bands on a yellowish-green background on most segments. The complete or partially circumscribed spots in the black areas may be deep yellow or orange. Head greenish-yellow with black stripes. Food plants are celery, parsley, carrots and related plants.

Figure I. Danaus plexippus L., monarch butterfly. F.g.l. 50 ± mm. Lateral view of last instar. Green or yellowish possessing one or more near-brown to black transverse stripes on all segments and the head. On most segments the median stripe of the three is most conspicuous. Paired, fleshy, near-black filaments occur on the dorsal half of the mesothorax and the eighth abdominal segments. Feeds on foliage of milkweeds.

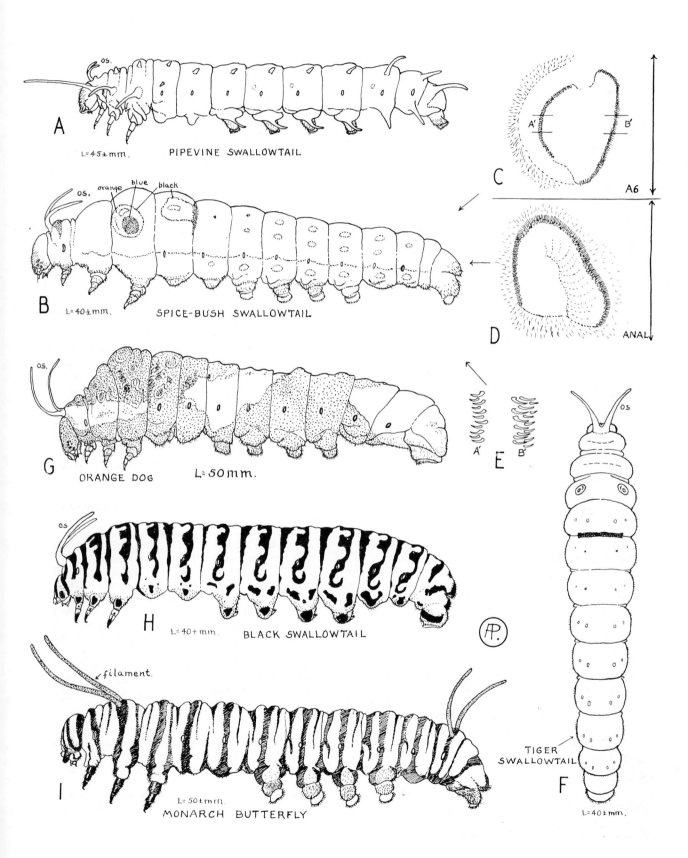

A — PIPEVINE SWALLOWTAIL — L=45±mm.

B — SPICE-BUSH SWALLOWTAIL — L=40±mm.

C — A6

D — ANAL

E — A' B'

G — ORANGE DOG — L=50mm.

H — BLACK SWALLOWTAIL — L=40±mm.

I — MONARCH BUTTERFLY — L=50±mm.

F — TIGER SWALLOWTAIL — L=40±mm.

EXPLANATION OF FIGURES L34, A-R

PHALAENIDAE

Figures A to E. Prodenia ornithogalli Guen., yellow-striped armyworm. F.g.l. 30-35 mm., slightly enlarged on the metathorax and abdominal segments, 1, 2, 7 and 8 and varies in general color from pale gray to jet black. Head usually brown with white adfrontals. Cervical shield brown with a faint median line which ends on the mesothorax. Subdorsal, elongated, triangular, near-black markings may be present on all abdominal segments 1 to 8. Below these occurs a bright yellow to cream colored stripe sometimes with four narrow lines in it and below the yellow stripe a dark band with spiracles in the lower edge. Spiracles light brown with black peritremes. The food plants include most common vegetables, grains, cotton, tobacco, violets, watermelons, petunia, peach and other cultivated plants and weeds. May climb and attack fruit buds. Crumb, 1929, Whelan, 1935.

Figure A. Cephalic view of head.

Figure B. Mesal view of right mandible.

Figure C. Lateral view of head to mesothorax.

Figure D. Lateral view of first abdominal segment showing characteristic distribution of pigment about spiracle.

Figure E. Lateral view of fourth abdominal segment.

Figures F to J. Prodenia eridania Cram., southern armyworm. F.g.l. 36 ± mm., uniform width throughout with the dorsum a general uniform gray tinged olivaceous or pinkish. Middorsal line, subdorsal stripe and subspiracular stripe unicolorous, whitish tinged with orange or pink. Laterally, on the dorsum, series of black, elongated, triangles occur usually on all segments expect the prothorax. Venter pinkish or orange flecked with white. Head pale yellow with bright rustly brown reticulations and no black coloration. Adfrontals brown, not white. Food plants include most vegetables, avocado, bean, blood root, castor beans, citrus, clover, cotton, crabgrass, oleander, sweet potato, tobacco, watermelon, willow and other cultivated plants and weeds. A good climber. Easily reared on bean seedlings in the laboratory. Crumb, 1929.

Figure F. Cephalic view of head.

Figure G. Mesal view of right mandible.

Figure H. Prothoracic tarsal claw.

Figure I. Lateral view of first abdominal segment showing characteristic distribution of pigment about spiracle.

Figure J. Lateral view of fourth abdominal segment.

Figures K to N. Peridroma margaritosa Haw., variegated cutworm. F.g.l. 38-45 mm., has a light to dark brown head with the pigment arranged as indicated (L34, K), body color from pale gray to a dark, mottled brown intermixed with red and yellow with yellowish mid-dorsal spots on the metathorax and at least the first four abdominal segments and a velvety black spot and yellow spot on the dorsum of the eighth abdominal segment. Skin smooth. Spiracles black within. Food plants extensive including most vegetables, corn, grains, grasses, tobacco, strawberries and many cultivated plants and weeds. Feeds mostly at night and does little climbing. Whelan, 1935.

Figure K. Cephalic view of head.

Figure L. Mesal view of right mandible.

Figure M. Lateral view of head to mesothorax inclusive.

Figure N. Lateral view of fourth abdominal segment.

Figure O to R. Euxoa ochrogaster Guen., red-backed cutworm. F.g.l. 37 ± mm., has a smooth, shiny, dirty-brown head with pigment arranged as in L34, O. Body light brown to gray, dorsum with a light median stripe bordered by two broad, reddish bands on either side, venter below the spiracles brown to light colored. Cervical shield light brown with fuscous spots about the caudal margin. Skin granules flat and pavement-like. Spiracles brown to black within. The food plants are many garden crops, flowering plants, corn and small grains. It feeds mostly underground, cutting off plants below soil level. Whelan, 1935.

Figure O. Cephalic view of head.

Figure P. Mesal view of right mandible.

Figure Q. Lateral view of head to mesothorax.

Figure R. Lateral view of fourth abdominal segment.

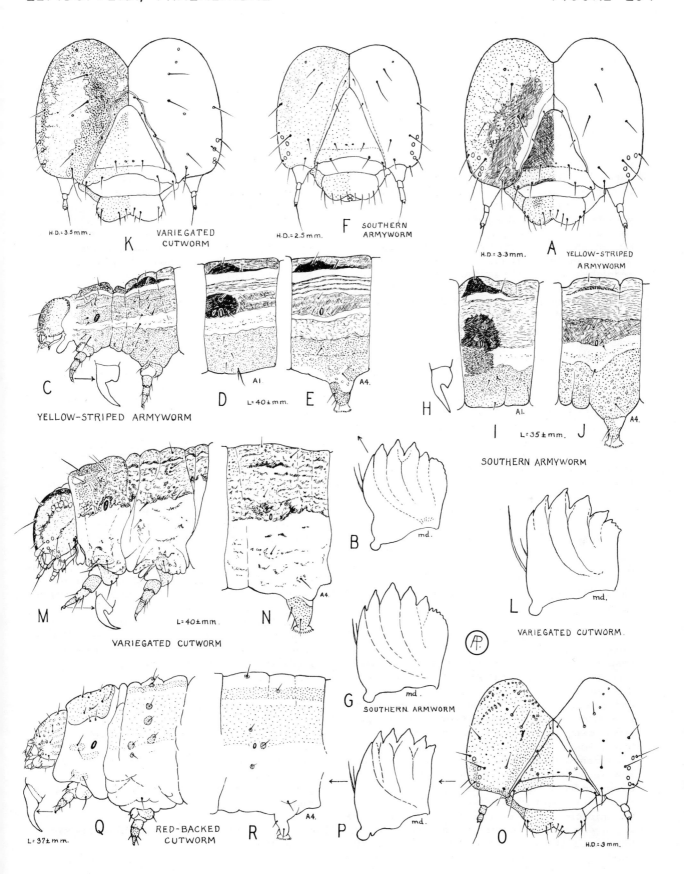

H.D.=3.5mm.
K   VARIEGATED
              CUTWORM

H.D.=2.5mm.
F   SOUTHERN
              ARMYWORM

H.D.=3.3mm.   A   YELLOW-STRIPED
                               ARMYWORM

C
YELLOW-STRIPED ARMYWORM

D   AI.
        L=40±mm.   E   A4.

H   I   AI.
              L=35±mm.   J   A4.

SOUTHERN ARMYWORM

B   md.

G   md.
SOUTHERN ARMWORM

L   md.
VARIEGATED CUTWORM.

M

N   A4.

L=40±mm.
VARIEGATED CUTWORM

Q   RED-BACKED
              CUTWORM

L=37±mm.

R   A4.

P   md.

O   H.D.=3mm.

LEPIDOPTERA

EXPLANATION OF FIGURES L35, A-L

PHALAENIDAE

Figures A to D. <u>Laphygma frugiperda</u> A. and S., fall armyworm. F.g.l. 35 $\pm$ mm., has a cream to brown colored head for the most part covered with dark reticulations and cream to near-white adfrontal areas. Body dark brown showing one median and one lateral light line. Laterad of the median line a broad, light brown band with reddish-brown mottlings, then laterad a narrow yellowish line just below setae beta (2), then a broader brown line and a reddish line of the same width the two merging on the thorax. Just below the spiracles a yellow band with reddish mottlings. Venter cream colored with reddish patches. Cervical shield dark brown with one medium and two lateral light lines. Pinacula about the setae black and conspicuous. Skin granules flat to pavement-like. Spiracles light to dusky within. Usually appears in greatest numbers in the early fall and is a good climber. Feeds on many plants in the garden, and field. Also attacks bent grass, cotton, tobacco, peanuts, and numerous legumes. Chittenden, 1901; Luginbill, 1928; Hinds and Dew, 1915

Figure A. Cephalic view of head.

Figure B. Mesal view of right mandible.

Figure C. Lateral view of head to mesothorax.

Figure D. Lateral view of fourth abdominal segment.

Figures E to H. <u>Cirphis unipuncta</u> Haw., armyworm. F.g.l. 35 $\pm$ mm., has a greenish brown head with numerous dark reticulations and dark streaks near the coronal and adfrontal sutures. The intensity of the pigment of the body varies considerably among individuals. Dorsum greenish-brown to black with a narrow, broken, light stripe along the dorsomeson. On each side a broad band of mottled brown darker at the edges and extending dorsad to seta beta (2) with a narrow white line below this followed by an orange or brown band edged with white, then a dark stripe to the spiracles edged with white. Below the spiracles a pale orange stripe unmottled and edged with white. Venter gray to cream with brownish mottlings. Cervical shield brown with markings. Skin noticeably granulated. Spiracles

dark brown to black. Brown lateral patches on ventral prolegs. Mandibles without dentes, see L35, F. Most abundant in late June to early August. Travels in armies and is a good climber. Food preference grains and cereals, however, it will consume most any plant when hungry. Crumb, 1927, Gibson, 1915, Davis and Satterthwait, 1916.

Figure E. Cephalic view of head.

Figure F. Mesal view of right mandible, a diagnostic character.

Figure G. Lateral view of head to mesothorax.

Figure H. Lateral view of fourth abdominal segment.

Figures I to L. <u>Nephelodes emmedonia</u> Cram., bronzed cutworm. F.g.l. 45 $\pm$ mm., has a light brown head with faint reticulations. Body color dark bronze-brown with five pale lines each about one-half as wide as the brown areas between them. Mid-dorsal line distinct throughout its length. The subdorsal light lines extend from the head through the anal plate. Immediately below the spiracles, which are located in the lower margin of the supraspiracular dark line, the lowest light line exists. Cervical shield bronze colored cut through with light lines. Skin smooth, not granulate. Spiracles black within. Sides of ventral prolegs brown. This northern species usually feeds near the ground but will climb fruit trees to feed on buds and leaves. Preferred foods are grasses, grain and corn. Crumb, 1926, Proc. Ent. Soc. Wash.

Figure I. Cephalic view of head.

Figure J. Mesal view of right mandible.

Figure K. Lateral view of head to mesothorax.

Figure L. Lateral view of fourth abdominal segment.

Note. For more information on cutworms see Whelan, 1935.

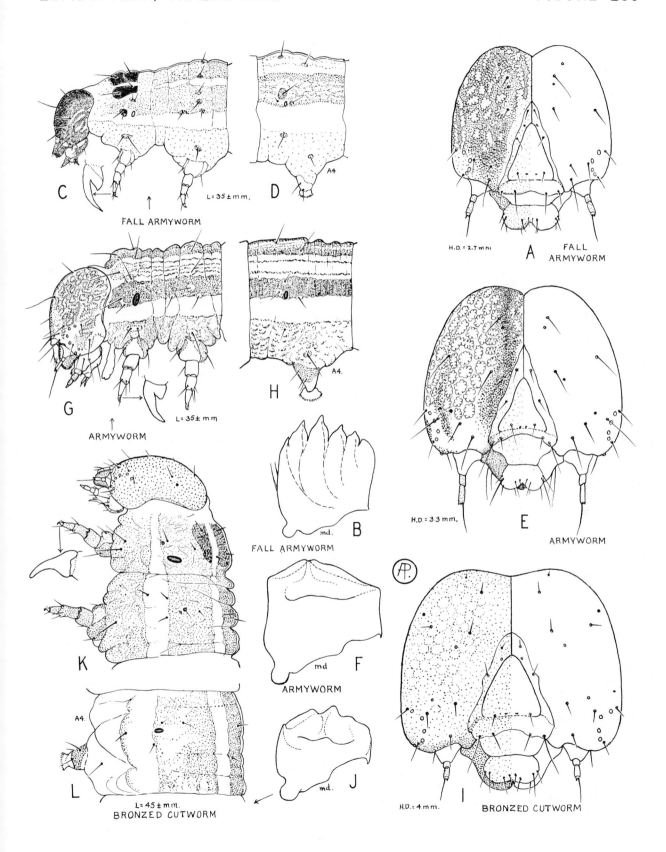

C FALL ARMYWORM L=35±mm. D A4

G ARMYWORM L=35±mm H A4.

B md. FALL ARMYWORM

K F md. ARMYWORM

L A4. J md. L=45±mm. BRONZED CUTWORM

A FALL ARMYWORM H.D.=2.7mm.

E ARMYWORM H.D.=3.3mm.

I BRONZED CUTWORM H.D.=4.mm.

P.

EXPLANATION OF FIGURES L36, A-P

PHALAENIDAE

Figures A to F. Heliothis virescens F., tobacco bud-worm. F.g.l. 35 ± mm., pale green to rust colored and marked with several pale longitudinal stripes. Head brown with faint pigmented spots. Cuticle, especially on the dorsal half, bears numerous slender microspines (L36, C and D). The prominent, pigmented tubercles (chalazae) of alpha (1) and beta (2) setae on abdominal segments 1, 2 and 8 are covered with tiny microspines similar to those found elsewhere on the cuticle. Near the center of the mesal (oral) aspect of the mandible (L36, F) a prominent tooth (retinaculum) occurs. Feeds in the buds or centers of unfolding leaves. Second generation larvae may attack the seed pods. Food plants are tobacco, cotton, ground cherry and other solanaceous plants, including Geranium and Ageratum.

Figure A. Lateral view of head to mesothorax.

Figure B. Lateral view of fourth abdominal segment.

Figure C. Pigmented area and distribution of microspines about the spiracle of fourth abdominal segment greatly enlarged.

Figure D. A small area bearing typical microspines greatly enlarged.

Figure E. Chalaza of setae alpha (1) of first abdominal segment greatly enlarged showing microspines.

Figure F. Mesal view of right mandible exhibiting a prominent, tooth-like projection (retinaculum) near the center of the oral surface.

Figures G to I. Heliothis virescens subflexa Gn., physalis fruit worm. F.g.l. 35 ± mm., greenish-yellow to dark brown. Head yellowish-brown with faint pigmented spots. Dark band above the spiracles due to pigment in the cuticle and the numerous, dark colored microspines. The prominent pigmented cone-shaped tubercles (chalazae), especially alpha (1) on segments 1, 2 and 8 of the abdomen, may possess a few microspines. Mandible possess a small bump near the center of the oral surface. Food plants are cultivated species of ground cherries or strawberry tomatoes especially the common Physalis pubescens, rarely on Physalis ixocarpa, (Col. H. E. Milliron).

Figure G. Pigmented area and distribution of microspines about the spiracle of fourth abdominal segment greatly enlarged.

Figure H. A small area bearing numerous, typical microspines greatly enlarged.

Figure I. Chalaza of setae alpha (1) of first abdominal segment greatly enlarged showing a small number of microspines on the cone-shaped tubercle.

Figure J. Mesal view of right mandible showing a small bump (not a prominent retinaculum) near the center of the oral surface.

Figures K tp P. Heliothis armigera Hbn., bollworm, corn earworm or tomato fruitworm. Also L6, E; L7, K. F.g.l. 35 ± mm., varies greatly in color from a light greenish-yellow or pink to deep brown or near black, especially on the dorsal aspect. Venter may be light green or flesh colored. Dark stripes on the dorsal aspect of the body are due, in part, to presence of numerous pigmented microspines only visible when seen through a lens. Prominent, pigmented tubercles (chalazae) of alpha (1) and beta (2) setae on abdominal segments 1, 2 and 8 are bare, without microspines. Head yellowish brown with faint markings. Mandibles possess no large tooth (retinaculum) on the mesal (oral) aspect. A general feeder attacking the foliage, stems, fruit or seed bearing portions of many plants, namely, corn, especially sweet corn, cowpeas, cotton, lima beans, tobacco, tomato, vetch and food plants. In greenhouses it may damage chrysanthemums and other flowers. Ditman and Cory, 1931; Garman and Jewett, 1914; Quaintance and Brues, 1905.

Figure K. Lateral view of head and mesothorax.

Figure L. Lateral view of fourth abdominal segment.

Figure M. Pigmented area and distribution of microspines about spiracle of fourth abdominal segment greatly enlarged.

Figure N. A small area bearing typical microspines greatly enlarged.

Figure O. Chalaza of seta alpha (1) of first abdominal segment greatly enlarged and without microspines.

Figure P. Mesal view of right mandible without a retinaculum.

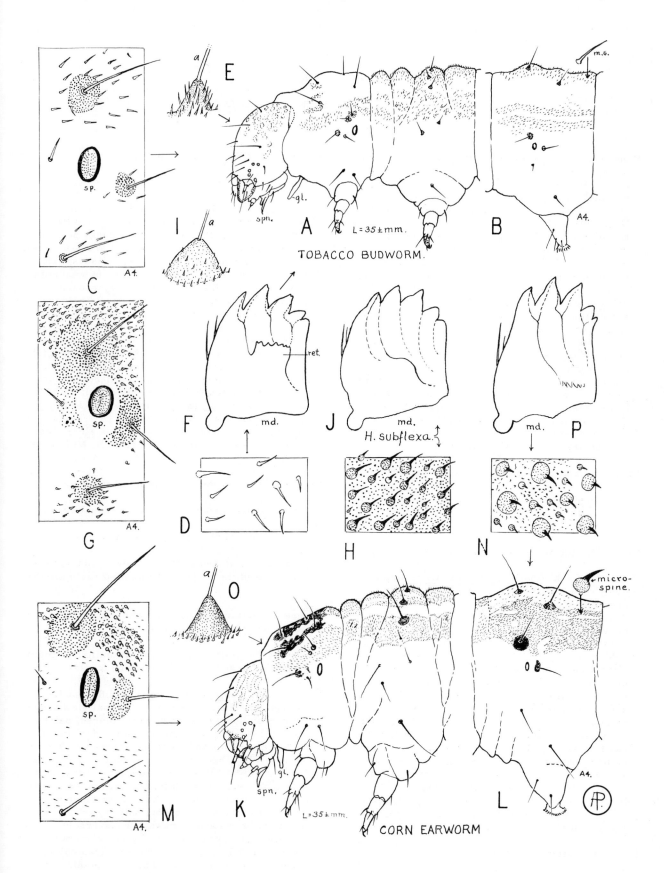

TOBACCO BUDWORM.

H. subflexa

CORN EARWORM

Figures A to D. Laphygma exigua Hbn., beet army-worn. F.g.l. 30-35 mm., possesses a brownish head with a number of near-white spots on the epicranium. Cervical shield smoky or green and cut by light lines. General color highly variable, light green, olivaceous to near black. Among extremely light or dark forms the following pigment distribution is obscure. Dorsum, between the light narrow, subdorsal lines, dotted and lined confusedly in green or near black, heaviest near pale dorso-mesal line. Area between subdorsal lines and the broad subspiracular greenish band is gray to black strongly dotted with near-white spots and frequently blotched in dull red. Bright near-white spots occur dorsad of the spiracles. Mesothorax possesses a prominent pigment spot on the spiracular line. Venter pale, mottled with white. Ventral prolegs green, thoracic legs brown. Food plants include numerous cultivated, garden and field crops and weeds. Some of these are Amaranth, asparagus, asparagus fern, beans, cotton, lettuce, onions, peas, peppers, potatoes, sugar beets, table beets, and tomatoes. J. W. Wilson, 1934.

Figure A. Lateral view of head to mesothorax.

Figure B. Lateral view of fourth abdominal segment.

Figure C. Cephalic view of head.

Figure D. Mesal view of right mandible.

Figures E to H. Chorizagrotis auxiliaris Grote, army cutworm. F.g.l. 25 ± mm. has a wide, light brown head covered with numerous groups of dark brown spots. Ocellar area dark brown. Pigmented cervical shield possesses dark brown spots and a light line on the dorsomeson. General color variable usually greenish gray to greenish brown with the dorsum pale mixed with white and without prominent marks. Two broad inconspicuous lighter subdorsal stripes may be seen. Area below spiracles near white. Cuticle very finely pavement granulose. Spiracles brown to black within. This spring species may travel in armies, climb and feed on the foliage or buds of many plants not cutting them off at ground level. The foot plants are chiefly grains, grasses and vegetables, namely, wheat, oats, barley and alfalfa among field crops. In gardens they may attack beet, cabbage, celery, corn, horseradish, onion, potato, rhubarb, strawberry, tomato, turnip and other plants.

Figure E. Lateral view of head to mesothorax.

Figure F. Lateral view of fourth abdominal segment.

Figure G. Cephalic view of head.

Figure H. Mesal view of right mandible.

Figures I to N. Heliothis ononis Schiff., flax boll-worm. F.g.l. 30 ± mm., has a light green head with lines of small circular near-black spots on the epicranium. General color dull green with two conspicuous longitudinal white or yellowish-white subdorsal and subspiracular stripes extending the entire length of the body. Narrow spiracular stripe light green and inconspicuous. The dark pigmented areas on the body are due to pigment in the cuticle and the numerous near black micro-spines (L37, L and M.). Compared with other species of Heliothis (L36, E, I and O) setae alpha (1) and beta (2) on abdominal segments 1, 2 and 8 are not located on cones (chalazae). It feeds almost exclusively on the fruit and seeds of cultivated flax, wild flax (Linum lewisii), cow cockle (Vaccaria vulgaris), purple milk-vetch (Astragalus goniatus) and sweet clover (Melilotus alba). Much of the above information taken from H. McDonald, 1947.

Figure I. Lateral view of head to mesothorax.

Figure J. Lateral view of fourth abdominal segment.

Figure K. Mesal view of right mandible.

Figure L. Pigmented area and distribution of micro-spines about the fourth abdominal spiracle greatly enlarged.

Figure M. A small portion of cuticle showing micro-spines and pigment greatly enlarged.

Figure N. Seta alpha (1) of first abdominal segment greatly enlarged exhibiting no cone (chalaza).

Figure O. Acronycta funeralis G. and R., paddle caterpillar. F.g.l. 25-30 mm., Dorsal view showing conspicuous, elongated, dark colored, paired, paddle-like structures (setae) on the dorsum of prothorax and all abdominal segments 1 to 9 except the seventh. Three pairs occur on the prothorax. The paddlelike setae arise from lateral margins of conspicuous, near-white, elliptical areas on the dorsum of each segment. Except for these near-white areas the entire dorsal half of each segment is a deep brown and somewhat transversely wrinkled. The ventral half of each segment is much lighter in color, yellowish to flesh color, except the pigmented pinacula. Food plants are deciduous trees, namely, apple, birch, elm, hickory and others.

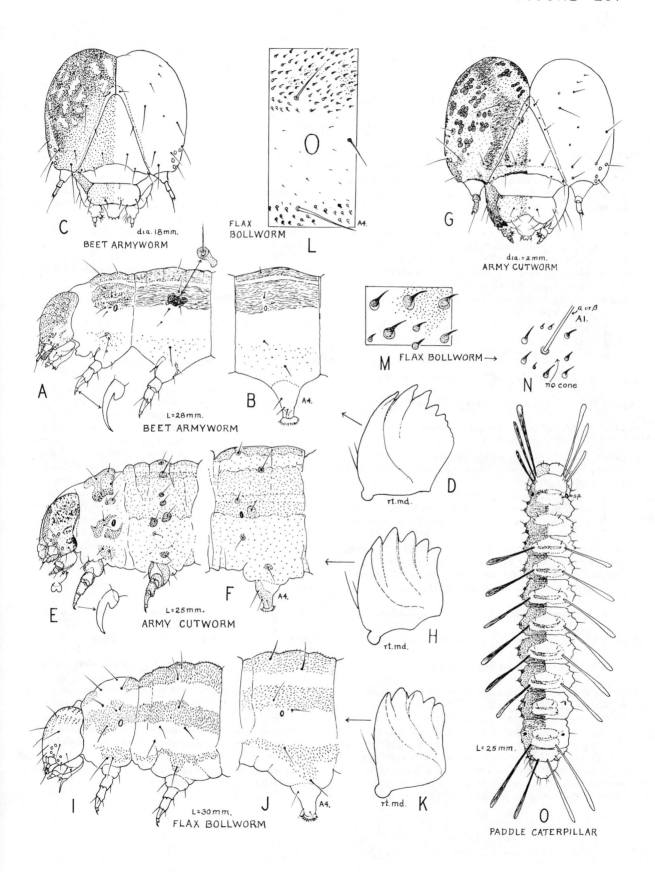

C
dia.18mm.
BEET ARMYWORM

FLAX BOLLWORM
O
A4.
L

G
dia.=2mm.
ARMY CUTWORM

A
L=28mm.
BEET ARMYWORM

B
A4.

M FLAX BOLLWORM →

N
a or β
A1.
no cone

D
rt.md.

E
F
A4.
L=25mm.
ARMY CUTWORM

H
rt.md.

I
J
A4.
L=30mm.
FLAX BOLLWORM

K
rt.md.

O
sp.
L=25mm.
PADDLE CATERPILLAR

EXPLANATION OF FIGURES L38, A-N

PHALAENIDAE

Figures A to C. Anticarsia gemmatilis Hbn., velvet-bean caterpillar. F.g.l. 35-38 mm. General body color variable, a dull green with near-white lines to olive brown. Head greenish yellow to orange. Cevical shield brown. Possesses bright colored, near-white, lines, one on the dorsomeson, two light lines above the spiracles and separated by a dark area and a distinct yellow to white, often pink to brown, broad spiracular band with a dark dorsal edge. Most setae conspicuous arising from pigmented pinacula. Feeds on foliage, often stripping plants. When disturbed it moves about violently. Food plants are chiefly legumes especially velvet beans (Stizolobium), horse beans (Canavoli), kudzu (Pueraria thunbergiana), soybeans and other plants such as locust sprouts and corn.

Figure A. Lateral view of head to mesothorax.

Figure B. Lateral view of fourth abdominal segment.

Figure C. Mesal view of right mandible.

Figures D to F. Macronoctua onusta Grote, iris borer, F.g.l. 45-50 mm., near-white to cream colored with a uniformly reddish-brown head. Faint to fairly conspicuous pigmented pinacula are associated with the setae, especially kappa (4). On the prothorax the Kappa group possesses one seta on an elevated pigmented pinaculum. All spiracles with black peritremes and a light center are elongated dorsoventrally especially those on the prothorax. A common borer in the roots and crowns of cultivated and wild iris and related plants.

Figure D. Lateral view of head to mesothorax.

Figure E. Lateral view of fourth abdominal segment.

Figure F. Mesal view of right mandible.

Figures G to J. Alabama argillacea Hbn., cotton leafworm, also L7, C. F.g.l. 35-40 mm. The last instar varies decidedly in color, light forms a bright yellow and dark forms a velvety black especially on the dorsal aspect. A narrow, light line occurs on the dorsomeson and on each side two light subdorsal lines and one light subspiracular broken line. The venter is light greenish yellow. Most of the setae on the body arise from dark colored pinacula which are very conspicuous in light forms. The head is yellow with several round dark spots on the epicranium. Ventral prolegs on abdominal segments 3 and 4 are subnormal in size. The food plant of this migrant larva is cotton foliage in the United States. The adults may feed on ripe fruit, especially peaches and grapes. Hinds, 1912.

Figure G. Lateral view of head to mesothorax.

Figure H. Lateral view of abdominal segments 3 to 5.

Figure I. Lateral view of abdominal segments 8 to 10.

Figure J. Mesal view of right mandible.

Figures K to M. Acronycta oblinita A. and S., smeared dagger moth, also L7, F; L8, B. F.g.l. 35-40 mm., has a black head and usually a velvety black body with yellow dots. Those along the subdorsal area coalesce more or less to form a broken subdorsal stripe. A broad, yellow, irregular stripe occurs along the spiracular line incised at each white spiracle. The verrucae are black and bear short bristly setae. Some light forms possess deep red verrucae and red areas in place of black. In such forms the yellow stripes are more conspicuous and continuous. It occurs in the early autumn on alder, buttonbush, poplar, willow and other deciduous trees.

Figure K. Lateral view of head to mesothorax.

Figure L. Lateral view of fourth abdominal segment.

Figure M. Mesal view of right mandible.

Figure N. Sudariophora acutalis Wlk., single filament looper. F.g.l. 30 $\pm$ mm., apparently is reddish brown in color with lighter stripes and patches as indicated. The most distinctive character is the two, single, fleshy, setaceous, prominent protuberances on the dorsomeson of the second and third abdominal segments. The entire larvae is covered with short secondary setae. Ventral prolegs are present on the fifth and sixth abdominal segments only. Collected in Florida.

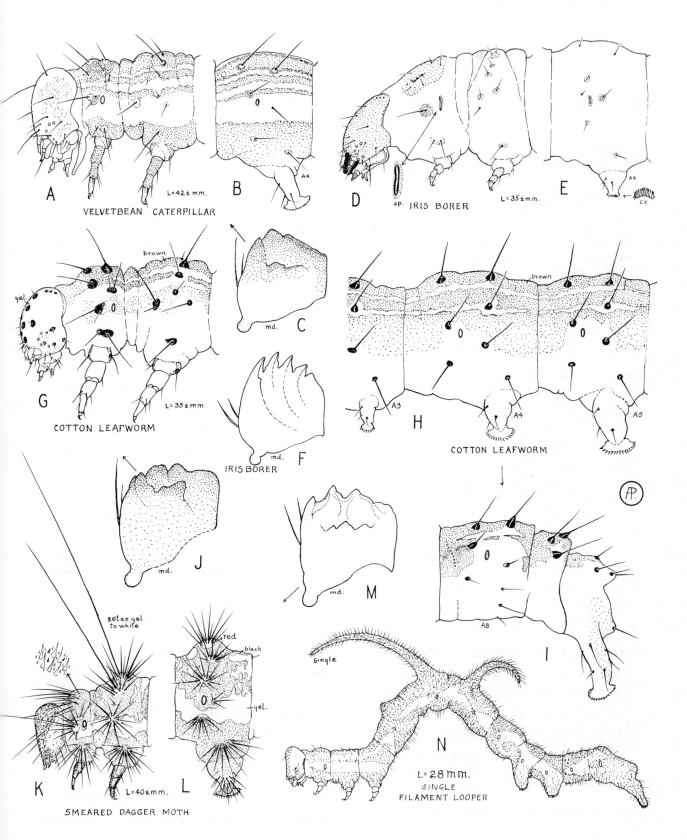

A VELVETBEAN CATERPILLAR L=42±mm.

B A4.

D sp. IRIS BORER L=35±mm.

E A4. c.r.

C md.

F IRIS BORER md.

G COTTON LEAFWORM L=35±mm. yel. brown

H COTTON LEAFWORM A3 A4 A5 brown 0

J md.

M md.

I A8

K setae yel. to white

L red black yel. L=40±mm.

SMEARED DAGGER MOTH

N single L=28mm. SINGLE FILAMENT LOOPER

EXPLANATION OF FIGURES L39, A-R

PHALAENIDAE

Figures A to C. <u>Scolecocampa liburna</u> Geyer, rotten-wood caterpillar. F.g.l. 45-50 mm., dirty white to cream colored possessing a brown head, cervical shield, anal plate and thoracic legs, long primary setae which arise from pigmented pinacula and black spiracles. The spiracles on the prothorax and eighth abdominal segment are much larger than the others. Ventral prolegs absent on third abdominal segment. The larva lives in moist, decayed, fallen logs.

Figure A. Lateral view of larva.

Figure B. Mesal view of right mandible.

Figure C. An enlarged eighth abdominal spiracle.

Figures D to G. <u>Trichoplusia ni</u> Hbn. (<u>Autographa brassicae</u> Riley), cabbage looper, F.g.l. 35-40 mm., grass green with a white, spiracular stripe and two, light, colored lines adjacent to the dorso-meson. Functional, ventral prolegs occur on the fifth and sixth abdominal segments. Feeds on cruciferous plants especially cabbage, cauliflower, kale and turnips. May also injure asparagus, beet, dandelion, dock, lettuce, pea, parsley, potato, tomato plants outdoors and carnation, mignonette and others in greenhouses.

Figure D. Lateral view of larva.

Figure E. Lateral view of head to mesothorax.

Figure F. Lateral view of fourth and fifth abdominal segments.

Figure G. Mesal view of right mandible.

Figures H to J. <u>Autographa oo</u>, a spotted cabbage looper, F.g.l. 35 ± mm., resembles closely the cabbage looper. It differs from this species in that dark pigmented pinacula may be present about many of the primary setae especially on the thorax and setae rho (3) on the abdominal segments. Black pigment occurs on the head (spots) and thoracic legs. The mesal (oral) surface of the mandible exhibits two secondary teeth on the ridges below dentes two and three. The food plants of this species are cruciferous crops.

Figure H. Lateral view of head to mesothorax.

Figure I. Lateral view of fourth and fifth abdominal segments.

Figure J. Mesal view of right mandible.

Figures K to M. <u>Plathypena scabra</u> F., green clover-worm, F.g.l. 20-25 mm., slender and uniformly pale green. The last instar of this semi-looper does not possess the fine, white to cream-colored longitudinal lines of the previous instar. Ventral prolegs occur on segments 4 to 6. Feeds chiefly on foliage of legumes, especially clover, however, it will occasionally defoliate peas, beans, lima beans, soybeans and vetch. Also attacks tickweed and strawberries. Hill, 1925.

Figure K. Lateral view of head to mesothorax.

Figure L. Lateral view of third and fourth abdominal segments.

Figure M. Mesal view of right mandible.

Figures N to P. <u>Ceramica picta</u> Harris., zebra caterpillar, F.g.l. 35-40 mm., velvety black with two, irregular, longitudinal, bright yellow stripes (subdorsal, and subspiracular) on each lateral aspect. Between these stripes narrow fine lines of the same color extend dorsoventrally especially on most of the abdominal segments. The head is orange and the thoracic and ventral prolegs yellowish. The larvae feed on garden crops, many flowers and weeds, especially in the late summer. Some of these are cabbage, gladioli, lilies, sweet peas and smartweed.

Figure N. Lateral view of head to mesothorax.

Figure O. Lateral view of fourth abdominal segment.

Figure P. Mesal view of right mandible.

Figures Q and R. <u>Catocala mira</u> Grt., a catocala caterpillar. F.g.l. 35 ± mm. A gray larva with a lined, pigmented head, numerous, small, fleshy forked projections on the venter and a conspicuous dorsal hump on the fifth abdominal segment. Taken from woodland foliage.

Figure Q. Lateral view of head to mesothorax.

Figure R. Lateral view of fifth abdominal segment.

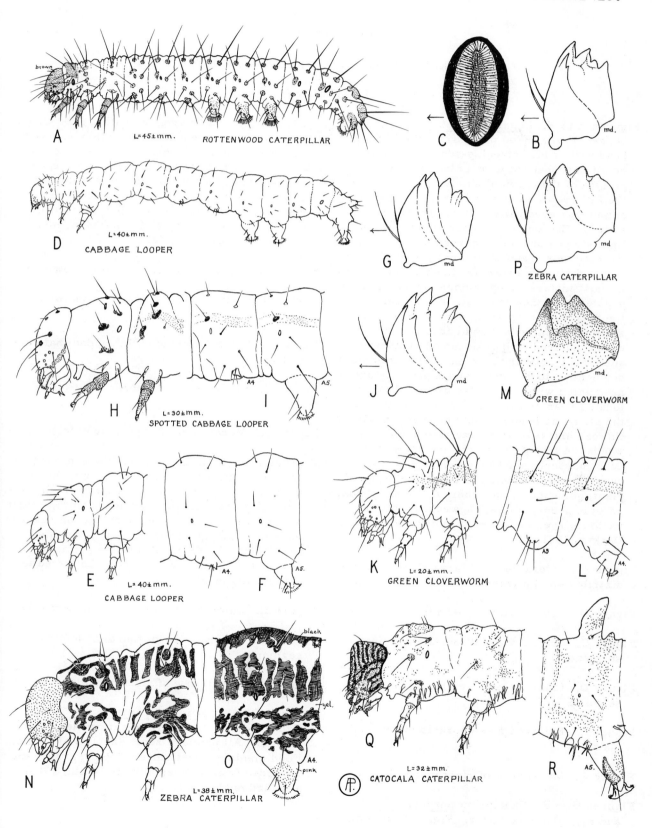

L=45±mm. ROTTENWOOD CATERPILLAR

A

B   md.

C

L=40±mm.
D   CABBAGE LOOPER

G   md.

P   ZEBRA CATERPILLAR   md

L=30±mm.
H   SPOTTED CABBAGE LOOPER   A4   A5.
I

J   md

M   GREEN CLOVERWORM   md.

L=40±mm.
E   CABBAGE LOOPER   A4.   A5.
F

L=20±mm.
K   GREEN CLOVERWORM   A3   A4.
L

black
N   O   yel.   A4.   pink

L=38±mm.
ZEBRA CATERPILLAR

Q   L=32±mm.   CATOCALA CATERPILLAR   R   A5.

LEPIDOPTERA

EXPLANATION OF FIGURES L40, A-P

PHALAENIDAE

Figures A to F. Papaipema nebris Guen., stalk borer. F.g.l. 35-40 mm., has a light brown head with a dark streak extending from the ocelli dorsocaudad to and along the ventral margin of the cervical shield. Except among the full grown larva this streak may continue and merge eventually with the spiracular stripe. The longitudinal areas between the light stripes and the mid-region, especially the metathorax and abdominal segments 1 to 3, are distinctly brown (reddish or purplish) in most instars except among larvae ready to pupate, when they are lost. A mid-dorsal light stripe occurs along dorsomeson of all segments. Subdorsal and subspiracular cream colored stripes occur on prothorax and mesothorax and also on caudal abdominal segments 4 to 9. Conspicuous pinacula are associated with most setae especially those located near spiracles. A common borer in the stems or tender shoots of many cultivated flowers and vegetables and also numerous weeds. A few of the plants are aster, barley, bean, burdock, blackberry, castor beans, currant, chrysanthemum, corn, dahlia, eggplant, goldenglow, gooseberry, lily hollyhock, pepper, peony, potato, ragweed, raspberry, rhubarb, rye, sunflower, timothy and tomato. Decker, 1931.

Figure A. Lateral view of larva showing usual distribution of pigment.

Figure B. Lateral view of head to mesothorax.

Figure C. Lateral view of fourth abdominal segment.

Figure D. Lateral view of eighth abdominal segment.

Figure E. Enlarged mesothoracic tarsus and claw.

Figure F. Mesal view of right mandible.

Figures G to K. Papaipema purpurifascia G. and R., columbine borer. F.g.l. 35-40 mm.,

salmon colored or brighter with a pale stripe along the dorsomeson. Head yellowish-brown cervical shield yellowish with a dark ventral margin. Anal plate and the pinacula, especially those adjacent to spiracles and on dorsomeson of eighth and ninth segments are deeply pigmented. A common borer in wild and cultivated varieties of columbine, Aquilegia sp. Matthewman, 1937.

Figure G. Lateral view of head to mesothorax.

Figure H. Lateral view of fourth abdominal segment.

Figure I. Lateral view of eighth abdominal segment.

Figure J. Englarged mesothoracic tarsus and claw.

Figure K. Mesal view of right mandible.

Figures L to M. Epizeuxis aemula Hbn. a dry pea hay caterpillar. F.g.l. 25 $\pm$ mm., has a light colored head with numerous reticulations, a light colored, spotted cervical shield, a light brownish streak along the dorsomeson between the subdorsal lighter areas, and pigmented small pinacula about most of the primary setae. It feeds on dry pea hay. Collected in North Carolina.

Figure L. Lateral view of head to mesothorax.

Figure M. Lateral view of fourth abdominal segment.

Figure N. Mesal view of right mandible.

Figures O to P. Epizeuxis americalis Guen. Probably a partially grown caterpillar found in Ohio. All primary setae knobbed at apicies. Food plants - sweet clover, "Hedysarum" and recorded from ant nests (J. B. Smith, 1909) and bird nests.

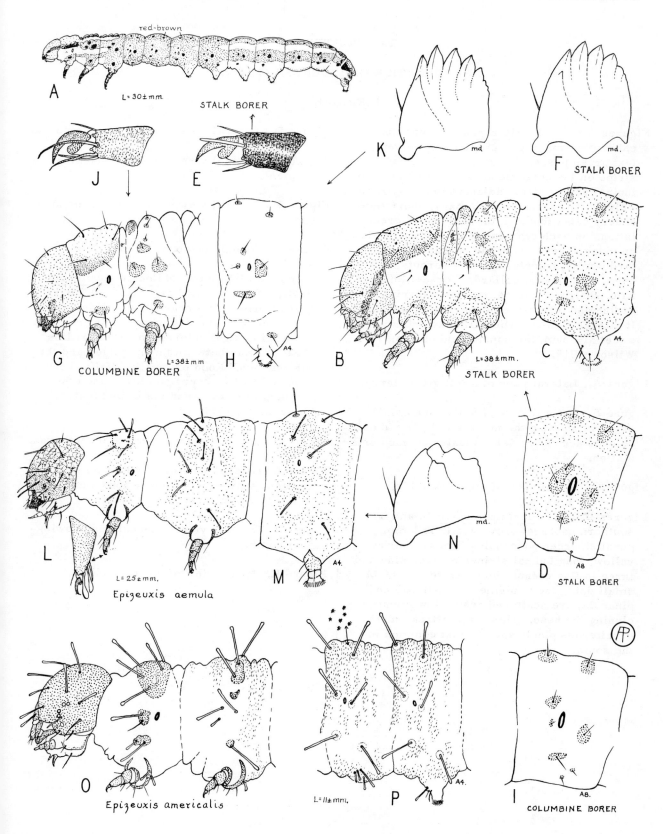

red-brown

A   L=30±mm.

STALK BORER

J

E

K   md.

F   STALK BORER

G   COLUMBINE BORER   L=38±mm

H   A4.

B   L=38±mm.

C   A4.   STALK BORER

L   L=25±mm.   Epizeuxis aemula

M   A4.

N   md.

D   A8   STALK BORER

O   Epizeuxis americalis

P   L=11±mm.   A4.

I   A8   COLUMBINE BORER

LEPIDOPTERA

EXPLANATION OF FIGURES L41, A-K

PIERIDAE

Figures A to C. Pieris rapae L., imported cabbageworm. F.g.l. 25-30 mm., velvety, leaf green possessing a narrow, yellowish stripe on the dorsomeson and a broken longitudinal yellow stripe adjacent to the spiracles. Velvety appearance due to many, short secondary setae found on the four to six crenulations on each segment of the body. Feeds on many vegetables of the cabbage or mustard family, namely, Brussel sprouts, cabbage, cauliflower, collards, horse-radish, kale, kohlrabi, lettuce, mustard, turnips, radish and others including related weeds. It attacks flowers especially nasturtiums, sweet alyssum, mignonette and others. H. F. Wilson, 1919.

Figure A. Lateral view of a full grown larva.

Figure B. Lateral view of fourth abdominal segment showing the numerous light and dark colored secondary setae located on each crenulation.

Figure C. Mesal view of right mandible.

Figures D to G. Pieris protodice B. and L., southern cabbageworm. F.g.l. 30 ± mm., purplish green possessing two, greenish-yellow, longitudinal stripes on each side and three to five crenulations per segment. Many small dots, due to pigmented chalazae and pinacula, are scattered over all segments including the head. This larva attacks many cruciferous plants and is most common in the south.

Figure D. Lateral view of head to mesothorax.

Figure E. Lateral view of fourth abdominal segment.

Figure F. Ventral view of caudal end, no anal comb.

Figure G. Mesal view of right mandible.

Figures H to K. Colias philodice eurytheme Bdvl., alfalfa caterpillar. F.g.l. 30 ± dark green worm with a near white spiracular stripe on each side including a faint red line and a faint, light colored, longitudinal line about halfway between the spiracles and the dorsomeson. Food primarily alfalfa, however, it occasionally occurs on clover and other legumes in Canada and the United States. Wildermuth, 1911.

Figure H. Lateral view of head to mesothorax.

Figure I. Lateral view of fourth abdominal segment showing six crenulations and numerous dark colored secondary setae.

Figure J. Ventral view of caudal end showing anal comb.

Figure K. Mesal view of right mandible.

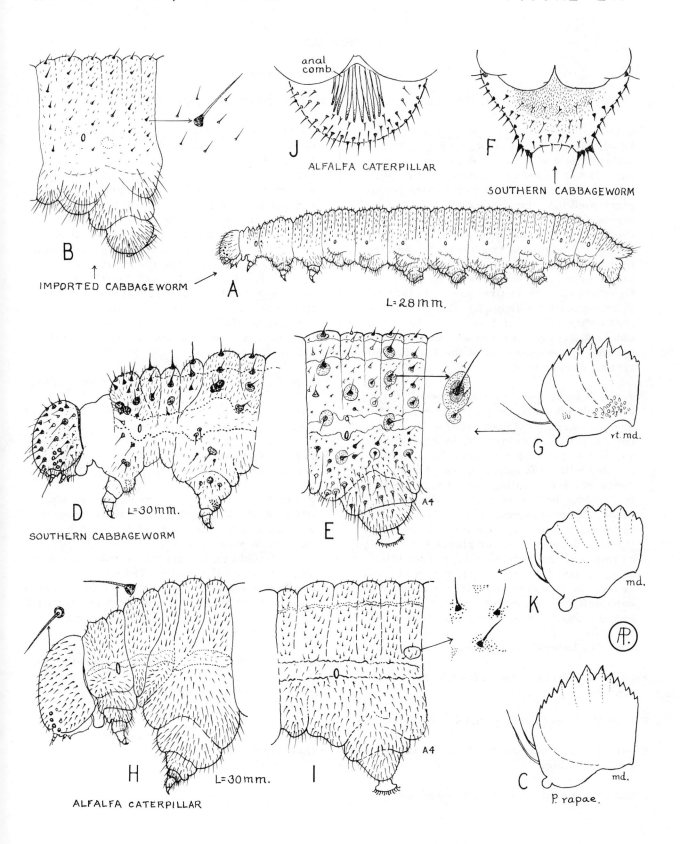

J
anal comb
ALFALFA CATERPILLAR

F
SOUTHERN CABBAGEWORM

B
IMPORTED CABBAGEWORM

A
L=28mm.

D
SOUTHERN CABBAGEWORM
L=30mm.

E
A4

G
rt. md.

K
md.

H
ALFALFA CATERPILLAR
L=30mm.

I
A4

C
P. rapae.
md.

EXPLANATION OF FIGURES L42, A-L

PSYCHIDAE A, PLUTELLIDAE B-F, YPONOMEUTIDAE G-I, THYATIRIDAE J-L

Figure A. <u>Thyridopteryx</u> <u>ephemeraeformis</u> Haw., bagworm. Also L6, I. F.g.l. 30 ± mm. Lateral view of a larva (♀) removed from its bag. It has a general dirty-white to light brown color with cephalic end more deeply pigmented than the abdomen. Dark brown pigment areas and spots are scattered over the head, thorax and anal plate. Cuticle of abdominal segments transversely and irregularly wrinkled. Long axis of spiracle on the prothorax is parallel with the dorsum. Crochets on each ventral proleg uniordinal, lateral penellipse (Fig. L3, H.). Bagworms feed on the foliage of a wide variety of deciduous and evergreen trees and shrubs. This species is common east of the Mississippi river. Baerg, 1928.

Figures B to F. <u>Plutella</u> <u>maculipennis</u> Curt., diamondback moth. F.g.l. 9 ± mm., pale green or cream colored with fairly conspicuous erect, dark colored setae on all of the segments including the head. Head yellowish mottled with dark brown spots. Feeds on the under surface of foliage or as a miner in the leaf producing foliage riddled with small holes. When disturbed on the plants the larva drops and suspends itself by a silken thread. Some of the food plants are cabbage, cauliflower, brussel sprouts, horseradish, kale, mustard, radish, rope, turnip and water cress. In the greenhouse it may also attack candytuft, stocks, sweet alyssum, wall flowers and other flowering plants. Marsh, 1917.

Figure B. Lateral view of head to mesothorax.

Figure C. Lateral view of fourth abdominal segment.

Figure D. Dorsal view of head and prothorax.

Figure E. Crochets on third abdominal, right, ventral proleg.

Figure F. Mesal view of right mandible.

Figures G to I. <u>Atteva</u> <u>aurea</u> Fitch, ailanthus webworm. Also L6, A; L7, L; L8, N, O. F.g.l. 25-28 mm., slender reddish to olive brown with long, light colored, primary setae arising from near-white pinacula. A fairly conspicuous, dark stripe bordered by white specks occurs above the spiracles and a lighter area below. Head, prothorax and true legs deeply pigmented. Ventral prolegs exhibit a multiserial or scattered distribution of crochets. The food plant is the Asiatic tree of heaven, <u>Ailanthus</u>. The gregarious larvae live within a thin silken web which encloses some of the foliage. It is most abundant in the south, not so common in Ohio or northern states.

Figure G. Lateral view of head to metathorax.

Figure H. Lateral view of fourth abdominal segment.

Figure I. Crochets on fourth abdominal, right, ventral proleg scattered.

Figures J to K. <u>Euthyatira</u> prob. <u>pudens</u> Gn. Also L8, A. F.g.l. 20 ± mm., light colored with the dorsal half more deeply pigmented than the venter possessing two distinct pigmented spots on the dorsal aspect of the head and also about the ocelli. The caterpillar resembles a sawfly larva in that the body tapers from a large thoracic region to a much smaller caudal end. The food plant is dogwood, species of Cornus.

Figure J. Lateral view of head to mesothorax.

Figure K. Lateral view of fourth abdominal segment.

Figure L. Crochets and setae of fourth abdominal, right, ventral proleg.

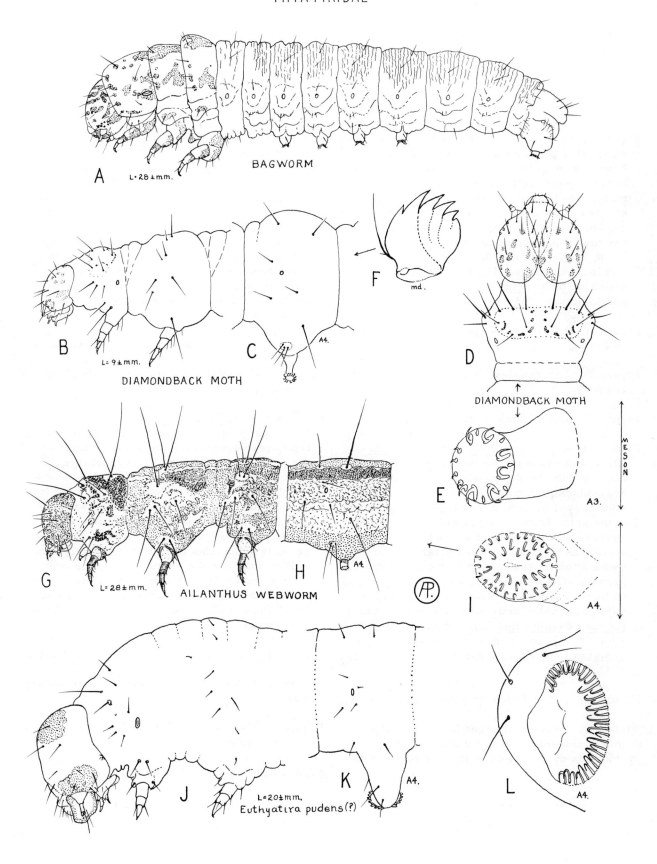

A   BAGWORM   L·28±mm.

B   DIAMONDBACK MOTH   L=9±mm.

C   A4.

D   DIAMONDBACK MOTH

E   A3.   MESON

F   md.

G   L=28±mm.   AILANTHUS WEBWORM

H   A4.

I   A4.

J   L=20±mm.   Euthyatira pudens(?)

K   A4.

L   A4.

LEPIDOPTERA

EXPLANATION OF FIGURES L43, A-K

PTEROPHORIDAE

Figures A to C. Oidaematophorus grandis Fish. F.g.l. 20 ± mm., creamy white with reddish-brown or purplish markings; lateral oblique, brownish-red dash on each abdominal segment; head large, brown, glossy with a darker area about ocelli; cervical shield reddish-brown; two short prongs (urogomphilike) on the caudal portion of the conspicuous, sclerotized, dorsal area of the ninth and tenth abdominal segments. The larvae are found in stems of Baccharis pilularis, a subtropical plant. Lange, 1939.

Figure A. Lateral view of prothorax and mesothorax.

Figure B. Lateral view of fourth abdominal segment.

Figure C. Dorsal view of caudal end.

Figures D and E. Platyptilia carduidactyla Riley, artichoke plume moth. F.g.l. 12 ± mm., yellowish to pinkish yellow possessing near-black pigment on the head, cervical shield, anal plate and true legs. All primary setae arise from dark pinacula. Entire body covered with short, fine secondary setae only visible under a lens. Feed externally or internally on most any part of the plant above ground. The most important injury is on and in floral heads. The food plants are cultivated artichoke, artichoke thistle or cardoon (Cynara cardunculus L.), indian thistle (C. edule Nutt.), common or bull thistle (C. lanceolatum) and related species. Lange 1941, 1942.

Figure D. Lateral view of head and prothorax.

Figure E. Greatly enlarged area about the fourth abdominal spiracle showing the distribution of the primary and secondary setae.

Figures F and G. Platyptilia antirrhina Lange, snapdragon plume moth. F.g.l. 10 ± mm., green or purplish including the head and all legs; two interrupted subdorsal lines and spiracular line whitish in last instar; no secondary setae present; primary setae whitish and arise from pigmented swollen pinacula and some of the setae have swollen apices. Early instars are leaf miners while later instars bore inside the stems or green seed-pods or feed on the flowers. Pests of snapdragons, especially in greenhouses. Lange 1939, 1942.

Figure F. Lateral view of head to metathorax.

Figure G. Lateral view of fourth abdominal segment.

Figures H to K. Pterophorus periscelidactylus Fitch, grape plume moth. F.g.l. 12-15 mm., light, yellowish-green possessing three or more pairs of verrucae per segment, each giving rise to six to eight light colored setae which may be slightly swollen at their apices. Numerous, short, secondary setae with enlarged apices are present on all segments. Ventral prolegs long and slender. Attacks growing grape shoots in May and early June, pulling together the edges of one or more leaves and feeds on the foliage within the webbed mass. One generation per season. Food plants cultivated grapes. Whitcomb and Tomlinson, 1940.

Figure H. Lateral view of head to metathorax.

Figure I. Lateral view of fourth abdominal segment.

Figure J. Crochets of sixth abdominal, right, ventral proleg.

Figure K. Crochets of right anal proleg.

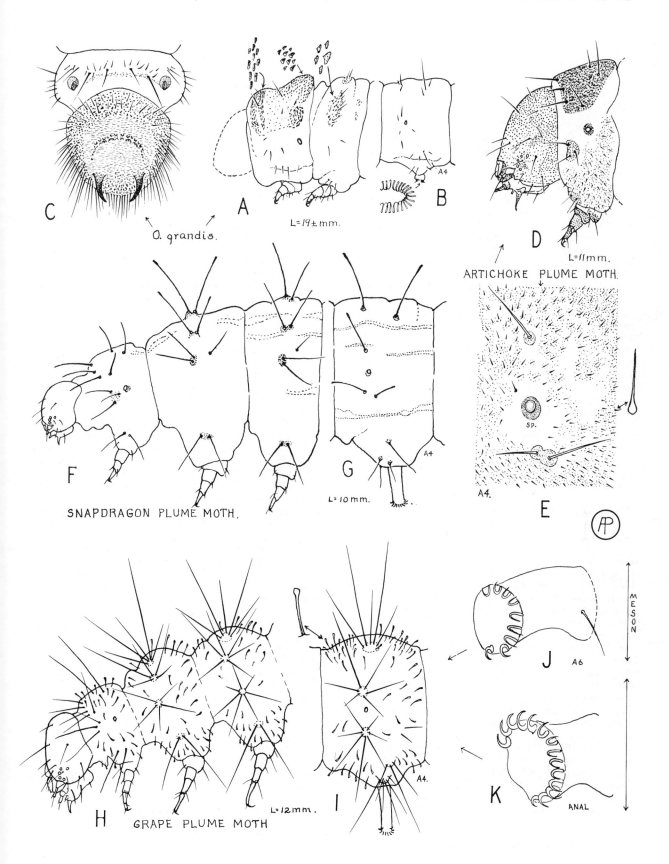

C

A   L=19±mm.

B   A4

O. grandis.

D   L=11mm.

ARTICHOKE PLUME MOTH.

F

SNAPDRAGON PLUME MOTH.

G   A4   L=10mm.

E   A4.   sp.

H   GRAPE PLUME MOTH

I   A4.   L=12mm.

J   A6   MESON

K   ANAL

EXPLANATION OF FIGURES L44, A-P

PYRALIDAE, CRAMBINAE

Figures A to D. Diatraea saccharalis F., sugarcane borer. F.g.l. 26 ± mm. Summer form possesses a rich brown head merging to black at the mouth parts, broad stocky mandibles each with four sharp and two rounded dentes plus a short sharp point at the base of the first tooth, setae SO^2 equally distant from fifth and sixth ocelli, cervical shield pale brown tinged with black ventrally, body white, pinacula and setae light brown, pinacula of seta alpha (1) on most abdominal segments large, conspicuous and very close together, lines passing through setae alpha (1) and beta (2) on most abdominal segments meet on the meson at a sharp angle (30° ±) outside bounds of the segment, alpha on ninth abdominal segment discernable and spiracles dark brown. Winter form differs from the summer form chiefly in almost complete loss of pigmentation, especially on cervical shield and pinacula, the head and spiracles retaining nearly the same amount of pigment. F.g.l. approximates 22 ± mm. The food plants are sugar cane, rice, corn, broom corn, Kafir corn, sorghum, Sudan grass, feather grass, vetiver, Panicum species and related plants. Holloway et al, 1928.

Figure A. Lateral view of head to mesothorax, summer form.

Figure B. Dorsal view of second abdominal segment, summer form.

Figure C. Cephalic view of head, summer form.

Figure D. Mesal view of right mandible.

Figure E to H. Diatraea crambidoides Grote, (D. zeacolella Dyar), southern cornstalk borer. F.g.l. 25 ± mm. Summer form possesses a yellow to brown head varying to black near the mouth parts, seta SO^2 usually equally distant from fifth and sixth ocelli or closer to fifth ocellus, mandibles broad, stocky each with four sharp dentes and a serrated cutting edge, cervical shield pale yellow, body dirty white, pinacula dark brown to near-black, pinacula of seta alpha (1) on abdomen conspicuous and further apart than one-half the greatest diameter of either pinaculum, lines drawn through setae alpha (1) and setae beta (2) on most abdominal segments meet on the meson at an acute angle (60° ±) usually within the bounds of the segment, pinacula of setae alpha (1) of ninth segment not discernible. Winter form more robust and pigmented areas exclusive of head much paler and not easily distinguished from ground color. The borers infest primarily leaves and stalks of corn. Also occur in sorghum, sugarcane, gama, grass, Johnson grass and related plants. Holloway, 1916; Leiby, 1920.

Figure E. Lateral view of head to mesothorax, summer form.

Figure F. Dorsal view of second abdominal segment, summer form.

Figure G. Position of setae about ocelli, especially SO^2.

Figure H. Mesal view of right mandible.

Figures I to P. Diatraea grandiosella Dyar, southwestern corn borer. F.g.l. 25 ± mm. Summer form borer sordid white with strongly sclerotized blackish-brown pinacula (pale, smoky or yellowish in winter forms), cervical shield broad, divided, pale yellow to brown with a transverse row of fuscous reticulations near anterior margin and a cluster on each side, a narrow, pigmented, shield on mesothorax caudad of alpha (1a) and beta (1b) bearing no setae, anal plate yellow with scattered fuscous reticulations, primary setae moderately long and yellowish to brown, Kappa pinaculum of prothorax, narrow, horizontal, bearing 2 setae, and ninth abdominal segment with six distinguishable setae on each side. Spiracles dark brown. Prothoracic spiracle twice size of those on segments 1 to 7. Spiracles on eighth segment larger than prothoracic spiracle and somewhat dorsad of others. Head yellow to yellowish-brown with distinct brownish reticulations. Setae SO^2 usually closer to sixth ocellus than to fifth. Mandibles with four distinct teeth and a rounded serrate cutting edge. Pinacula of setae alpha (1) on most abdominal segments about as far apart as one half the lateromesal length of each pinaculum, also lines drawn through setae alpha (1) and beta (2) on each side will meet on the meson outside the area of the segment on which they are located. Infests all portions of a corn plant. Also attacks broom corn, most grain sorghums, sugar cane and Johnson grass. Hibernates in corn stubble near ground level. Found in portions of Arizona, New Mexico, Texas, Oklahoma and Kansas. Davis et al, 1933.

Figure I. Lateral view of head to mesothorax, summer form.

Figure J. Lateral view of fourth abdominal segment, summer form.

Figure K. Lateral view of head to mesothorax, winter form.

Figure L. Lateral view of fourth abdominal segment, winter form.

Figure M. Dorsal view of second abdominal segment, summer form.

Figure N. Cephalic view of head, summer form.

Figure O. Mesal view of right mandible.

Figure P. Position of setae about ocelli, especially SO^2.

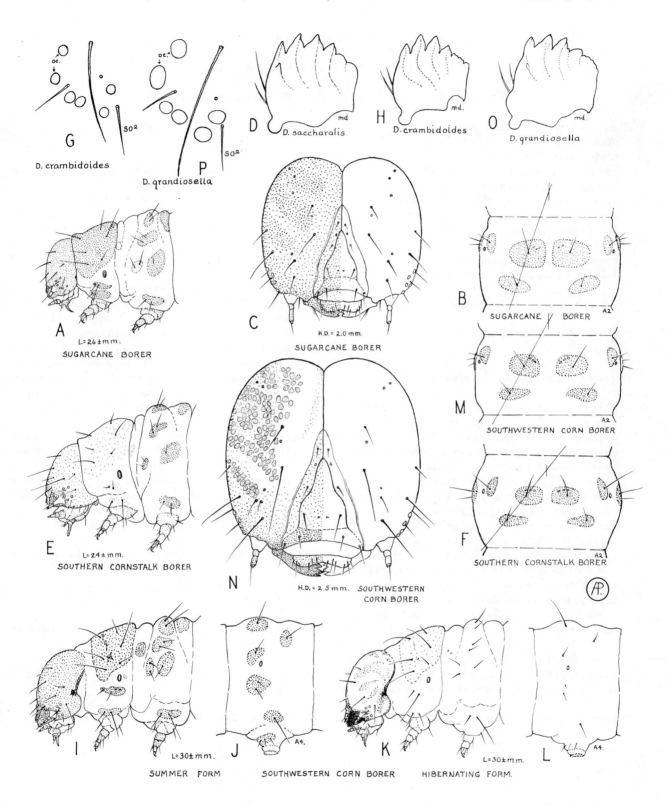

G
D. crambidoides

P
D. grandiosella

D
D. saccharalis

H
D. crambidoides

O
D. grandiosella

A
L=26±mm.
SUGARCANE BORER

C
H.D.=2.0 mm.
SUGARCANE BORER

B
SUGARCANE BORER

E
L=24±mm.
SOUTHERN CORNSTALK BORER

N
H.D.=2.5 mm.   SOUTHWESTERN CORN BORER

M
SOUTHWESTERN CORN BORER

F
SOUTHERN CORNSTALK BORER

I
L=30±mm.
SUMMER FORM

J
SOUTHWESTERN CORN BORER

K
L=30±mm.
HIBERNATING FORM.

L

EXPLANATION OF FIGURES L45, A-M

PYRALIDAE, EPIPASCHIINAE A-E, GALLERIINAE D-M

Figures A to C. Tetralopha robustella Zell., pine webworm. F.g.l. 13-16 mm., (alcoholic material) a very light brown with darker sub-dorsal and superspiracular stripes extending from the prothorax to the ninth abdominal segment inclusive. Head light brown with near-black, conspicuous, pigment areas on the dorsal and caudal portions. Larvae attack the terminal branches of pines producing brown masses or balls of silk and frass 1 to 3 inches long and 1 to 2 inches thick.

Figure A. Lateral view of head to mesothorax.

Figure B. Lateral view of fourth abdominal segment.

Figure C. Mesal view of right mandible.

Figures D to H. Achroia grisella F. lesser wax moth. F.g.l. 15-18 mm., slender, white to pale grayish-white except brown head and darker mouth parts, brown cervical shield, near-black spiracles, and pale yellowish-brown setae, true legs and crochets. Ocelli absent. Black peritremes of spiracles thicker on caudal aspects. Crochets numerous and partly triordinal. Kappa group setae of prothorax on a line ventrad (or nearly so) of spiracles, also kappa (4) and eta (5) setae of abdominal segments 1 to 8 in a vertical position. Mandibles with a prominent, rounded, thin, protuberance immediately distad of condyle. Larvae found in wild and commercial honey bee hives, especially in the trash on the bottom board, not so often in the combs of the apiary or in storage. Also reared from dried apples, raisins, crude sugar and dried insects. Forbes, 1923; Hinton, 1943.

Figure D. Lateral view of head to mesothorax.

Figure E. Lateral view of fourth abdominal segment.

Figure F. Crochets and setae of sixth abdominal, right, ventral proleg.

Figure G. Crochets and setae of right anal proleg.

Figure H. Mesal view of right mandible.

Figures I to M. Galleria mellonella L. wax moth. Also L7, B. F.g.l. 23-28 mm., stout, pale yellowish to grayish brown except the brown head, dark mouth parts, yellowish-brown cervical shield and pale yellowish spiracles, suranal plate, true legs and crochets. Possesses four pairs of ocelli (1 and 2 combined), yellowish spiracular peritremes of uniform thickness, crochets few in number and partially biordinal, Kappa group setae of prothorax on a line dorsad of spiracle, kappa (4) and eta (5) setae of abdominal segments 1 to 8 in an oblique position and mandible stout without a conspicuous thin protuberance immediately distad of condyle. Larvae found in wild and commercial honey bee combs in the apiary or in storage. Hinton, 1943.

Figure I. Lateral view of head to mesothorax.

Figure J. Lateral view of fourth abdominal segment.

Figure K. Crochets and setae of sixth abdominal, right, ventral proleg.

Figure L. Crochets and setae of right anal proleg.

Figure M. Mesal view of right mandible.

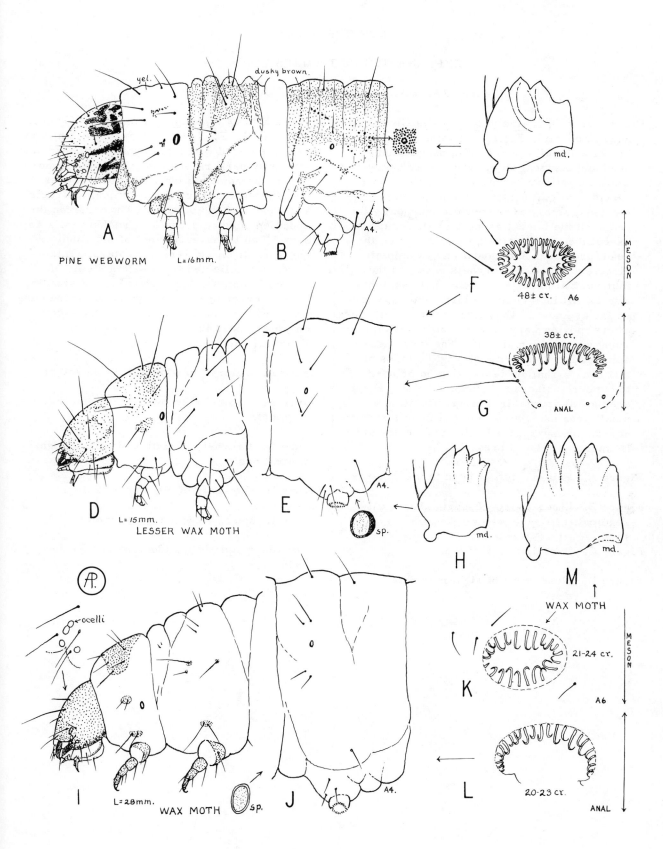

PINE WEBWORM   L=16mm.

LESSER WAX MOTH   L=15mm.

WAX MOTH   L=28mm.

LEPIDOPTERA

EXPLANATION OF FIGURES L46, A-I

PYRALIDAE, NYMPHULINAE, AQUATIC

Figures A to D. Catoclysta fulicalis Clem., an aquatic pyralid. F.g.l. 12 $\pm$ mm., greyish to brown with yellowish-brown, prognathous head and cervical shield which may be near-white or yellowish-brown. Spiracles absent except vestigial scars on the abdomen. Filementous, smoky to near-white tracheal gills occur on the lateral aspects of all segments except the head. Setae absent except on the head, prothorax and caudal end. Complete circles of biordinal crochets occur on the four ventral prolegs of abdominal segments 2 to 6. All instars of the larva are aquatic so far as known. They live on stones or rocks where moving water occurs, riffles, rapids or along wave beaten shores. The larva usually spins and lives under a sheet-like mass of silk over a shallow depression on or near the under surface of a stone. The silk sheet over a full grown larva is restricted to a small area usually not more than 15 mm. across and surrounded with small holes about its margin. Lloyd, 1914.

Figure A. Lateral view of head to mesothorax.

Figure B. Lateral view of fourth abdominal segment.

Figure C. Dorsal view of larva.

Figure D. Mesal view of right mandible.

Figures E to I. Nymphula prob. gyralis Hbst. Also L6, G. F.g.l. 10-12 mm., dirty white to cream colored with a pale yellowish head and a slightly darker cervical shield. Setae occur on the head and thorax but are almost completely absent on the abdomen. Spiracles are absent on the prothorax but occur on the abdomen, segments 1 to 8. Tracheal gills absent. Two transverse rows of biordinal crochets occur on the ventral prolegs. This larva was collected from within stems of cat-tails plants below the surface of standing water. Other species of Nymphula possessing numerous tracheal gills have been collected on water cress in cold spring water in Franklin County, Ohio.

Figure E. Lateral view of head to mesothorax.

Figure F. Lateral view of fourth abdominal segment.

Figure G. Crochets of sixth abdominal, right, ventral proleg.

Figure H. Crochets of right anal proleg.

Figure I. Mesal view of right mandible.

For other aquatic Lepidoptera see Frohne, 1939.

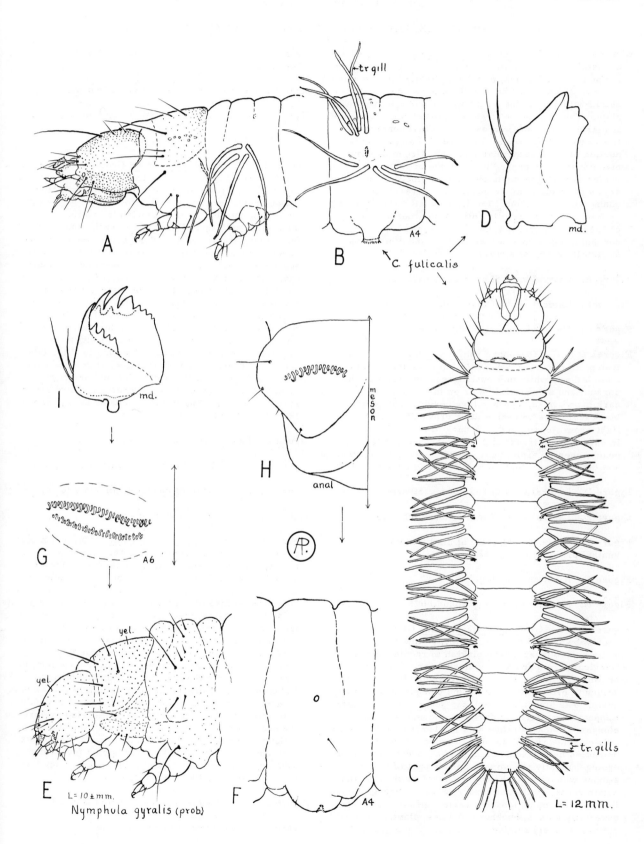

A

tr gill

B   A4

C. fulicalis

D   md.

I   md.

G   A6

H   meson   anal

AP.

C   tr. gills

                 L=12mm.

E   L=10±mm.
     yel.   yel.   yel.

Nymphula gyralis (prob.)

F   A4

EXPLANATION OF FIGURES L47, A-Q

PYRALIDAE, PHYCITINAE A-H, L-Q, CRAMBINAE I-K

Figures A to C. Elasmopalpus lignoscellus Zell., lesser cornstalk borer. F.g.l. 13-15 mm., nile green, brown-striped with a fuscous, polished, slightly bilobed and somewhat depressed head, a dark brown cervical shield with a pale line on the meson and a brown anal plate. The dorsum between the spiracles on each side is marked with nine narrow longitudinal near-brown lines crossed by broad brown areas near the caudal portion of each abdominal segment. Green to white pigment is interspersed between the brown lines. The venter is pale green without much pigment. This borer, most common in the south, may severely injure young corn near ground level, especially when grown on thin sandy or gravelly soil. Also attacks beans, cowpeas, crab grass, Johnson grass, peas, peanuts, sorghum, sugarcane, wheat, turnips and other crops. Luginbill and Ainslie, 1917.

Figure A. Lateral view of head to mesothorax.

Figure B. Lateral view of fourth abdominal segment.

Figure C. Mesal view of right mandible.

Figures D to H. Euzophera semifuneralis Wlkr., American plum borer. F.g.l. 20-25 mm., varies in color from a dingy white to a dusky green or brown on the dorsum and somewhat lighter on the venter. It has a dark brown head, a pale yellow cervical shield with black markings on each side, a brown anal plate and light brown legs tipped with dark brown. The borer infests injured trunks and larger branches of plum, peach, cherry, apple, pear, mountain ash, persimmon and other trees. Blakeslee, 1915; S. A. Forbes, 1890.

Figure D. Lateral view of head to mesothorax.

Figure E. Lateral view of fourth abdominal segment.

Figure F. Crochets and setae of sixth abdominal, right, ventral proleg.

Figure G. Right anal proleg.

Figure H. Mesal view of right mandible.

Figures I to K. Crambus caliginosellus Clem., corn root webworm. F.g.l. 16-20 mm., yellowish to dirty white and younger larvae pinkish to reddish brown. Cervical shield and head yellowish-brown merging to brown near mouth parts. Large pigmented pinacula, yellow to brown, occur about the conspicuous brown setae. The pinaculum about the setae of the prothorax Kappa group nearly or partially encompasses the elongated black spiracle, this is also true of the pinacula of setae rho (3) on the abdominal segments. Spiracles near black. Circles of crochets on ventral prolegs, mostly triordinal. Spends part of its time in a loose web or tubes below soil level. Feeds on and within roots, stalks and tender leaves of young plants. Food plants, corn, tobacco, various grasses and weeds especially asters, buckhorn, daisies, plantain and wild carrot. Closely related species of Crambus attack

various grains and grasses including timothy. Ainslie, 1918 to 1930.

Figure I. Lateral view of head to mesothorax.

Figure J. Lateral view of fourth abdominal segment.

Figure K. Mesal view of right mandible.

Figures L to O. Acrobasis caryae Grote, pecan nut casebearer. F.g.l. 15-17 mm., pale yellowish-brown to light grey brown; head reddish-brown with deeper brown spots, cervical shield, prothoracic Kappa pinaculum and suranal plate yellowish to brown. Pigment differentiation of the cuticle on the body due to the density of microscopic dark spots. Setae rho on mesothorax and eighth abdominal segments arise from near-white spots surrounded by assymmetrical dark brown rings similar to those found in Ephestia. Two most distinctive characters are setae gamma on the cervical shield much nearer epsilon than alpha (twice as far from alpha as from epsilon) and on ninth abdominal segment alpha (1) as near (or nearer) to rho (3) as beta (2) and not on the same pinaculum with beta (2). Pecan appears to be the only food for this species. It attacks tender shoots or immature nuts entering the young nuts on the side and destroying them especially in the first generation. Third generation larvae are found in the shucks or hulls. Bilsing, 1927; Gill, 1925; and Hinton, 1943.

Figure L. Lateral view of head to mesothorax.

Figure M. Lateral view of fourth abdominal segment.

Figure N. Dorsal view of caudal segments 9 to 10.

Figure O. Mesal view of right mandible.

Figures P and Q. Acrobasis juglandis LeB., pecan leaf case bearer. F.g.l. 16-18 mm., dark greyish brown to purplish (microscopic stipple-like spots dense), head deep reddish brown to near black, spiracles near black, cervical shield and suranal plate a bright brown. Setae rho on mesothorax and eighth abdominal segments arise from a clear area surrounded by an assymmetrical dark ring, most conspicuous on the mesothorax (similar to Ephestia). Two most distinctive characters are seta gamma on the cervical shield approximately the same distance from alpha and epsilon, in some cases somewhat nearer epsilon and on ninth abdominal segment seta alpha is definitely nearer beta than rho and frequently located on the same pinaculum with beta (2). This species shows a decided preference for pecan trees. A few observers have found it on hickory, Japanese walnut and other trees. It attacks new leaves and young buds in the spring frequently webbing together leaflets and twigs, causing defoliation. See Hinton, 1943 and Gill, 1917.

Figure P. Dorsal view of caudal segments 9 and 10.

Figure Q. Mesal view of right mandible.

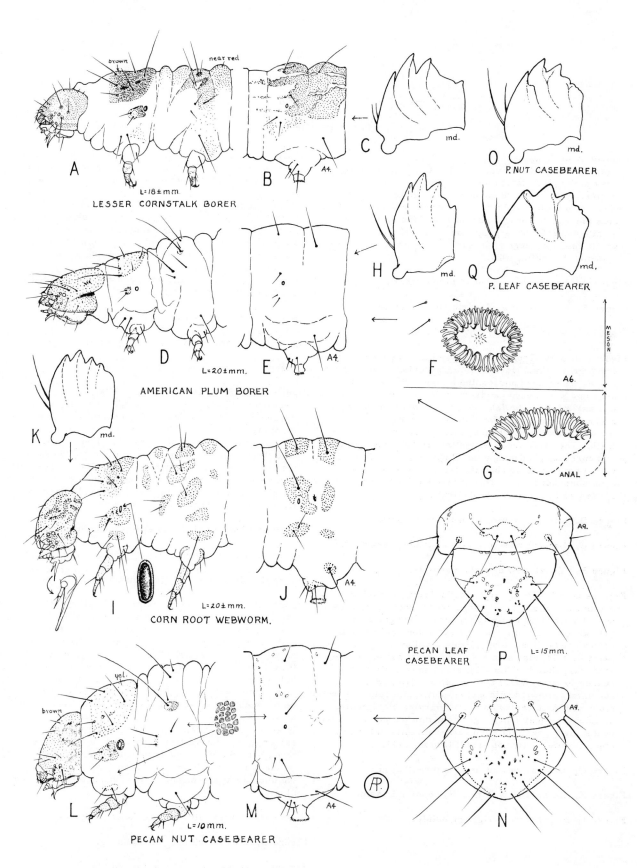

LESSER CORNSTALK BORER
L=18±mm.

AMERICAN PLUM BORER
L=20±mm.

CORN ROOT WEBWORM.
L=20±mm.

PECAN NUT CASEBEARER
L=10mm.

P. NUT CASEBEARER

P. LEAF CASEBEARER

PECAN LEAF CASEBEARER
L=15mm.

LEPIDOPTERA

EXPLANATION OF FIGURES L48, A-R

PYRALIDAE, PHYCITINAE

Figures A to C. <u>Mineola vaccinii</u> Riley, cranberry fruitworm. F.g.l. 18-20 mm., nearly all green or may be rosy pink on the dorsal half and grass green on the venter. Possesses no conspicuous pigmented areas. Head yellowish to light brown. Setae, cervical shield, anal plate and crochets almost colorless or the same as other parts. Infests and consumes the contents of one to four cranberries before it completes its development. Franklin, 1928.

Figure A. Lateral view of head to mesothorax.

Figure B. Lateral view of fourth abdominal segment.

Figure C. Mesal view of right mandible.

Figures D to F. <u>Zophodia convolutella</u> Hbn., gooseberry fruitworm. F.g.l. 15-17 ± mm., greenish with a yellow to brown head possessing a pigmented ocellar area and a darkened caudal margin. Cervical shield and anal plate yellowish. Setae yellowish and without pigmented pinacula. Mandible with three prominent teeth and a wide roughened, cutting edge mesad of the teeth. The larva feeds within the fruit of gooseberry and currants producing premature coloring. If an infested berry is disturbed the larva may emerge and hang suspended on a silken thread until all danger is passed when it returns to the fruit.

Figure D. Lateral view of head to mesothorax.

Figure E. Lateral view of fourth abdominal segment.

Figure F. Mesal view of right mandible.

Figures G to I. <u>Etiella zinckenella</u> Treit., lima-bean pod borer. F.g.l. 17-20 mm., green, reddish to brown with dorsum frequently ruddy pink. Younger larvae pale green to cream color. Head amber yellow with brown caudal line, cervical shield yellowish with a few pairs of dots, also seta beta (2a) somewhat nearer to alpha (1a) than to delta (2b), also rho (2c) distinctly nearer to epsilon (1c) than to gamma (1b). Setae on abdomen yellowish with no pigmented pinacula. Mandible with four dentes on distal margin. Peritremes of spiracles near black. Feeds within the pods of lima beans, field peas, common rattlebox, milk vetch and other legumes. Hyslop, 1912; Hinton, 1943.

Figure G. Lateral view of head to mesothorax.

Figure H. Lateral view of fourth abdominal segment.

Figure I. Mesal view of right mandible.

Figures J to L. <u>Monoptilota pergratialis</u> Hulst., lima-bean vine borer. F.g.l. 22-25 mm., robust, cylindrical, glaucous, bluish-green with the dorsum of abdominal segments often a dull carneous or pinkish cast. Head shining brown. Cervical shield bright olive brown. Prothoracic Kappa group pinaculum and anal plate yellowish brown. Pinacula of most setae inconspicuous. Peritremes of spiracles near-black. Mandible obtusely pointed with three dentes on the distal margin. Larva produces a gall-like swelling in the vines of pole lima beans and probably other legumes. See U.S.D.A. (1900). Bul. 23.

Figure J. Lateral view of head to mesothorax.

Figure K. Lateral view of fourth abdominal segment.

Figure L. Mesal view of right mandible.

Figures M to O. <u>Tlascala finitella</u> Wlk., Hills cranberry fireworm. F.g.l. 20-23 mm., light to medium brown, (younger individuals definitely reddish) with four longitudinal, broken, light lines between the spiracles and the dorsomeson on most segments. Head fuscous, also the cervical shield, suranal plate and thoracic legs a deep brown. Peritremes of spiracles near black. Colorless primary setae as long as each segment. Crochets of ventral prolegs circular and triordinal. Larvae feed on cultivated cranberries.

Figure M. Lateral view of head to mesothorax.

Figure N. Lateral view of fourth abdominal segment.

Figure O. Mesal view of right mandible.

Figures P to R. <u>Psorosina hammondi</u> Riley, apple leaf skeletonizer. F.g.l. 9-11 mm., including the head and cervical shield, vary in color from near green to reddish brown and are flecked with numerous near-white small areas especially about the setae. Venter paler than dorsum. Setae light colored and moderately long. Seta epsilon (1c) on the prothorax arises from a deeply pigmented pinaculum. Setae rho (2b) and epsilon (2a) on the mesothorax are adjacent and have about their bases a conspicuous sclerotized, pigmented ring. This is also somewhat true of rho (3) on the eighth abdominal segment. Larva lives under a thin layer of silken threads on the lower surface of foliage where it feeds on the soft tissue leaving a network of veins. Most common on apple foliage, occasionally on quince and plum.

Figure P. Lateral view of head to mesothorax.

Figure Q. Lateral view of mesothorax.

Figure R. Mesal view of right mandible.

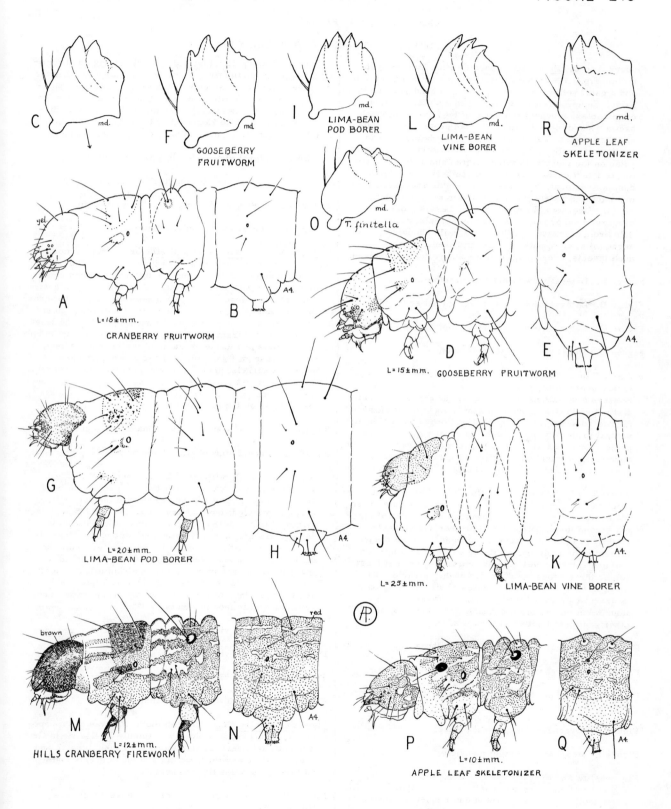

C   md.

F   GOOSEBERRY
    FRUITWORM

I   LIMA-BEAN
    POD BORER   md.

L   LIMA-BEAN
    VINE BORER   md.

R   APPLE LEAF
    SKELETONIZER   md.

O   md.   T. finitella

A   yel
    L=15±mm.
    CRANBERRY FRUITWORM

B   A4.

D   E   A4.
    L=15±mm.   GOOSEBERRY FRUITWORM

G   L=20±mm.
    LIMA-BEAN POD BORER

H   A4.

J   L=25±mm.

K   A4.
    LIMA-BEAN VINE BORER

M   brown   L=12±mm.
    HILLS CRANBERRY FIREWORM

N   red   A4.

AP.

P   L=10±mm.
    APPLE LEAF SKELETONIZER

Q   A4.

EXPLANATION OF FIGURES L49, A-S

PYRALIDAE, PHYCITINAE A-O, PYRALINAE P-S

Figures A to D. Plodia interpunctella Hbn. Indian-meal moth. F.g.l. 10-13 mm., possesses a near-white cuticle and a pale, yellowish or reddish-brown head and mouth parts. Setae, cervical shield, suranal plate, peritremes of spiracles, crochets and parts of legs pale-yellowish brown. Mandible with three distinct dentes, the middle one the largest. Front extends two-thirds distance to vertical triangle. No pinacula or sclerotized rings about setae on the mesothorax, metathorax and abdominal segments 1 to 9 except rho (3) on mesothorax and eighth abdominal segment. Spiracle on the eighth abdominal segment approximately half way between seta rho (3) and eta (5). Crochets biordinal circle. Infests stored and prepared food products, especially cereals, dried fruits, dried roots, grasses, herbs, meal, milk chocolate, powdered milk, nuts, nuts in candy and seeds. Also feeds on dead insects, excrement, exuviae and pollen in beehives.

Figure A. Lateral view of head to mesothorax.

Figure B. Lateral view of fourth abdominal segment.

Figure C. Lateral view of eighth abdominal segment.

Figure D. Mesal view of right mandible.

Figures E to O. Phycitinae, Ephestia species. Full grown larvae near-white, pinkish, yellowish or pale green. Possess a yellowish to brown head and cervical shield, distinct yellowish to brown pinacula about most of the pigmented setae, except epsilon, yellowish spiracles and ventral prolegs with circular and usually biordinal crochets. Each seta rho (2b and 3) on mesothorax and eighth abdominal segment with a circular clear membranous area about its base surrounded by a sclerotized ring.

Figures E to I. Ephestia kühniella Zell., Mediterranean flour moth. F.g.l. 15-18 mm., near white to pale green. Mandible with outer tooth subventral and mesad of largest second tooth. Diameter of prothoracic spiracle slightly greater than distance between setae on Kappa (prespiracular) group. Distance between seta epsilon (3a) and spiracle on eighth abdominal segment at least two or three times the diameter of the spiracle. The larva in feeding produces masses of silk webbing on or in grain or prepared food products. Favorite food is flour, also infests bran, cereals, corn, meal, wheat, other grains and pollen in beehives.

Figure E. Lateral view of head and prothorax.

Figure F. Lateral view of eighth abdominal segment.

Figure G. Crochets of sixth abdominal, right, ventral proleg.

Figure H. Crochets of right anal proleg.

Figure I. Mesal view of right mandible.

Figures J to M. Ephestia elutella Hbn., tobacco moth. F.g.l. 10-15 mm., near-white to pinkish. Mandible with outer tooth distinct and part of outer margin. Diameter of prothoracic spiracle distinctly less than distance between setae on Kappa (prespiracular) group. Distance

between seta epsilon (3a) and spiracle on eighth abdominal segment distinctly greater than the largest diameter of the spiracle. Diameter of the eighth abdominal spiracle about two-thirds as broad as membranous area about base of seta rho (3), also distinctly less than distance between setae kappa (4) and eta (5). Infests cured tobacco, chocolate, nuts and dried vegetable products.

Figure J. Lateral view of head to mesothorax.

Figure K. Lateral view of fourth abdominal segment.

Figure L. Lateral view of eighth abdominal segment.

Figure M. Dorsal view of caudal segments.

Figures N to O. Ephestia figulilella Greg., raisin moth. F.g.l. 10 ± mm., near-white. Diameter of prothoracic spiracle approximately equal to distance between setae of Kappa (prespiracular) group. Distance between epsilon (3a) and spiracle or eighth abdominal segment approximately that of the largest diameter of spiracle. Most setae very long, two or more times longer than the length of the segment from which they arise. Field hosts include fallen fruits and waste products of mulberries, plums, prunes, grapes, figs, apricots, nectarines, peaches, peach pit kernels, pears, cherries, apples and dates. They also infest drying fruits and storage products consisting of dried fruits or nuts. Rarely do they attack fresh fruits on the plant.

Figure N. Lateral view of eighth abdominal segment.

Figure O. Dorsal view of caudal segments.

Figures P to S. Pyralis farinalis L., meal moth. F.g.l. 20-25 mm., dirty white except the medium brown head, cervical shield, true legs, crochets and the decidedly grayish (stippled) thorax, first abdominal and caudal segments. Head with front covering one-half distance to vertical triangle and with four distinct ocelli. Mandible broad usually with two apical teeth (if not eroded). No distinct sclerotized pinacula about setae immediately dorsad and ventrad of spiracles on abdominal segments 1 to 6. Spiracles somewhat elliptical with thick dark peritremes. Infests moist or mouldy bran, grain, corn, seeds or stored food products.

Figure P. Lateral view of head to mesothorax.

Figure Q. Lateral view of fourth abdominal segment.

Figure R. Lateral view of eighth abdominal segment.

Figure S. Mesal view of right mandible.

Ephestia cautella Wlkr. almond moth. Larvae of this species from all reports closely resemble E. figulilella Greg. The cuticle is darker, also more yellowish, pinkish and greyish-white and the pinacula are more deeply pigmented than the species figured here.

For further information on all of the above species see Hinton, 1943.

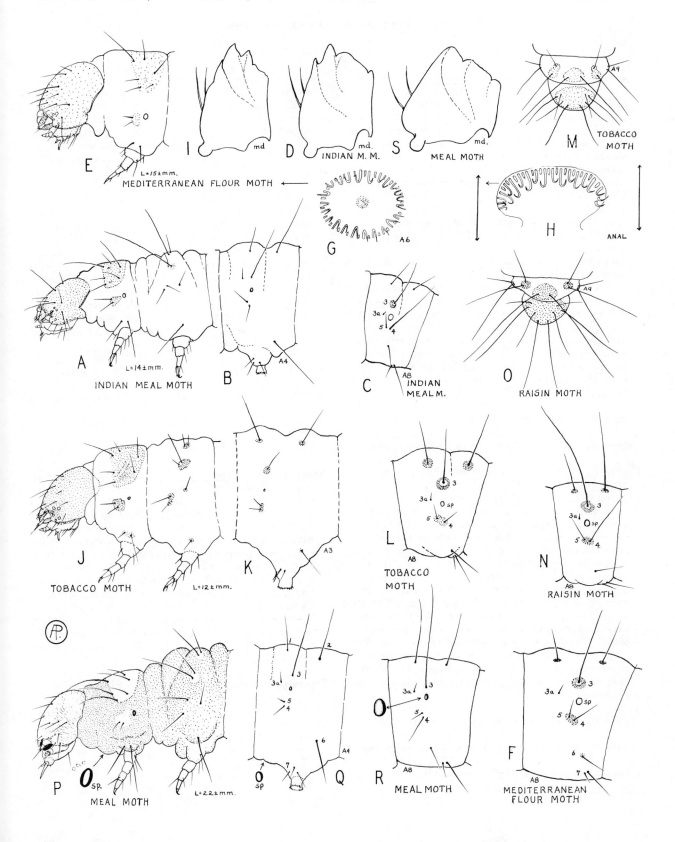

E MEDITERRANEAN FLOUR MOTH L=15±mm.

I md.

D INDIAN M. M. md.

S MEAL MOTH md.

M TOBACCO MOTH A9

G A6

H ANAL

A INDIAN MEAL MOTH L=14±mm.

B A4

C INDIAN MEAL M. A8

O RAISIN MOTH A9

J TOBACCO MOTH L=12±mm.

K A3

L TOBACCO MOTH A8

N RAISIN MOTH A8

P MEAL MOTH L=22±mm.

Q A4

R MEAL MOTH A8

F MEDITERRANEAN FLOUR MOTH A8

EXPLANATION OF FIGURES L50, A-Q

PYRALIDAE, PYRAUSTINAE

Figurea A to C. Hymenia recurvalis F., Hawaiian beet webworm. F.g.l. 23 ± mm., slender pale green with a light colored head possessing conspicuous groups of round, brown spots. A prominent near-black pinaculum about setae epsilon (2a) on the mesothorax. On the yellowish cervical shield a dark spot occurs caudad of gamma (1b). Most of the pinacula, if visible, are almost the same color as the cuticle. Larva may or may not spin a web over its feeding areas. Feeds on foliage of beets, mangels, sugar beets, Swiss chard, spinach and other plants including several weeds belonging to Amaranthus and Chaenopdium.

Figures D to F. Pantographa limata G. and R., basswood leaf roller. F.g.l. 35 ± mm., bright green with a deep brown to near-black head, cervical shield and thoracic legs. Pinacula on the thorax more conspicuous than those on the abdomen. No pigmented anal plate. Larva cuts a basswood leaf halfway across and rolls the severed portion into a tube in which it lives and feeds. Later it constructs a smaller hibernating nest by folding the edge of a leaf over its body. Food plants, basswood foliage.

Figure D. Lateral view of head to mesothorax.

Figure E. Lateral view of fourth abdominal segment.

Figure F. Mesal view of right mandible.

Figures G to I. Loxostege similalis Guen., garden webworm. F.g.l. 20-25 mm., green to yellowish-green, possessing a yellowish, speckled head and no definite cervical shield. Deeply pigmented pinacula conspicuous, especially those on the abdomen dorsad of the spiracles. Living specimen shows a distinct light streak along the dorsomeson between three pairs of very dark pinacula on the dorsum of each segment. Pinacula ventrad of the spiracles have light centers from which the setae arise. Mandibles usually possess four irregular teeth. The larva is a general foliage feeder, spinning light webs over the leaves. Some of the many plants it feeds upon are alfalfa, beans, beets, clover, cowpeas, lamb's quarters, peas, pigweed and ragweed.

Figure G. Lateral view of head to mesothorax.

Figure H. Lateral view of fourth abdominal segment.

Figure I. Mesal view of right mandible.

Figure J. Loxostege commixtalis Wlkr., alfalfa webworm. F.g.l. 22 ± mm., closely resembles larva of L. similalis. Mandibles of the specimens seen possess five more or less regular dentes. When abundant may migrate in armies from pasture land or roadside weeds to cultivated crops and feed upon alfalfa, barley, clover, corn and other food plants.

Figure J. Mesal view of right mandible.

Figures K to N. Evergestis rimosalis Guen., cross-striped cabbageworm. F.g.l. 20 ± mm., bluish-gray with several distinct transverse near-black stripes on the dorsum of each segment. A wide, bright yellow, spiracular line extends from the mesothorax to the caudal end. Venter green, mottled with yellow. Head light yellow, cervical shield darker. Pinacula above spiracles are near-black. It feeds on new leaves of cabbage and related plants including nasturtium.

Figure K. Lateral view of head to mesothorax.

Figure L. Lateral view of fourth abdominal segment.

Figure M. Dorsal view of fourth abdominal segment.

Figure N. Mesal view of right mandible.

Figures O to Q. Hellula undalis F., cabbage webworm. F.g.l. 15-17 mm., grayish-yellow with five prominent brown to purplish longitudinal stripes on the dorsum. Lighter stripes occur on the sides and below the spiracles. Head dark brown to near-black. Cervical shield shiny, purplish gray. Pinacula, when present, inconspicuous. The larva in feeding, except the first instar, covers its feeding area with a silk web on which faeces and dirt collects. Attacks young leaves and heart of plants. At times destructive in seed beds. Some of the food plants are beet, cabbage, cauliflower, collard, horseradish, mustard, radish turnip (including roots), shepherd's purse, and purslane. Chittenden and Marsh, 1912.

Figure O. Lateral view of head to mesothorax.

Figure P. Lateral view of fourth abdominal segment.

Figure Q. Mesal view of right mandible.

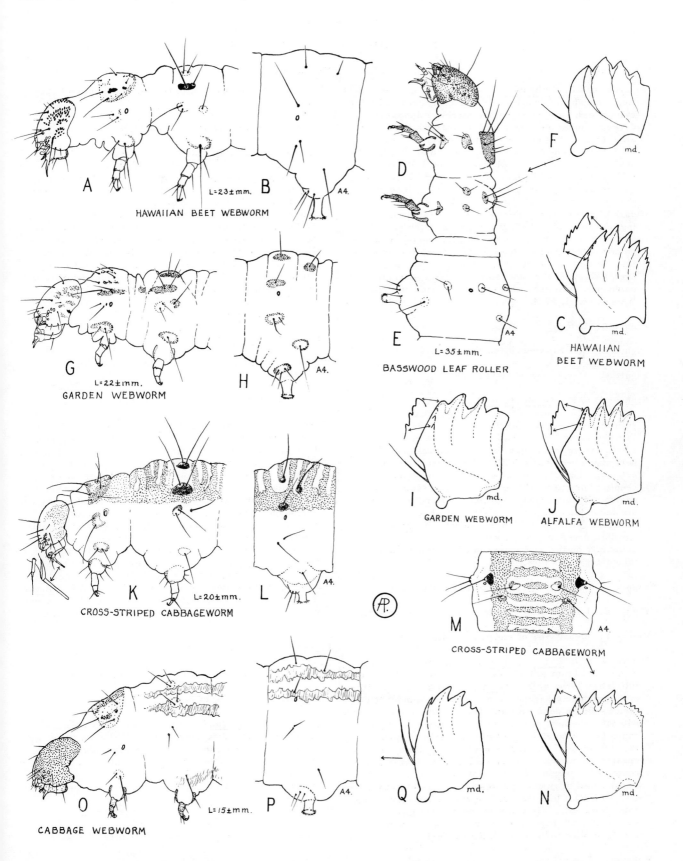

A
L=23±mm.
B
A4.
HAWAIIAN BEET WEBWORM

D
E
L=35±mm.
BASSWOOD LEAF ROLLER
A4

F
md.

C
md.
HAWAIIAN BEET WEBWORM

G
L=22±mm.
GARDEN WEBWORM
H
A4.

I
md.
GARDEN WEBWORM

J
md.
ALFALFA WEBWORM

K
L=20±mm.
CROSS-STRIPED CABBAGEWORM
L
A4.

M
A4.
CROSS-STRIPED CABBAGEWORM

O
CABBAGE WEBWORM
L=15±mm.
P
A4.

Q
md.

N
md.

EXPLANATION OF FIGURES L51, A-R

PYRALIDAE, PYRAUSTINAE

Figures A to C. Phlyctaenia rubigalis Guen., celery leaf tier; greenhouse leaf tier. F.g.l. 17-19 mm., slender, cylindrical, pale green with a narrow, middorsal, darker green stripe bordered by near-white. When alive trachea visible through translucent cuticle. All legs, long, slender and pale green. No anal fork. An oval dark spot on cervical shield caudad of gamma (1b) or dorsad of rho (2c). Spiracles small and rounded. Setae pale yellow, moderately long. Head small, pale greenish-yellow, faintly mottled. Ocelli with dark pigment spots. Feeds on a wide range of flowering, ornamental and vegetable plants in the greenhouse and outdoors. Consumes foliage, frequently tying together two contiguous leaves. On celery it may bore into the stalks. A few of the many host plants are beet, celery, chrysanthemum, cineraria, carnation, calendula, geranium, snapdragon, spinach and violet. Weigel, et. al. 1924.

Figure A. Lateral view of head to mesothorax.

Figure B. Lateral view of fourth abdominal segment.

Figure C. Mesal view of right mandible.

Figures D to F. Desmia funeralis Hbn., grape leaf folder. F.g.l. 20 ± mm., slender, glossy, translucent, yellowish-green with the dorsum somewhat darker than the sides. Head and dorsal portion of cervical shield are yellow to light brown. Ventral (or lateral) part of the cervical shield and the pinaculum about setae epsilon (2a) and rho (2b) on the mesothorax are deeply pigmented. All setae yellowish, those on abdomen without pigmented pinacula. Mandibles with six dentes and rounded at distal end. Feeds on the foliage of wild and cultivated grapes, also attacks Virginia creeper and two varieties of red bud. Feeds primarily on the upper surface of the leaf within a folded edge. Strauss, 1916.

Figure D. Lateral view of head to mesothorax.

Figure E. Lateral view of fourth abdominal segment.

Figure F. Mesal view of right mandible.

Figures G to I. Diaphania hyalinata L., melonworm. F.g.l. 25-30 mm., greenish to yellow resembling the full grown larva of D. nitidalis. Earlier instars without pigmented pinacula and possess two slender white stripes on the dorsomeson. Head yellowish-brown and without a pigment spot on the caudal margin. Seta kappa (4) on the eighth abdominal segment approximately the same distance from the spiracle as the greatest diameter of the spiracle. Mandible with five dentes not covering the entire distal margin, an additional small projection present on the distolateral margin. Chiefly a leaf feeder, late generation larvae may enter the fruit. It is a serious pest in the gulf coast states on cantaloupe, cucumber, squash and pumpkin, rarely on watermelon. R. I. Smith, 1911.

Figure G. Lateral view of head and prothorax.

Figure H. Setae adjacent to the eighth abdominal spiracle.

Figure I. Mesal view of right mandible.

Figures J to L. Diaphania nitidalis Stoll., pickleworm. F.g.l. 25-30 mm., greenish to yellowish-green, without the pigmented pinacula typical of earlier instars especially the fourth. Head yellowish-brown and with a distinct pigmented spot on the lower half of its caudal margin. Seta kappa (4) on eighth abdominal segment, two or more times as far away from the spiracle as the greatest diameter of the spiracle. Mandible with five dentes extending over the entire distal margin. May feed on and in blossoms or buds or bore into stems or leaf petioles. Greatest damage occurs within the fruit. Food plants are chiefly cantaloupe, cucumber, squash and watermelon. Pumpkins are immune. Quaintance, 1901; R. I. Smith, 1911.

Figure J. Lateral view of head and prothorax.

Figure K. Setae adjacent to the eighth abdominal spiracle.

Figure L. Mesal view of right mandible.

Figures M to O. Pachyzancla bipunctalis F., southern beet webworm. F.g.l. 22-25 mm., dark, dirty green (glossy and semi-transparent) with a dark brown mottled head and a cervical shield near black on lateral aspects and without pigmentation on the dorsomeson. Pinacula about all setae, most conspicuous in preserved specimens especially those dorsad of spiracles. One large, irregular, pinaculum on each side of the mesothorax includes setae, alpha (1a), beta (1b), epsilon (2a) and rho (2b). Right mandible possesses seven or more dentes on distal margin and a distinct broad, triangular projection on the outside lateral margin above the condyle. Feeds on foliage of beets, cauliflower, cabbage and weeds, especially species of Amaranthus (pigweed, spiny amaranth, etc.), folding and webbing the leaves together by silken threads. Chittenden, 1911.

Figure M. Lateral view of head to mesothorax.

Figure N. Lateral view of fourth abdominal segment.

Figure O. Mesal view of right mandible.

Figures P to R. Pyrausta futilalis Led., Indian hempworm, F.g.l. 23 ± mm., with dorsum reddish-brown to orange and venter much lighter, head, cervical shield and anal plate yellowish, mottled with conspicuous dark areas or spots. Pinacula about all setae conspicuous and deeply pigmented. A leaf worm on Indian hemp or dogbane.

Figure P. Lateral view of head to mesothorax.

Figure Q. Lateral view of fourth abdominal segment.

Figure R. Mesal view of right mandible.

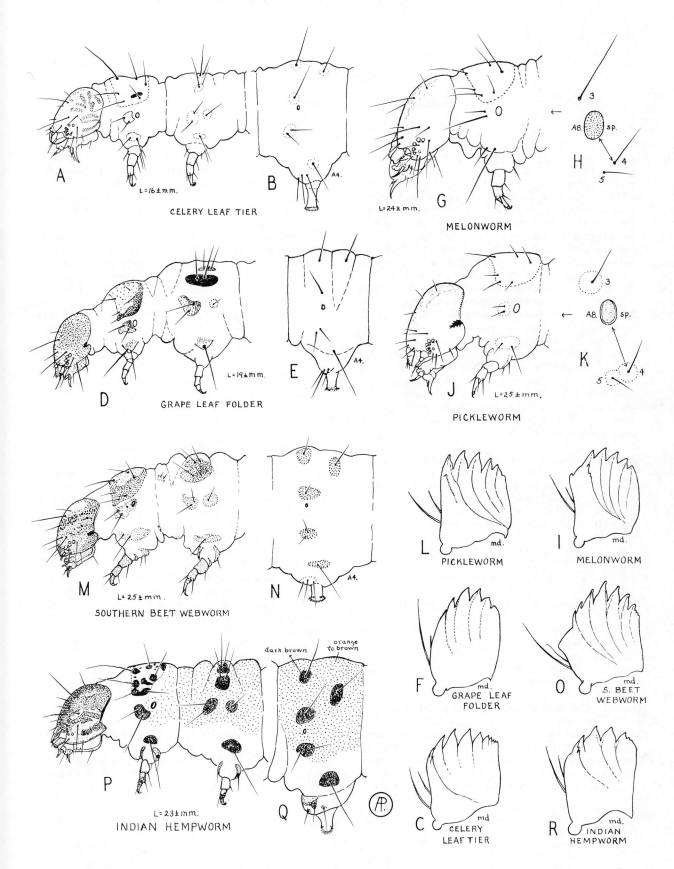

A

L=16±mm.

CELERY LEAF TIER

B   A4.

G

L=24±mm.

MELONWORM

H   3   A8   sp.   4   5

D

L=19±mm.

GRAPE LEAF FOLDER

E   A4.

J

L=25±mm.

PICKLEWORM

K   3   A8   sp.   4   5

M

L=25±mm.

SOUTHERN BEET WEBWORM

N   A4.

L   md.   PICKLEWORM

I   md.   MELONWORM

F   md.   GRAPE LEAF FOLDER

O   md.   S. BEET WEBWORM

P

L=23±mm.

INDIAN HEMPWORM

Q

dark brown   orange to brown

C   md   CELERY LEAF TIER

R   md.   INDIAN HEMPWORM

EXPLANATION OF FIGURES L52, A-P

PYRALIDAE, PYRAUSTINAE

Figures A to I. Pyrausta nubilalis Hbn. European corn borer, also L6, D; L7, A. F.g.l. 23-25 mm., dirty white varying in color on the dorsum from a pink, slate gray or "smoky-fuscous" to a light brown. Skin granules (L52, G) are most dense on the dorsum and produce a distinct stripe. Lateral and ventral integument dirty white. Head brown mottled with blackish. Ocellar pigment black. Anterior setae A^1, A^2 and puncture A in almost a straight line. Mandibles nearly square each with five dentes. Pinaculum of prothoracic Kappa group in most specimens has a definite pigment spot on the side nearest the spiracle. Pigmented pinacula about alpha (1) setae on most abdominal segments about the same distance apart (x) as the diameter of each pinaculum. Attacks many herbaceous plants. Its chief economic host is corn boring into most any portion above ground. It also infests asters, beans, beets, celery, chrysanthemums, gladioli, potatoes and other vegetables, flowers and weeds, altold over 200 kinds of plants. One or two generations per season.

Figure A. Cephalic view of head.

Figure B. Area on head capsule showing position of setae A^1, A^2 and puncture A.

Figure C. Mesal view of right mandible.

Figure D. Lateral view of prothorax.

Figure E. Lateral view of eighth abdominal segment.

Figure F. Dorsal view of second abdominal segment.

Figure G. Skin granules on dorsum of second abdominal segment.

Figure H. Crochets and setae of sixth abdominal, right, ventral proleg.

Figure I. Crochets and setae of right anal proleg.

Figures J to M. Pyrausta ainsliei Hnr., smartweed borer. F.g.l. 18-20 mm. Superficially this smaller borer closely resembles P. nubilalis. Dorsum slate gray to plumbeous and venter dirty white. Head uniformly, distinct brown to deep black.

Most reliable character for separating the two species is the position of the anterior setae on the head, namely setae A^1 and A^2 and puncture A form a distinct angle not a straight line. On the prothorax no definite pigment spot occurs on the Kappa pinaculum adjacent to the spiracle. The distance between the pinacula of setae alpha (1) on most of abdominal segments (y) is usually less than the diameter of each pinaculum. Mandibles square, each with five dentes. The most common food plants are several smartweeds. They also infest other weeds, namely, cocklebur, ragweed, Joe-pye weed, spreading dogbane, cat-tail and lamb's quarter. In the late season they may be found in several shelter hosts, namely, corn, goldenrod, beggar-ticks, cotton and others.

Figure J. Area on head capsule showing position of setae A^1, A^2 and puncture A.

Figure K. Mesal view of right mandible.

Figure L. Lateral view of prothorax.

Figure M. Dorsal view of second abdominal segment.

Figures N to P. Pyrausta penitalis Grote, lotus borer. F.g.l. 30-35 mm., decidedly larger than P. nubilalis. Dorsum brownish-black and plumbeous, venter near-white. Head light yellowish and mottled with brown pigment. Mandibles decidedly elongated (not square) with five dentes. Kappa group pinaculum on prothorax does not possess a definite pigmented spot adjacent to the spiracle. The distance between the pinacula of the setae alpha (1) on most of the abdominal segments (z) is usually greater than diameter of each pinaculum. Common food plants are lotus and smartweeds. Shelter plants are corn, rhubarb and weeds.

Figure N. Mesal view of an elongated right mandible.

Figure O. Lateral view of prothorax.

Figure P. Dorsal view of second abdominal segment.

Note: For more details concerning above species see Ainslie and Cartwright 1921, 1922; Drake and Decker, 1927; Ellis 1925; Heinrich 1919; Mosher 1919.

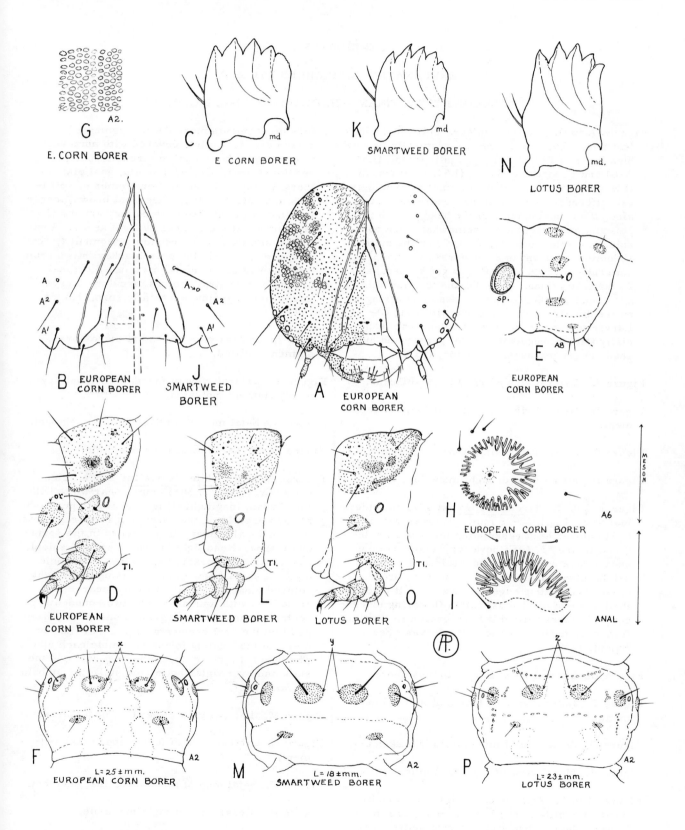

G
E. CORN BORER

C
E CORN BORER
md

K
SMARTWEED BORER
md

N
LOTUS BORER
md.

B EUROPEAN
CORN BORER

J
SMARTWEED
BORER

A EUROPEAN
CORN BORER

E
EUROPEAN
CORN BORER
sp.
A8

D
EUROPEAN
CORN BORER
Ti.

L
SMARTWEED BORER
Ti.

O
LOTUS BORER
Ti.

H
EUROPEAN CORN BORER
MESON
A6

I
ANAL

F
x
L=25±mm.
EUROPEAN CORN BORER
A2

M
y
L=18±mm.
SMARTWEED BORER
A2

P
z
L=23±mm.
LOTUS BORER
A2

LEPIDOPTERA

EXPLANATION OF FIGURES L53, A-P

PYRALIDAE, PYRAUSTINAE A-H, PYRALINAE I-L, CRAMBINAE M-P

Figures A to D. Lineodes integra Zell., nightshade leaf tier. F.g.l. 14-16 mm., structurally resembles larva of Phlyctaenia rubigalis Guen., (L51, A-C) and P. tertialis Guen., (L53, E-H) except it is smaller. Some of the distinct morphological differences are: a narrow near-black streak along the caudal margin of the head capsule; pinacula on the prothorax somewhat more conspicuous; seta alpha (1), (L53, C) on the ninth abdominal segment is caudodorsad of rho (3) not cephalodorsad as in P. rubigalis Guen., and P. tertiralis Guen., (L53, G) and the mandibles are rounded with six distinct dentes covering the entire distal margin (compare with L51, C). Larvae feed on the foliage of Solanaceae, especially tomato, eggplant, potato, pepper and nightshade in greenhouses. Compton, 1937.

Figure A. Lateral view of head to mesothorax.

Figure B. Lateral view of fourth abdominal segment.

Figure C. Setal map of ninth abdominal segment.

Figure D. Mesal view of right mandible.

Figures E to H. Phlyctaenia tertialis Guen., elder leaf tier. F.g.l. 20-22 mm., all green with a light colored head resembling larva of P. rubigalis, figure 51, A-C, however, it does not possess a dark spot on the inconspicuous cervical shield, also mandibles have a smooth, broad, distomesal cutting edge, not serrate. It feeds on the foliage of Sambucus, called flowering elderberry. Others record it from grapes in Virginia. It may tie together some of the leaves. See Balduf, 1930.

Figure E. Lateral view of head to mesothorax.

Figure F. Lateral view of fourth abdominal segment.

Figure G. Setal map of ninth abdominal segment.

Figure H. Mesal view of right mandible.

Figures I to L. Aglossa caprealis Hbn., murky meal caterpillar. F.g.l. 25-28 mm., brownish to near black, often with a bronze lustre. Crev-

ices on segments more deeply pigmented than raised areas. Cuticle covered with numerous microscopic, hexagonal to circular spots. Head reddish-brown. Cervical shield, anal plate and thoracic legs yellowish. Peritremes of spiracles near black. Most setae light brown, longer than the segments from which they arise and surrounded at their bases by light areas. Position of setae on ninth abdominal segment typical of species. Mandibles near-black with two prominent dentes on the distal margin. Biordinal crochets on ventral prolegs circular. Larvae infest stored grains, especially corn. Hinton, 1943.

Figure I. Lateral view of head to mesothorax, pigment omitted.

Figure J. Lateral view of fourth abdominal segment, pigment indicated.

Figure K. Setal map of ninth abdominal segment.

Figure L. Mesal view of right mandible.

Figures M to P. Chilo plejadellus Zinck., rice stalk borer. F.g.l. 30-33 mm., near white with two, broad, longitudinal, light brown to purplish stripes present on the dorsum of most segments. An additional fainter stripe occurs in the spriacular area. Head light brown. Cervical shield, anal plate and thoracic legs yellow with some pigment spots. Setae brown arising from light colored pinacula. Oval spiracles near-black. Mandibles with four sharp and two rounded dentes on the distal margin and one small sharp point on the oral surface near the margin. Summer and hibernating forms resemble each other. The borer attacks rice, living as a borer in the stalk and overwintering in rice stalks or stubble. Ingram, 1927.

Figure M. Lateral view of head to mesothorax.

Figure N. Lateral view of fourth abdominal segment.

Figure O. Setal map of ninth abdominal segment.

Figure P. Mesal view of right mandible.

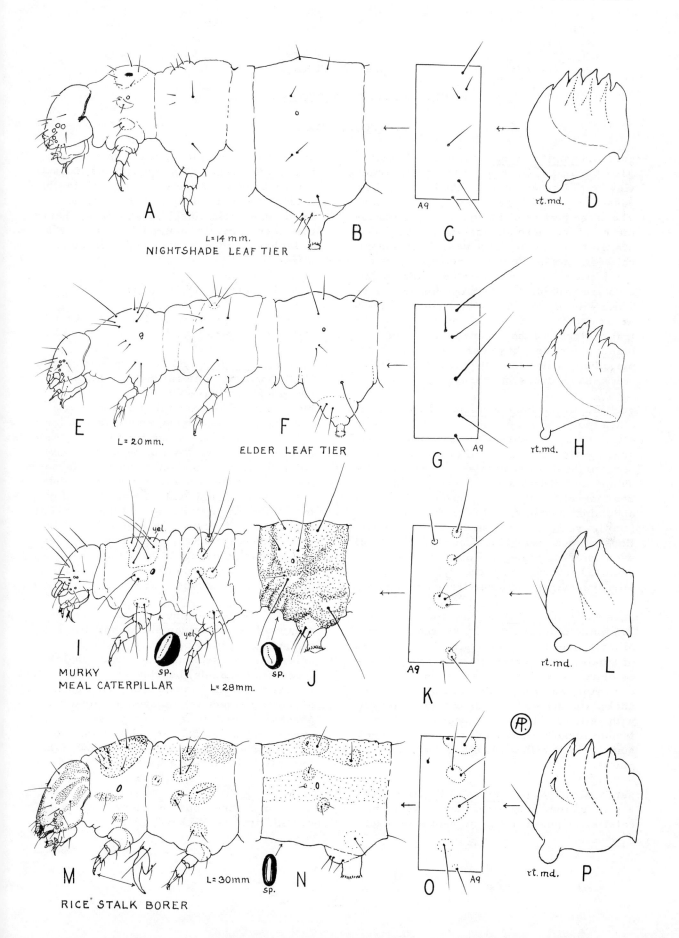

A

L=14 mm.
NIGHTSHADE LEAF TIER

B

C

A9

D

rt.md.

E

L= 20 mm.

ELDER LEAF TIER

F

G

A9

H

rt.md.

I

MURKY
MEAL CATERPILLAR

yel

yel

sp.

L=28mm.

J

sp.

K

A9

L

rt.md.

M

RICE STALK BORER

L=30mm

N

sp.

O

A9

P

rt.md.

EXPLANATION OF FIGURES L54, A-G

SATURNIIDAE

Figure A. Samia cecropia L., cecropia moth. Also L6, L; L7, G. F.g.l. 80-90 mm. Lateral view of pea green, smooth, thick caterpillar possessing a few, conspicuous, colored scoli. The large beta scoli located near the dorsomeson of the meso and metathorax are deep orange to red while the beta scoli on abdominal segments one to eight are yellow. All other scoli dorsad and ventrad of the spiracles are pale blue. The spiracles are near-white with narrow black peritremes. Yellow areas occur on the lateral aspects of the ventral prolegs and the suranal plate. Food plants apple, ash, boxelder, cottonwood, maple, plum, willow and other deciduous fruit trees, shade trees and shrubs.

Figure B. Callosamia promethea Drury, promethea moth. F.g.l. 60± mm. Lateral view of bluish green to bluish white caterpillar possessing prominent pairs of orange to red tubercles (scoli without setae) on the mesothorax and metathorax and a median orange to red tubercle on the dorsomeson of the eighth abdominal segment. All other tubercles (scoli) are near black, small, shiny projections. Black areas also occur on the lateral aspects of the prolegs. Food plants ash, azalea, barbery, birch, cherry, lilac, maple, tulip, sassafras and other trees and shrubs.

Figure C. Tropea luna L., luna moth. F.g.l. 70± mm. Lateral view of pea green caterpillar possessing yellow spiracles, six rows of small pink tubercles (scoli) each with one or more black hairs and a few white ones, a faint yellow subspiracular line and a brown anal plate and anal shields bordered in part with yellow. Food plants, beech, birch, butternut, hickory, ironwood, oak, plum, sweet gum, walnut, willow and other deciduous plants.

Figures D and E. Automeris io F., io moth. F.g.l. 60± mm., pea green, spiny, venomous caterpillar possesses prominent scoli each armed with many, long, greenish spines tipped with black and a conspicuous, subspiracular, reddish stripe edged with white which extends the entire length of the abdomen. Food plants alder, ash, beech, birch, cherry, elm, locust, maple, oak, poplar, sassafras and other deciduous trees and herbaceous plants.

Figure D. Lateral view of larva.

Figure E. Lateral view of sixth and seventh abdominal segments.

Figure F. Hemileuca maia Drury, buck moth. F.g.l. 55± mm. Lateral view of the sixth and seventh abdominal segments of a purple-black, venomous caterpillar possessing a reddish head, numerous, small whitish (or yellow) ovoid spots on the body bearing short fuscous setae, two rows of reddish (tawny) colored, short, spiny scoli along the dorsomeson of the metathorax to the eighth abdominal segment, prominent long black scoli on the prothorax, metathorax and the lateral aspects of the abdominal segments, red spiracles, a deep red anal plate, red prolegs and glossy black thoracic legs. Food plants oaks, willow, hazelnut, wild cherry, rose and probably other deciduous species.

Figure G. Telea polyphemus Cram., polyphemus moth or American silkworm. F.g.l. 60± mm. Lateral view of a stout, light green caterpillar possessing small, reddish-brown tubercles (pinacula) bearing white setae, some silvered at their bases. Setae (rho) on the abdomen immediately above the spiracles possess at their bases conspicuous silvered areas. Spiracles salmon colored and the cervical shield is bordered by yellow. The food plants comprise a wide variety of deciduous trees, shrubs and herbs.

Note: For descriptions and colored figures of above species see Packard, 1912.

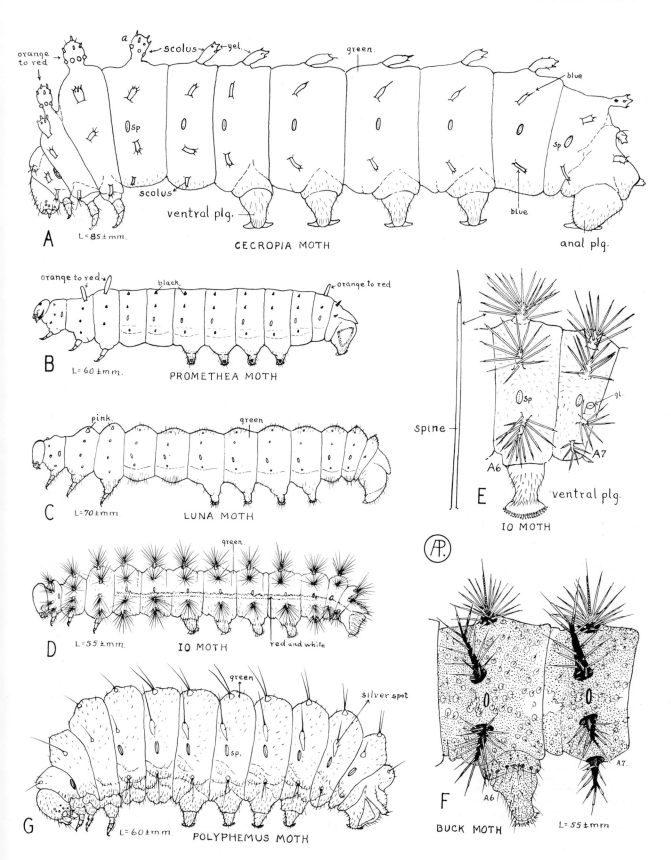

A — CECROPIA MOTH — L=85±mm.

B — PROMETHEA MOTH — L=60±mm.

C — LUNA MOTH — L=70±mm.

D — IO MOTH — L=55±mm.

E — IO MOTH — spine

F — BUCK MOTH — L=55±mm.

G — POLYPHEMUS MOTH — L=60±mm.

EXPLANATION OF FIGURES L55, A-O

SPHINGIDAE

Figures A and B. Lapara bombycoides Wlk., pine needle sphinx. F.g.l. 65 ± mm., slender, green, longitudinally striped with red, white and yellow lines or blotches. A conspicuous, more or less continuous, brick-red line on the dorsomeson is flanked by narrow white lines. Between each white line and the spiracles a broad green area containing a narrow yellow line occurs. Immediately ventrad of spiracles a narrow white line is flanked by red areas above and below, but more extensively ventrad, frequently covering most of the lateroventral aspects including the prolegs. Head triangular, conical with an inverted V-shaped dark stripe. No caudal horn. Food pine needles on scrub pine and other species.

Figure A. Lateral view of larva.

Figure B. Cephalic view of head.

Figure C. Pholus achemon Drury, achemon sphinx. Also L56, C (anal horn on an early instar). F.g.l. 75-80 mm., pale straw-yellow to reddish brown on dorsum and deep brown on venter. Usually a broken, brown line occurs on the dorsomeson and a more continuous, subdorsal, brown line on each side. Six, conspicuous, diagonal rows of light, contiguous spots occur on abdominal segments 2 to 7. Spiracles are located in the enlarged ventral spot of each series. Scattered, small, dark colored rings about secondary setae present on all segments. Head, anal plate and lateral plates of anal prolegs light to deep brown. Anal horn reduced to shiny black spot surrounded by a lighter ring. Food, foliage of grapes and Virginia creeper.

Figure C. Lateral view of larva.

Figures D to F. Protoparce quinquemaculata Haw., tomato hornworm. F.g.l. 80-90 mm., green to dark reddish brown with conspicuous V-shaped greenish-white marks on each abdominal segment. Black spiracle on each segment located within the point of the V-shaped mark. One portion of the V-shaped mark is a diagonal line in front of and above the spiracle and the other a longitudinal irregular line ventrad of the spiracle. Anal horn is green with near-black marks on the sides and tip. This northern hornworm feeds on the foliage of tomato, tobacco, eggplant, pepper, potato and others including weeds.

Figure D. Lateral view of head and prothorax.

Figure E. Lateral view of fourth abdominal segment.

Figure F. An enlarged all-black abdominal spiracle.

Figures G to J. Protoparce sexta Johan., tobacco hornworm. F.g.l. 90 ± mm., green with conspicuous diagonal, elongated, greenish-white lines above the spiracles on each abdominal segment. Black pigment occurs in varying amounts between the crenulations. Oval spiracles light in color at top and bottom. Anal horn curved and near-red. This southern hornworm feeds on foliage of tobacco, tomato, eggplant, pepper, potato and others including weeds.

Figure G. Lateral view of larva.

Figure H. Lateral view of fourth abdominal segment with small amount of black pigment.

Figure I. Lateral view of fourth abdominal segment with large amount of black pigment.

Figure J. An enlarged, partly black, abdominal spiracle.

Figure K. Ceratomia amyntor Hbn., five pronged sphinx. F.g.l. 80-85 mm., stout, pale green or reddish brown, with one, conspicuous, caudal horn on the eighth segment and four prominent scoli on the thorax (one pair on the mesothorax and one on the metathorax). Abdominal segments 1 to 7 with 6 to 8 crenulations per segment. Along the dorsomeson of the abdomen a distinct ridge exists consisting of white to pink protuberances usually one per crenulation, each bearing secondary setae. Seven, similar, near-white, diagonal ridges dorsad of the spiracles occur on abdominal segments 1 to 8. Each diagonal ridge covers two segments. Head, thoracic legs and lateral aspects of all prolegs usually yellow to yellowish-brown. Elevated secondary setae numerous. Found in September on foliage of beech, birch, elm, linden, and probably ash. Felt, 1905.

Figure K. Lateral view of head to mesothorax.

Figures L to M. Celerio lineata F., white-lined sphinx, also L56, A. F.g.l. 75-85 mm., greenish yellow to near black. Among very light forms (L55, M) the black pigment occurs about the spiracles and large white spots or a line cephalodorsad of the spiracles while among deeply pigmented forms (L56, A) the entire dorsum may be black, with or without a middorsal line and with a few small light colored spots above the spiracles in rows or scattered. Venter never as deeply pigmented as dorsum. Head, cervical shield, anal plate and lateral plates on anal prolegs yellowish flecked with white pinacula of numerous setae. Caudal horn yellow and prominent. Food plants beech, elm, linden, ash and other deciduous plants.

Figure L. Lateral view of head to mesothorax.

Figure M. Lateral view of fourth abdominal segment.

Figures N and O. Ceratomia catalpae Bdv., catalpa sphinx. F.g.l. 75± mm., pale yellow, usually with a broad black band on the dorsum flanked with narrow white and black lines on each side. Spiracular area pale yellow marked with near-black vertical spots between the crenulations and bounded ventrally by an irregular near-black line. Among light colored forms no black pigment occurs in the spiracular area or below it, also a wide area along the dorsomeson on the abdominal segments may possess no black pigment. Head black. Black caudal spine on dorsomeson of eighth segment conspicuous. Larvae feed on foliage of all common species of catalpa, C. bungei most subject to attack. Baerg, 1935.

Figure N. Lateral view of head to mesothorax.

Figure O. Lateral view of fourth abdominal segment.

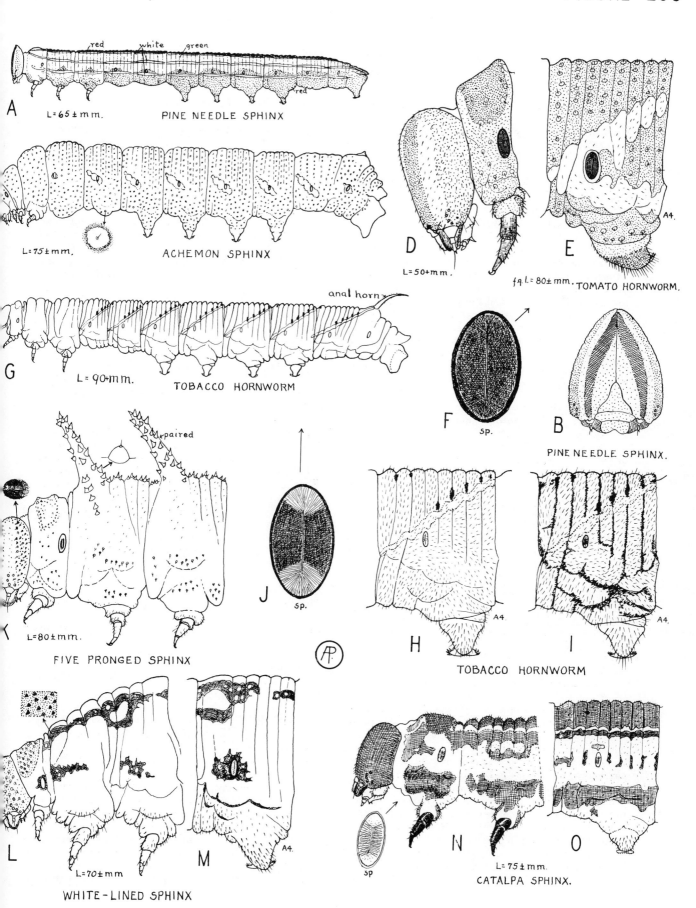

A L=65±mm. PINE NEEDLE SPHINX

red white green

ACHEMON SPHINX L=75±mm.

D L=50+mm.

E f.g.l.=80±mm. TOMATO HORNWORM.

G L=90+mm. TOBACCO HORNWORM

anal horn

F sp.

B PINE NEEDLE SPHINX.

paired

K L=80±mm. FIVE PRONGED SPHINX

J sp.

H A4.

I A4.

TOBACCO HORNWORM

L L=70±mm WHITE-LINED SPHINX

M A4.

N

O

sp.

L=75±mm. CATALPA SPHINX.

EXPLANATION OF FIGURES L56, A-M

SPHINGIDAE A-C, GEOMETRIDAE D-I, PHALAENIDAE J-M

Figure A. Celerio lineata F., white-lined sphinx. Lateral view of fourth segment of a deeply pigmented form. See L55, L-M for more details.

Figure B. Pholus satellitia L., var. pandorus Hbn. F.g.l. 75-80 mm., reddish brown to olive green with six, conspicuous, near-white oval spots on abdominal segments 2 to 7. Black spiracles are located within all of these spots except on the second segment where the spot is greatly reduced in size and dorsad of the spiracle. Scattered, small, near-black, round specks occur in the cuticle on some of the segments especially on the meso and metathorax and the first three abdominal segments. Head, cervical shield, anal plate, lateral plates of anal prolegs and ventral prolegs yellowish. Anal horn reduced to round, black, lustrous spot surrounded by yellow and white rings. Food, foliage of grapes and Virginia creeper. Lateral view of last instar.

Figure C. Pholus achemon Drury, achemon sphinx. Lateral view of abdominal segments 7 to 10 of a young, red larva (length 35 mm) possessing a well developed anal horn or process on the dorsomeson of the eighth abdominal segment. See L55, C for more details.

Figures D and E. Nemoria rubifrontaria Pack., a winged looper. F.g.l. 15-20 mm., sienna to yellow brown covered with coarse rugosities. Frequently suffused with orange, yellow or green. Lateral extensions more or less reddish brown. Surface of body covered with many blunt spine-like projections. Spiracles with dark brown peritremes located on the dorsum near bases of winged lateral projections on segments 2 to 4. Foodplant Comptonia asplendifolia Ait. For more detailed description see Dethier, 1942.

Figure D. Lateral view of larva.

Figure E. Dorsal view of second abdominal segment.

Figure F. Nematocampa limbata Haw., filament bearer or paired filament looper. F.g.l. 18-20 mm. Lateral view of looper showing one set of two unequal pairs of distended, elongated, fleshy filaments arising from the second and third abdominal segments, the caudal pair somewhat shorter than the cephalic pair. Over-all color mottled dusky brown, light gray to near-black. Filaments brown to black tipped with near-white. Head rusty red, also short rounded tubercles on first and eighth abdominal segments. Anal legs rusty lined with a whitish line. Food plants; oak, maple, crataegus, currant and strawberry. Packard, 1890.

Figures G to I. Itame ribearia Fitch., currant spanworm. F.g.l. 28-30 mm., near-white with broad yellow stripes on the dorsum and lateral aspects. Conspicuous deep brown to near-black, pinacula or spots, variable in size about all setae and elsewhere, so distributed that they produce broken longitudinal rows. Head yellowish with near-black pigment on the frons, about the ocelli and the dorsolateral aspects of the epicranium. Cervical shield and anal plate with few small dark spots. Spiracles near-black. Food, foliage of currant, gooseberry, blueberry and huckleberry.

Figure G. Lateral view of head to mesothorax.

Figure H. Lateral view of fifth to tenth abdominal segment.

Figure I. Mesal view of right mandible.

Note: Pigment of spots omitted on prothorax and abdominal segments 6 to 10.

Figures J to M. Meropleon cosmion Dyar., pink sugarcane borer. F.g.l. 35± mm., cream colored with dorsum distinctly pink in living specimens. Head, cervical shield, thoracic legs and small pinacula about setae yellow to yellowish brown. Anal plate yellowish-brown flecked with brown spots and caudal margin heavily sclerotized. Oval spiracles near-black, those on prothorax and eighth abdominal segments much larger than others. Crochets on prolegs homoideous mesoseries. Food plants, sugarcane, grasses and corn. Bynum and Holloway, 1924.

Figure J. Lateral view of head to mesothorax.

Figure K. Lateral view of fourth abdominal segment

Figure L. Lateral view of eighth to tenth abdominal segment.

Figure M. Mesal view of right mandible.

**Herse cingulata F., sweetpotato hornworm. F.g.l. 90± mm., greenish larva with a brownish head possessing three dark lines on each side of the head. The median stripe is the largest surrounding the ocelli at the ventral end. A light streak occurs along the dorsomeson flanked by two darker lines of approximately the same width. All of the spiracles are near-black each surrounded by a deeply pigmented circular area. Caudal horn prominent and near-black. True legs, lateral portions of the ventral prolegs and anal prolegs deeply pigmented. Food pland sweetpotato, morning glory and probably other Ipomaea and Convolvulus.

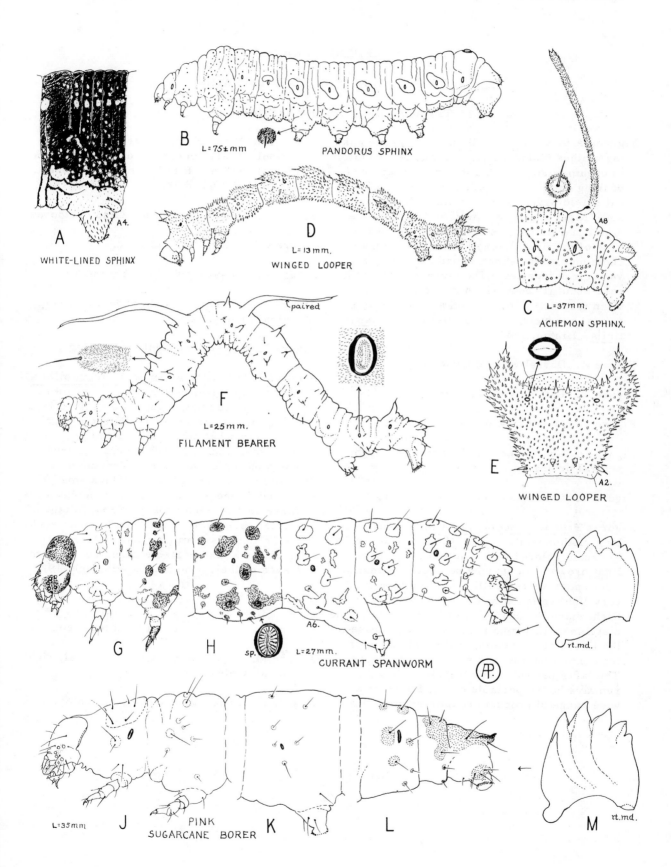

A. WHITE-LINED SPHINX A4.

B. PANDORUS SPHINX L=75±mm.

C. ACHEMON SPHINX. L=37mm. A8

D. WINGED LOOPER L=13mm.

E. WINGED LOOPER A2.

F. FILAMENT BEARER L=25mm. paired

G.

H. CURRANT SPANWORM L=27mm. A6. sp.

I. rt.md.

J. PINK SUGARCANE BORER L=35mm.

K.

L.

M. rt.md.

LEPIDOPTERA

EXPLANATION OF FIGURES L57, A-N

TINEIDAE A-J, INCURVARIIDAE K-N

Figures A to E. Tinea pellionella L., casemaking clothes moth. F.g.l. 8± mm., near-white to cream colored with a distinct brown head bearing one pair of ocelli and a brown cervical shield without pigment along the dorsomeson. Right mandible with five dentes on the distal margin and a small projection at the base of the first (lateral) tooth. Many crochets on prolegs short, broad at base and very close together. The larva constructs a case about its body which it carries about when feeding. They feed on a wide range of animal products. See food list for T. bisselliella. Hinton, 1943.

Figure A. Dorsal view of head and prothorax.

Figure B. Lateral view of head.

Figure C. Mesal view of right mandible.

Figure D. Crochets of sixth abdominal, right ventral proleg.

Figure E. Crochets of right anal proleg.

Figures F to J. Tineola bisselliella Hum., webbing clothes moth. F.g.l. 9± mm., near-white to cream colored with a distinct yellow to light brown head bearing no ocelli or vestigial light spots where ocelli should be found and a very light yellow to near white cervical shield. Right mandible usually with four dentes on the distal margin and no projection at the base of the first (lateral) tooth. All crochets on prolegs short, narrow and some distance apart. The larva produces silk webbing along its runways but no portable case. Feeds on a wide range of products containing animal ma-

terial such as bristles, hair, feathers, leather or wool. It also occurs in dried animal meat (meals), fish meal, milk powder, casein, dead insects and stuffed animals. Hinton, 1943.

Figure F. Dorsal view of head and prothorax.

Figure G. Lateral view of head.

Figure H. Mesal view of right mandible.

Figure I. Crochets of sixth abdominal, right, ventral proleg.

Figure J. Crochets of right anal proleg.

Figures K to N. Paraclemensia acerifoliella Fitch, maple leaf cutter. F.g.l. 6-7 mm., cream colored with light brown sclerotized areas on the dorsum of all thoracic segments. Body somewhat depressed. Head prognathous, depressed and yellowish-brown with rugose areas on the cephalodorsal aspects of the epicranium. Crochets of prolegs small ovals, hooked at one end and arranged in one transverse row on each proleg. Food, foliage of maples, especially sugar maple, and beech. Early stage is a miner. Late instars construct disk-like portable cases cut from the leaves of their food plants. Herrick, 1923.

Figure K. Dorsal view of larva.

Figure L. Lateral view of head to mesothorax.

Figure M. Crochets of sixth abdominal, right, ventral proleg.

Figure N. Crochets of right anal proleg.

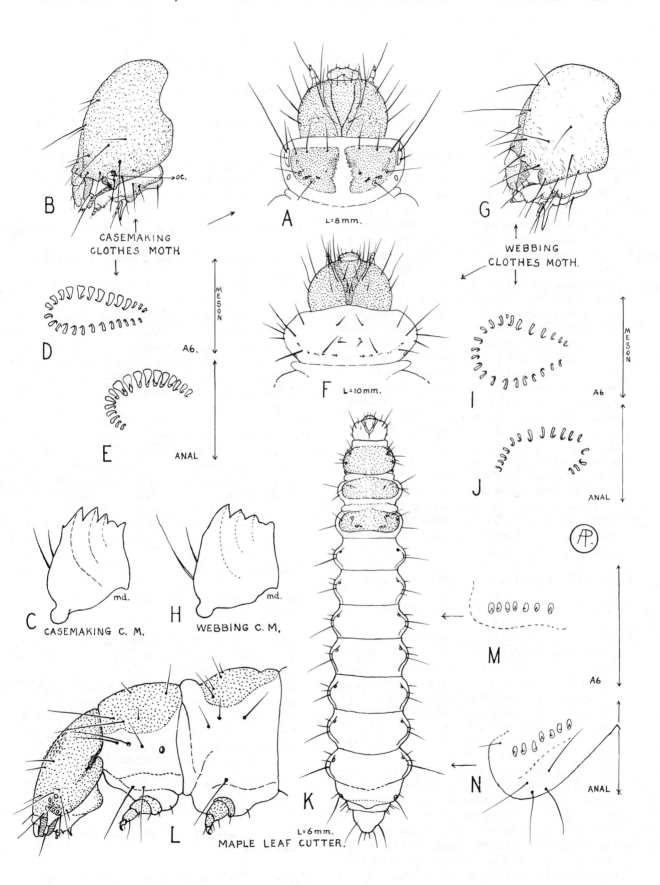

B

CASEMAKING
CLOTHES MOTH

D

E

A   L=8mm.

F   L=10mm.

MESON

A6.

ANAL

C   CASEMAKING C. M.

H   WEBBING C. M.

L

K   L=6mm.
MAPLE LEAF CUTTER.

G

WEBBING
CLOTHES MOTH.

I

J

MESON

A6

ANAL

M

A6

N

ANAL

LEPIDOPTERA

EXPLANATION OF FIGURES L58, A-J

ZYGAENIDAE A-D, PRODOXIDAE E-G, BOMBYCIDAE, H-J

Figures A and B. Harrisina brillians B. and McD., western grape skeletonizer. F.g.l. 16-18 mm., robust, slug-like and sulfur yellow with transverse rows of prominent verrucae on most segments. On the dorsum of the abdomen the setae on verrucae dorsad of the spiracles are near-black on all segments except 3 and 5 where they are light colored. The combined alpha (1) and beta (2) verrucae on the two sides of each segment are large and almost meet on the dorsomeson. The two transverse purplish bands present at the end of the thorax and on the sixth and seventh segments in living caterpillars are invisible in preserved specimens. Head brown to near black and retractible. Cervical shield and the narrow, transverse, anal plate are light brown and bear long black setae. Some very long, near-white, beaded setae arise from the verrucae ventrad of the spiracles, on the thorax and near the caudal end. Eversible glands dorsad of prothoracic legs. Partly grown larvae feed side by side and skeletonize foliage of wild and cultivated grapes and Virginia creeper. Larger larvae consume entire areas of the leaves and also attack leaf petioles and fruit, Wehrle, 1939, Lange, 1944.

Figure A. Lateral view of larva.

Figure B. Mesal view of right mandible.

Figures C and D. Harrisina americana Guer., grape leaf skeletonizer. Also L8, C. F.g.l. 11-13 mm., in many respects (sulfur yellow, retractile head, eversible glands and long beaded setae) resembles H. brillians except it is smaller. The preserved specimens examined show four longitudinal rows of dark verrucae on the dorsum which are less conspicuous than those on H. brillians, also there appears to be no color difference in the verrucae on the third and fifth abdominal segments. Some of the specimens show a narrow pigmented stripe on the dorsomeson and two wider pigmented stripes on the sides above the spiracles including rho (3) verrucae. Transverse pigmented bands may also occur between the thorax and the first abdom-

inal segment and between abdominal segments 6 and 7. Feeds in parallel groups skeletonizing the foliage of wild and cultivated grapes and Virginia creeper. Jones, 1909.

Figure C. Lateral view of head to mesothorax.

Figure D. Lateral view of fourth abdominal segment.

Figure E. Tegeticula yuccasella Riley, yucca moth. F.g.l. 14± mm. Lateral view of larva, pinkish to light red, especially the dorsum of all segments. Body somewhat c-shaped, with yellowish thoracic legs but no prolegs. Head yellowish to near-brown about mouth parts. Feeds on the developing seeds of Yucca filamentosa.

Figures F and G. Prodoxus quinquepunctella Cham., bogus yucca moth. F.g.l. 8± mm., short, stout, cyphosomatic, completely legless, shiny, cream colored, grub-like larva. Setae absent or minute, especially on the dorsal aspect. Head small, yellowish and retractible. Feeds in flower stem or flesh of the fruit of Yucca filamentosa.

Figure F. Lateral view of larva.

Figure G. Ventral view of head and mouth parts.

Figures H to J. Bombyx mori L., silkworm. F.g.l. 45± mm., near-white to cream colored, covered with numerous, small, secondary setae and a short caudal horn on the eighth abdominal segment but no crenulations (annulets) on the abdominal segments. Ventral prolegs far apart bearing biordinal crochets in a mesoseries. Food, chiefly foliage of several varieties of mulberry and osage orange.

Figure H. Lateral view of head to metathorax.

Figure I. Lateral view of fourth abdominal segment.

Figure J. Lateral view of abdominal segments 8 to 10.

226

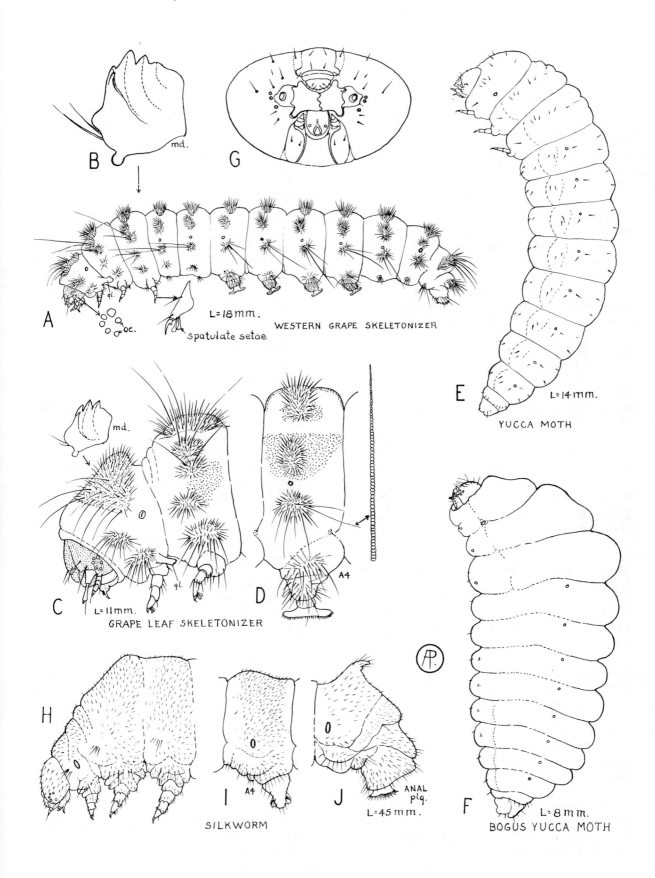

B md.

G

A gl. oc. spatulate setae L=18mm. WESTERN GRAPE SKELETONIZER

E L=14mm. YUCCA MOTH

C md. gl. L=11mm. GRAPE LEAF SKELETONIZER

D A4

H

I A4 SILKWORM

J ANAL plq. L=45mm.

F L=8mm. BOGUS YUCCA MOTH

A SELECTED BIBLIOGRAPHY FOR LARVAE OF LEPIDOPTERA

This bibliography contains many of the publications which give good to excellent descriptions or figures of larvae of nearctic species of Lepidoptera only, that are common, important or unusual. Also see excellent figures and descriptions of caterpillars which occur in some of the publications listed under "A selected general bibliography on nymphs and larvae of insects," (page 56). A complete listing of all papers has not been attempted.

In this bibliography the scientific name (that used by each author) of each larva described has been added to the title in most cases where it does not appear in the original.

Ainslie, G. G.
1918. Contributions to a knowledge of the Crambinae of North America. I. Ann. Ent. Soc. Amer. 11:51-62.

1922. Contributions to a knowledge of the Crambinae, II. Crambus laqueatellus Clemens. Ann. Ent. Soc. Amer. 15:125-136.

1923. Striped sod webworm, (Crambus mutabilis Clemens). Jour. Agr. Res. 24:399.

1923. Silver-striped webworm, (Crambus praefectellus Zincken). Jour. Agr. Res. 24:415.

1927. The large sod webworm, (Crambus trisectus Walk.). U.S.D.A. Tech. Bul. 31.

1930. The bluegrass webworm, (Crambus teterrellus Zincken). U.S.D.A. Tech, Bul. 173.

Ainslie, G. G. and W. B. Cartwright.
1921. Biology of the smartweed borer, (Pyrausta ainsliei Heinrich). Jour. Agr. Res. 20:837.

1922. Biology of the lotus borer, (Pyrausta penitalis Grote). U.S.D.A. Bul. 1076.

Balduf, W. V.
1930. The cycles and habits of Phlyctaenia tertialis, Guen, Proc. Ent. Soc. Wash. 32:31.

Baerg, W. J.
1923. The strawberry tiger moth, (Haploa reversa Stretch). Ark. Agr. Exp. Sta. Bul. 183.

1928. The three shade tree insects, (Thyridopteryx ephemeraeformis Haw, Datana integerrima G. and R., Hyphantria cunea Drury). Ark, Agr. Exp. Sta. Bul. 224.

Beckham, C. M.
1947. Biology of the spotted tentiform leafminer Lithocolletis crataegella Clem. on apple. Masters thesis, Ohio State Univ., Columbus, Ohio.

Beutenmüller, W.
1901. Monograph of the Sesiidae of America, north of Mexico. Mem. Amer. Mus. N. H. Memoir 1. Pt. VI, 215-352.

Bilsing, S. W.
1927. Studies on the biology of the pecan nut case bearer (Acrobasis caryae Grote). Texas Agr. Exp. Sta. Bul. 347.

Bishopp, F. C.
1923. The puss caterpillar and the effects of its sting on man, (Megalopyge opercularis S. and A.). U.S.D.A. Dept. Circ. 288.

Blakeslee, E. B.
1915. American plum borer, (Euzophera semifuneralis Walk.). U.S.D.A. Bul. 261.

Borror, D. J.
1943. Caterpillars. School Nature League Bull. Nat. Audubon Soc., Series 14. Bul. 1 Sept. 4 pages.

Bottimer, L. J.
1926. Notes on some Lepidoptera from eastern Texas. Jour. Agr. Res. 33:797.

Breakey, E. P.
1930. Contribution to a knowledge of the spindle worm, (Achatodes zeae Harris). Ann. Ent. Soc. Amer. 23:175-191.

Brooks, F. E.
1918. Papers on deciduous fruit insects. II. The grape root-borer (memthyrus polistiformis Harris, Aegerüdae). U.S.D.A. Bul. 730, p. 21-28.
1920. Pear borer (Aegeria pyri Harris). U.S.D.A. Bul. 887.

LEPIDOPTERA

Brunner, J.
1915. The Zimmerman pine moth, (Pinipestis zimmermani Grote). U.S.D.A. Bur. Ent. Bul. 295.

Burgess, A. F., and S. S. Crossman.
1927. The satin moth, a recently introduced pest. (Stilpnotia salicis L.) U.S.D.A. Bul. 1469.

1929. Imported insect enemies of the gypsy moth and brown tail moth (colored plates of larvae). U.S.D.A. Tech. Bul. 86.

Busck, A.
1915. The European pine-shoot moth, a serious menace to pine timber in America (Evetria (Rhyacionia) buoliana Schiff.). U.S.D.A. Bul. 170.

1917. The pink bollworm, (Pectinophora gossypiella Saund,, and Pyroderces rileyi Wlsm.). Jour. Agr. Res. 9:343-370.

1928. Phthorimaea lycopersicella, new species (Gelechiidae), a leaf feeder on tomato, Hawaiian Ent. Soc. Proc. 7:171.

Bynum, E. K. and T. E. Holloway.
1924. The new pink borer of sugar cane and corn, (Meropleon cosmion Dyar) Ann. Ent. Soc. Amer. 17:469.

Capps, H. W.
1939. Keys for the identification of some lepidopterous larvae frequently intercepted at quarantine. U.S.D.A. Bur. Ent. and P.Q. E-475 (mimeographed).

1946. Description of the larva of Keiferia peniculo Heinrich, with a key to the larvae of related species attacking eggplant, pepper, potato, and tomato in the United States. Ann. Ent. Soc. Amer. 39:561.

Chapman, T. A.
1902. The classification of Gracilaria and allied genera. Entomologist 35:81, 138-142 and 159-164.

Chittenden, F. H.
1901. The fall army worm and variegated cutworm, (Laphygma frugiperda S. and A. and Peridroma saucia Hbn.). U.S.D.A. Div. Ent. Bul. 29. n.s.

1899. Squash vine borer, (Melittia satyriniformis Hbn.). U.S.D.A. Bur. Ent. Cir. 38. 2d. s.

1911. The southern beet webworm (Pachyzancla bipunctalis Fabr.). U.S.D.A. Bur. Ent. Bul. 109, pt. 2.

1912. The larger canna leaf roller, (Calpodes ethlius Cram.). U.S.D.A. Bur. Ent. Circ. 145.

1912. The imported cabbage webworm (Hellula undalis Fab.). U.S.D.A. Bur. Ent. Bul. 109, pt. 3.

1913. The rose slug-caterpillar, (Euclea indetermina Boisd.) U.S.D.A. Bur. Ent. Bul. 124.

1913. The Florida fern caterpillar, (Eriopus floridensis Guen.). U.S.D.A. Bur. Ent. Bul. 125.

1913. The abutilon moth, (Cosmophila erosa Hbn.). U.S.D.A. Bur. Ent. Bul. 126.

1913. The spotted beet webworm, (Hymenia perspectalis Hbn.). U.S.D.A. Bur. Ent. Bul. 127.

1916. The pink corn-worm. An insect destructive to corn in the crib, (Batrachedra rileyi Wals.). U.S.D.A. Bul. 363.

1919. The rice moth, (Corcyra cephalonica Staint.). U.S.D.A. Bul. 783.

1920. The red-banded leaf-roller, (Eulia velutinana Walk.). U.S.D.A. Bul. 914.

1921. The European horse-radish webworm, (Evergestis straminalis Hbn.). U.S.D.A. Bul. 966.

Compton, C. C.
1937. Lineodes intergra Zell., a potential pest of greenhouse tomatoes. Jour. Econ. Ent. 30: 451-454.

Comstock, J. A.
1927. Butterflies of California. Publ. by author, 501 Edwards-Wildey Bldg., Los Angeles, California.

Cook, W. C.
1930. Field studies of the pale western cutworm, (Porosagrotis orthogonia Morr.). Colored plate. Montana A.E.S. Bul. 225.

1934. Cutworms and army worms, Minn. Agr. Exp. Sta. Extn. Circ. 48.

Crumb, S. E.
1915. Key to the cutworms affecting tobacco. J. Econ. Ent. 8:392-96.

1926. The bronzed cutworm (Nephelodes emmedonia Cramer), Lepidoptera. Proc. Ent. Soc. Wash. 28:201.

1926. The nearctic budworms of the lepidopterous genus Heliothis. Proc. U. S. Nat. Mus. 68:1-8.

1927. The army worms. Bul. Brooklyn Ent. Soc. 22:41-53.

1929. Tobacco cutworms. (many species). U.S.D.A. Tech. Bul. 88.

1932. The more important climbing cutworms. Bul. Brooklyn Ent. Soc. 27:73-98.

1934. A classification of some noctuid larvae of the sub-family Hypeninae. Ent. Amer. 14:133-196. n.s.

Davenport, D. D. and V. G. Dethier.
1937. Bibliography of the described life-histories of Rhopalocera of America north of Mexico, (1889-1937). (1947 supplement of Dethier), Entomologica Americana, 17:155-194.

Davis, E. G., J. R. Horton, C. H. Gable, E. V. Walter, R. A. Blanchard, and C. Heinrich.
1933. The southwestern corn borer, (Diatraea grandiosella Dyar). U.S.D.A. Tech. Bul. 388.

Davis, J. J. and A. F. Satterthwait.
1916. Life history studies of Cirphis unipuncta, the true army worm. Jour. Agr. Res. 6:799.

Decker, G. C.
1930. The biology of the four-lined borer, (Luperina stipata Morr.) Iowa Agr. Exp. Sta. Res. Bul. 125.

1931. The biology of the stalk borer, (Papaipema nebris Gn.). Iowa Agr. Exp. Sta. Res. Bul. 143.

Dethier, V. G.
1941. Antennae of lepidopterous larvae. Bul. Mus. Comp. Zool. Harvard, 87:455.

1942. Notes on the life histories of five common Geometridae. Canadian Ent. 74:225-234.

1946. Supplement to the bibliography of the described life-histories of the Rhopalocera of America north of Mexico. Psyche 53:15-20.

Ditman, L. P. and E. N. Cory.
1931. The corn earworm biology and control, (Heliothis obsoleta Fab.). Maryland Agr. Exp. Sta. Bul. 328.

Drake, C. J. and G. C. Decker.
1927. Some caterpillars frequently mistaken for the European corn borer. Iowa Agr. Exp. Sta. Circ. 103.

Dunnam, E. W.
1924. The apple trumpet leaf miner, (Tischeria malifoliella Clem.). Iowa State Col. Agr. Exp. Sta. Bul. 220.

Dyar, H. G.
1890. The genus Datana. Ent. Americana 6:129-132.

1893. On the larval cases of North American Psychidae. Ent. News. 4:320-21.

1894. A classification of lepidopterous larvae. Ann. N. Y. Acad. Sci. 3:194-232.

1895. Additional notes on the classification of lepidopterous larvae. Trans. N. Y. Acad. Sci. 14:49-63.

1895-1899. The life histories of the New York slug caterpillars. 18 articles and conclusion. Jour. N. Y. Ent. Vols. 3-7. First papers with E. L. Morton.

1896. Notes on the head setae of Lepidopterous larvae, with special reference to the appendages of Perophora melsheimerii Harr. (Lacosomidae). Jour. N. Y. Ent. Soc. 4:92.

1896. A new Anisota, (Anisota consularis Dyar). Jour. N. Y. Ent. Soc. 4:166.

1898. Descriptions of the larvae of fifty North American Noctuidae. Proc. Ent. Soc. Wash. 4:315-32.

1900. Preliminary notes on the larvae of the genus Arctia. Jour. N. Y. Ent. Soc. 8:34-47.

1914. The pericopid larvae in the National Museum. Insecutor Inscitiae Menstruvs. 2:62-64.

Edwards, W. H.
1868-72, 1884, 1897. The butterflies of North America. Vol. 1. Amer. Ent. Soc. Phil., Vol. 2 and 3 Houghton, Mifflin and Co., Boston & N. Y.

Ellis, W. O.
1925. Some lepidopterous larvae resembling the European corn borer, (Pyrausta nubilalis Hbn.). Jour. Agr. Res. 30:777.

Evenden, J. C.
1926. The pine butterfly, (Neophasia menapia Felder). Jour. Agr. Res. 33:339.

Fink, D. E.
1915. The verbena bud moth, (Olethreutes hebesana Walk.) U.S.D.A. Bur. Ent. Bul. 226.

Flint, W. P. and J. R. Malloch.
1920. The European corn borer and some similar native insects. Ill. Nat. Hist. Survey Bul. 13:art. X, 287-305.

Forbes, S. A.
1890. The American plum borer, (Euzophera semifuneralis Wlkr.). Psyche 5:295.

1905. Cutworms attacking corn. 23 Rept. Ill. State Ent., p. 231.

Forbes, W. T. M.
1906. Field tables of Lepidoptera. Worcester, Mass, 141 p.

1910. The aquatic caterpillars of Lake Quinsigamond. (Keys to species of Nymphuline caterpillars.) Psyche 17:219-227

1911. A structural study of some caterpillars. Ann. Ent. Soc. Amer. 3:94-132.

1910. A structural study of some caterpillars - II, the Sphingidae. (Key to species.) Ann. Ent. Soc. Amer. 4:261-279.

1923. The Lepidoptera of New York and neighboring states. Cornell Agr. Exp. Sta. Memoir 68, 729 pages.

Fracker, S. B.
1915.(revised 1930). The classification of lepidopterous larvae. Univ.of Ill. Biol. Monograph, Vol. 2, No. 1.

Friend, R. B.
1927. The biology of the birch leaf skeletonizer (Bucculatrix canadensisella Chamb.). Conn. Agr. Exp. Sta. Bul. 288.

1931. The squash vine borer.(Melittia satyriniformis Hbn.). Conn. Agr. Exp. Sta. Bul. 328.

Frohne, W. C.
1939. Biology of Chilo forbesellus, and hygrophilous crambine moth. Trans. Amer. Micro. Soc. 58:304.

1939. Observations on the biology of three semiaquatic lacustrine moths, (Nepticula sp., Schoenobius melinellus dispersellus Robinson and Occidentalia comptulatalis Hulst.). Trans. Amer. Micro. Soc. 58:327-348.

Frost, S. W.
1921. Lepidoptera injurious to the apple in Pennsylvania (including a key to the Microlepidoptera of Pennsylvania which feed on the foliage and fruit of apple). Penn. State Col. Agr. Exp. Sta. Bul. 169.

1927. Notes on the life history of the bud moth, (Spilonota ocellana D. and S.). Jour. Agr. Res. 35:347.

Garman, H. and H. H. Jewett.
1914. The life history and habits of the corn ear-worm,(Chloridea obsoleta Fab.). Colored plate of larvae. Ky. Agr. Exp. Sta. Bul. 187.

Garman, H.
1920. Observations on the structure and coloration of the larval corn ear-worm, the budworm and a few other lepidopterous larvae. Ky. Agr. Exp. Sta. Bul. 227 (Res.).

1921. A destructive bud worm of apple trees (Haploa lecontei Guer.). Ky. Agr. Exp. Sta. Circ. 25.

Garman, P.
1917. The oriental peach pest. (Laspeyresia molesta Busck). Maryland Agr. Exp. Sta. Bul. 209.

1918. A comparison of several species of Lepidoptera infesting peach and apple in Maryland with additional notes on the oriental peach moth. Maryland Agr. Exp. Sta. Bul. 223.

Gerasimov, A.
1937. Bestimmungstabelle der familien von schmetterlingsraupen (Lep.). Stett. Ent. Zeitung 98:281.

Gibson, A.
1915. The army-worm Cirphus (Leucania) unipuncta Haw. Dom. Canada Dept. Agr. Ent. Bul. 9.

1920. Boring caterpillars affecting corn and other crops and which are liable to be mistaken for the European corn borer. Can. D. A. Ent. Br. Circ. 14, Tech.

Gill, J. B.
1917. The pecan leaf case- bearer, (Acrobasis nebulella Riley). U.S.D.A. Bul. 571.

1925. The pecan nut case- bearer, (Acrobasis hebescella Hulst.). U.S.D.A. Bul. 1303.

Gilliatt, F. C.
1929. A key to certain tortricid larvae occuring in Nova Scotia with notes on their habits and life histories. Sci. Agr. Canada, Vol. 10:120-127.

Graf, J. E.
1917. The potato tuber moth (Phthorimaea operculella Zell.). U.S.D.A. Bur. Ent. Bul. 427.

Griswold, G. H.
1944. Studies on the biology of the webbing clothes moth, (Tineola bisselliella Hum.). Cornell Univ. Agr. Exp. Sta. Memoirs 262.

Hanson, A. J. and R. L. Webster.
1936. The pea moth, (Laspeyresia nigricana Steph.). Wash. Agr. Exp. Sta. Bul. 327.

Hawley, N. M.
1926. The fruit tree leaf roller and its control by oil sprays (Archips argyrospila Walk.). Utah Agr. Exp. Sta. Bul. 196.

Heinrich, C.
1916. On the taxonomic value of some larvae characters in the Lepidoptera. Proc. Ent. Soc. Wash. 18:155.

1919. Notes on the European corn borer (Pyrausta nubilalis Hbn.) and its nearest American allies with descriptions of larvae, pupae and one new species. Jour. Agr. Res. 18:171.

1921. Some Lepidoptera likely to be confused with the pink bollworm (Pectinophora gossypiella Saund.). Jour. Agr. Res. 20;807.

Herrick, G. W. and R. W. Leiby.
1915. The fruit tree leaf roller, (Archips argyrospila Wlk.). Cornell Univ. Agr. Exp. Sta. Bul. 367.

1923. The maple case-bearer, (Paraclemensia acerifoliella Fitch). Cornell Univ. Agr. Exp. Sta. Bul. 417.

Hill, C. C.
1925. Biological studies of the green clover worm, (Plathypena scabra Fabr.). U.S.D.A. Bul. 1336.

Hinds, W. E.
1912. Cotton worm or "caterpillars," (Alabama argillacea Hbn.). Ala. Agr. Exp. Sta. Bul. 164.

Hinds, W. E. and J. A. Dew.
1915. The grass worm or false army worm, (Laphygma·frugiperda, A. and S.). Alabama Agr. Exp. Sta. Bul. 186.

Hinton, H. E.
1943. Larvae of the Lepidoptera associated with stored products. Bul. Ent. Res. 34:163.

Holland, W. J.
1903. The moth book. Doubleday, Page and Co., Garden City, N. Y.

1914, (revised 1942). The butterfly book. Doubleday, Page and Co., Garden City, N. Y.

Holloway, T. E.
1916. Larval characters and distribution of two species of Diatraea (D. saccharalis crambdoides Fab. and D. zeacolella Dyar). Jour. Agr. Res. 6:621.

Holloway, T. E., W. E. Haley, U. C. Loftin and C. Heinrich.
1928. Sugar cane moth borer in the United States, (Diatraea saccharalis Fab.). U.S.D.A. Tech. Bul. 41. Also see U.S.D.A. Bul. 746 (1919).

Howard, L. O. and F. H. Chittenden.
1907. The catalpa sphinx, (Ceratomia catalpae Bdv.). U.S.D.A. Bur. Ent. Circ. 96.

1909. The leopard moth, (Zeuzera pyrina Fab.). U.S.D.A. Bur. Ent. Circ. 109.

1909. The green-striped maple worm (Anisota rubicunda Fab.). U.S.D.A. Bur. Ent. Circ. 110.

Howard, L. O. and W. F. Fiske.
1911. The importation into the United States of the parasites of the gypsy moth and the brown-tail moth, (colored figures of larvae). U.S.D.A. Bur. Ent. Bul. 91.

Hutchings, C. B.
1924. The lesser oak carpenter worm and its control. (Prionoxystus macmurtrei Guer.). Can. D. A. Ent. Br. Circ. 23.

Hyslop, J. A.
1912. The legume pod moth, (Etiella zinckenella schistocolor Zell.). U.S.D.A. Bur. Ent.
Bul. 95, pt. 6

Ingerson, H. G.
1918. The striped peach worms, (Gelechia
confusella Cham.). U.S.D.A. Bur, Ent. Bul.
599.

Isely, D.
1918. Orchard injury by the hickory tiger-
moth, (Halisidota caryae Harr.). U.S.D.A.
Bur. Ent. Bul. 598.

1920. Grapevine looper, (Lygris diversilineata Hbn.). U.S.D.A. Bul. 900.

Jones, P. R.
1909. The grape-leaf skeletonizer (Harris-
ana americana Guen.). U.S.D.A. B, E. Bul.
68, pt. 8.

Jones, T. H. 1923. T
1923. The egg plant leaf miner, (Phthaori-
maea glochinella Zell.). Jour. Agr. Res.
26:567.

Johnson, F. and A. G. Hammar.
1912. The brape berry moth, (Polychrosis
viteana Clem.). U.S.D.A. Bur. Ent. Bul. 116,
pt. 2, pp. 15-71.

Keifer, H. H.
1935-1937. California Microlepdoptera VII,
X, XI and XII. Calif. Dept. Agr. Monthly Bul.
24:195; 25:349; 26:177; and 26:334.

King, J. L.
1917. The lesser peach tree borer, (Synanthedon pictipes G. & R.). Ohio Agr. Exp. Sta.
Bul. 307.

Knowlton, G. F. and M. W. Allen.
1937. Oblique-banded leaf roller, a dewberry
pest in Utah, (Cacoecia rosaceana Harr.).
Jour. Econ. Ent. 30:780-785.

Lange, W. H., Jr.
1939. Early stages of California plume moths.
No. 1. So. Cal. Acad. Sci. 38:20.

1939. Two new California plume moths. So.
Cal. Acad. Sci. 38:157.

1941. The artichoke plume moth (Platyptilia
carduidactyla Riley) and other pests injurious
to the globe artichoke. Calif. Agr. Exp. Sta.
Bul. 653.

1942. Certain plum moths of economic importance in California, (Platyptilia species).
Jour. Econ. Ent. 35:718.

1944. The western grape leaf skeletonizer
Harrisina brillians in California. Cal. Bul.
Dept. Agr. Vol. 33:98.

Leach, Br. R.
1916. The apple leaf-sewer (Ancylis nubecu-
lana Clem.). U.S.D.A. Bur. Ent. Bul. 435.

Leiby, R. W.
1920. The larger corn stalk borer in North
Carolina, (Diatraea zeacolella Dyar). N. C.
Dept. Agr. Vol. 41, No. 13.

Lloyd, J. T.
1914. Lepidopterous larvae from rapid
streams, (Elophila fulicalis Clem.). Jour.
N. Y. Ent. Soc. 22:145.

Lopez, A. W.
1929. Morphological studies of the head and
mouth parts of the mature codling moth larva,
(Carpocapsa pomonella Linn.). Univ. of Calif.
Publ. Ent. 5:19-36.

Luginbill, P. and G. G. Ainslie.
1917. The lesser corn stalk-borer, (Elasmopalpus lignosellus Zell.). U.S.D.A. Bul. 539.

Luginbill, P.
1928. The fall army worm, (Laphygma frugiperda S. and A.). U.S.D.A. Tech. Bul. 34.

McDonald, H.
1947. Biology and control of Heliothis ononis
Schiff. An important new pest of flax in western Canada. Ph. D. thesis, Ohio State University, Columbus, Ohio.

McDunnough, J.
1936. Further notes on Canadian plume moths-
Pterophoridae. Can. Ent. 68:63-69.

1938-39. Check list of the Lepidoptera of
Canada and the United States of America.
Mem. So. Calif. Acad. Sci., Part 1. Macro-
lepidoptera; part 2, Microlepidoptera.

McGuffin, W. C., A. W. A. Brown and M. R.
MacKay.
1942-1946. A series of publications presenting detailed description and some figures of
larvae of forest insects, chiefly Geometridae,
Phalaenidae and Tortricidae. The Can. Ent.
Vols. 74-78.

Marsh, H. O.
1912. The sugar-beet webworm, (Loxostege sticticalis L.). U.S.D.A. Bur. Ent. Bul. 109, pt. 6.

1913. The striped beet caterpillar (Mamestra trifolii Rott.) U.S.D.A. Bur. Ent. Bul. 127, pt. 2.

1916. The Hawaiian beet webworm, (Hymenia fascialis Cram.) U.S.D.A. Bur. Ent. Bul. 109, pt. 1.

1917. Life history of Plutella maculipinnis, the diamond-back moth. Jour. Agr. Res. 10:1.

Matthewman, W. G.
1937. Observations on the life history and habits of the columbine borer, (Papaipema purpurifascia G. and R.). Ent. Soc. Ont. Rept. 67:69-72.

Meyrick, E.
1928. Revised handbook of British Lepidoptera, London, England.

Neiswander, C. R.
1941. Coryphista meadii Pack., a new pest of Japanese barberry. Jour. Econ. Ent. 34:386-389.

Nelson, R. H.
1936. Observations on the life history of Platynota stultana Wlsm. on greenhouse rose. Jour. Econ. Ent. 29:306-312.

Packard, A. S.
1895-1912. Monograph of the Bombycine moths of North America including their transformations and origin of the larval markings and armature. Memoirs National Acad. of Sci. 1895, Vol. 7, part 1, Notodontidae. 1905, Vol. 9, part 2, Ceratocampidae, Ceratocampinae. 1912, Vol. 12, part 3, Ceratocampidae (exclusive of Ceratocampinae), Saturniidae, Hemileucidae and Brahmeidae.

1895. On the larvae of the Hepialidae. Jour. N. Y. Ent. Soc. 3:69-73.

Parker, J. R., A. L. Strand and H. L. Seamans.
1921. Pale western cutworm (Porosagrotis orthogonia Morr.) Jour. Agr. Res. 22:289.

Parrott, P. J., and W. J. Schoene.
1912. The apple and cherry ermine moths. (Yponomeuta malinellus Zell and Y. padellus L.). N. Y. Agr. Exp. Sta. Geneva Tech. Bul. 24.

Patch, E. M.
1908. The saddled prominent, (Heterocampa guttivitta Walk.). Maine Agr. Exp. Sta. Bul. 161.

1921. A meadow caterpillar, "the adventurer" (Ctenucha virginica Charp.), (colored plate). Maine Agr. Exp. Sta. Bul. 302.

Patterson, J. E.
1921. Life history of Recurvaria milleri, Busck, the lodgepole pine needle miner, in the Yosemite National Park, California. Jour. Agr. Res. 21:127-142.

1929. The pandora moth, a periodic pest of western pine forests, (Coloradia pandora Blake). U.S.D.A. Tech. Bul. 137.

Peterson, A.
1912. Anatomy of the tomato worm larva, Protoparce carolina L. Ann. Ent. Soc. Amer. 5:247.

1923. The peach tree borer in New Jersey, (Sanninoidea exitiosa Say). N. J. Agr. Exp. Sta. Bul. 391.

Porter, B. A.
1924. The cankerworms, (Alsophila pometaria Harr. and Paleacrita vernata Peck.). U.S.D.A. Bul. 1238.

1924. The bud moth, (Spilonota ocellana D. and S.). U.S.D.A. Bul. 1273.

Porter, B. A. and P. Garman.
1923. The apple and thorn skeletonizer, (Hemerophila pariana Clerck) Conn. Agr. Exp. Sta. Bul. 246.

Quaintance, A. L.
1898. Three injurious insects, bean leaf-roller (Endamus proteus Linn.), Corn Delphax (Delphax maidis Ash), and canna leaf-roller (Hydrocampa cannalis Fern.). Florida Agr. Exp. Sta. Bul. 45.

1901. The pickle-worm, (Margaronia nitidalis Cram.). Georgia Agr. Exp. Sta. Bul. 54.

Quaintance, A. L. and C. T. Brues.
1905. The cotton bollworm (corn earworm, Heliothis obsoleta Fab.). U.S.D.A. Bur. Ent. Bul. 50.

Reinhard, H. J.
1929. The cotton-square borer, (Strymon melinus Hbn.). Texas Agr. Exp. Sta. Bul. 401.

Richards, O. W. and Thomson, W. S.
1932. A contribution to the study of the genera Ephestia Gn. (including Strymax, Dyar) and Plodia Gn. (Lep., Phycitidae), with notes on parasites of the larvae. Ent. Soc. London, Trans. 80:169-250.

Ripley, L. B.
1924. The external morphology and postembryology of noctuid larvae. Ill. Biol. Monographs 8, pt. 4, 102 pp.

Rockwood, L. P. and S. K. Zimmerman.
1931. A seed catarpillar, Grapholitha conversana Wlsm., on a native clover in north Pacific region. Jour. Agr. Res. 43:57.

Scammell, H. B.
1917. Cranberry girdler, (Crambus hortuellus Hbn.). U.S.D.A. Bul. 554.

Scudder, S. H.
1889. The butterflies of the eastern United States and Canada. Cambridge, Mass. 3 volumes. Vol. 1, Nymphalidae and Satyrinidae. Vol. 2. Lycaenidae, Paplilionidae and Hesperidae. Vol. 3, illustrations.

1890. A study of the caterpillars of North America swallowtail butterflies. I. Psyche 8:206-210.

1893. Brief guide to the common butterflies of the northern United States and Canada. Henry Holt & Co., N. Y.

Silver, J. C.
1933. Biology and morphology of the spindle worm or elder borer, (Achatodes zeae Harr.). U.S.D.A. Tech. Bul. 345.

Simpson, C. B.
1903. The codling moth, (Carpocapsa pomonella L.). U.S.D.A. Div. Ent. Bul. 41.

Slingerland, M. V.
1896. Green fruit worms, (Xylina antennata Walk., X. laticinerea Grt. and X. grotei Riley). Cornell Univ. Agr. Exp. Sta. Bul. 123.

1897. The pistol-case-bearer, (Coleophora malivorella Riley). Cornell Univ. Agr. Exp. Sta. Bul. 124.

1904. The grape berry moth, (Polychrosis viteana Clem.). Cornell Agr. Exp. Sta. Bul. 223.

Smith, H. B. and H. G. Dyar.
1898. A revision of Acronycta (Ochsenheimer) and of certain allied genera. Proc. U. S. Nat. Mus. 21:1-194.

Smith, R. I.
1911. Two important cantaloupe pests, (Diaphania nitidalis Stoll. and Diaphania hyalineata L.). N. C. Agr. Exp. Sta. Bul. 214.

Snodgrass, R. E.
1922. The resplendent shield-bearer, (Coptodisca splendoriferella) and the ribbed-cocoon-maker (Bucculatrix pomifoliella). Smithsonian Rept. 1920, p. 485. (No. 2641.)

Strauss, J. F.
1916. The grape leaf-folder, (Desmia funeralis Hbn.). U.S.D.A. Bul. 419.

Strohecker, H. F.
1938. The larval and pupal stages of two tropical American butterflies. (Athena petreus Cramer figured.) Ohio Jour. Sci. 38:294-295.

Symons T. B. and L. M Peairs.
1910. The codling moth, Carpocapsa pomonella L.). Maryland Agr. Exp. Sta. Bul. 142.

Thomas, C. A.
1936. The tomato pin worm.(Gnorimoschima lycopersicella Busck.) Penn. Agr. Exp. Sta. Bul. 337.

Tietz, H. M.
1936. The Noctuidae of Pennsylvania (food plants). Penn. State College Agr. Ept. Sta. Bul. 335.

Vickery, R. A.
1926. Observations on Cirphis latiuscula H. Sch. in the gulf coast region of Texas. Jour. Agr. Res. 32:1099-1119.

Webster, R. L.
1909. The lesser apple leaf-folder, (Peronea minuta Rob.). Iowa State Col. Agr. Exp. Sta. Bul. 102.

1911. The wheat-head army-worm as a timothy pest, (Meliana albilinea Hbn.) Iowa Agr. Exp. Sta. Bul. 122.

Wehrle, L. P.
1924. The clover-seed caterpillar, (Laspeyresia interstinctana Clem.). Cornell Agr. Exp. Sta. Bul. 428.

1929. The clover-leaf caterpillar (Olethreutes cespitana Hbn.) and the clover-leaf tyer (Anchylopera angulifasciana Zell.). Cornell Agr. Exp. Sta. Bul. 489.

Weed, C. M.
1887. Life history of Danais archippus. Prairie Farmer. 30, July 59: 487.
1899. The spiny elm caterpillar, (Nymphalis antiopa L.). N. H. Agr. Exp. Sta. Bul. 67.

Weigel, C. A., B. M. Broadbent, A. Busck and C. Heinrich.
1924. The greenhouse leaf-tyer, (Phlyctaenia rubigalis Guen.). Jour. Agr. Res. 29:137.

Welch, P. S.
1916. Contribution to the biology of certain aquatic Lepidoptera. (Nymphula). Ann. Ent. Soc. Amer. 9:159-187.

Whelan, D. B.
1935. A key to the Nebraska cutworms and army worms that attack corn. Nebraska Agr. Exp. Sta. Res. Bul. 81.

Whitcomb, W. D. and W. E. Tomlinson, Jr.
1940. The grape plum moth, (Oxyptilus periscelidactylus Fitch). Jour. Econ. Ent. 33:372.

Wildermuth, V. L.
1911. The alfalfa caterpillar, (Eurymus eurytheme Bdvl.). U.S.D.A. Bur. Ent. Circ. 133.

1916. The New Mexico range caterpillar and its control, (Hemileuca oliviae Ckll.). U.S.D.A. Bur. Ent. Bul. 443.

Wilson, H. F.
1919. The common cabbage worm in Wisconsin (Pontia rapae Linn.). Wisc. Agr. Exp. Sta. Res. Bul. 45.

Wilson, J. W.
1934. The asparagus caterpillar; its life history and control, (Laphygma exigua Hbn.). Florida agr. Exp. Sta. Bul. 271.

Wolcott, G. H.
1933-1934. Lima bean pod-borer caterpillars of Puerto Rico, (Maruca testularis Geyer, Fundella cistipennis Dyar and Etiella zinckenella Treit.). Jour. Dept. Agr. Puerto Rico 17:241 and 18:429.

Wood, W. B. and E. R. Selkregg.
1918. Further notes on oriental peach moth (Laspeyresia molesta, Busck. Jour. Agr. Res. 13:59.

LARVAE OF HYMENOPTERA

Chiefly Plant Infesting Species

Larval stages of the Hymenoptera are probably less well known than those of any of the four major orders possessing larvae. This is particularly true in the suborder Apocrita (Clistogastra) containing the following superfamilies, Ichneumonoidea, Cynipoidea, Chalcidoidea, Serphoidea, Bethyloidea, Formicoidea, Chrysidoidea, Specoidea, Vespoidea and Apoidea.

Structurally the external morphology of the larvae of the Apocrita is more simplified than that of the Symphyta (Chalastogastra) especially among late instar individuals. Among the Formicoidea and Apoidea the larvae are soft bodied, frequently c-shaped, faintly segmented and pointed at the head end. Among the Apoidea no distinct sclerotized head is apt to be present and sclerotized mouth parts are usually wanting. Inconspicuous spiracles may be present on most thoracic and abdominal segments. Among the families possessing species parasitic on or in other insects a partial or distinctly sclerotized head possessing sharp pointed, opposable mandibles may be present. This is particularly true of the first instar of many species. Late instars, especially the last, may not possess a sclerotized head or well defined mandibles, also they may be soft bodied, faintly segmented, straight, cyphosomatic or c-shaped. For descriptions and figures of larvae of many parasitic Hymenoptera see Clausen, 1940, and the numerous references cited.

The following discussion presents a condensed survey of the habits and external morphology of the Symphyta. It is far from complete yet presents the information a beginning student needs to classify most larvae of this suborder. For a more thorough presentation read pages 14 to 34 in Yuasa, 1922. Also for detailed discussions of the names, which some investigators apply to various folds and areas that occur on the tergum, pleurum and sternum, see Middleton, 1921 (Jour. Agr. Res.) or Atwood and Peck, 1943.

Larvae of the Symphyta feed on plant tissues except the Orussidae which are parasites of wood boring Coleoptera. Most species feed openly on the foliage of many kinds of plants, especially trees and bushes. Some are gregarious and live in silken webs. Other species are leaf rollers, gall producers, leaf miners or borers in buds, fruits, petioles, stems, twigs, branches or trunks of coniferous or deciduous plants.

Most larvae of the Symphyta are caterpillar-like (H1,A) nearly cylindrical, with the diameter of the caudal segments usually somewhat smaller than those near the cephalic end. Among leaf miners the segments are apt to be distinctly depressed. Body division and segments are usually distinct, consisting of a well defined head, three thoracic segments and ten abdominal segments. In most species the segments are subdivided into transverse annulets (crenulations, plicae or pleats) particularly on the dorsal aspect, (H1, I). Larvae in this group vary considerably in size, some of the leaf miners are very small, in some cases not more than 5 mm. in length while other species of leaf feeders and some wood borers may be fairly large, 50 mm. or more in length. Most external leaf feeding species are 15 to 30 mm. long.

Head. (H1, K and L.) All larvae of the Symphyta possess a distinct head with opposable, chewing mouth parts which resemble the mouth parts found in larvae of many Coleoptera or Lepidoptera. In the vast majority of species the head and mouth parts are hypognathous while among some leaf miners and wood boring species they are prognathous or nearly so. Most species possess a well exposed head. Among a few leaf miners and wood borers, the prothorax covers a portion of the dorsal and lateral aspects.

The head capsule is nearly globose and decidedly circular on the cephalic aspect especially among the external leaf feeding Tenthredinoidea. The head may be deeply or lightly pigmented. Its surface may be smooth, polished, roughened or granulate. Fine or peglike setae may be numerous on the entire head or confined to the ventral and cephalic aspects or practically absent. There is no indication that a consistent setal pattern exists, however, setal distribution and structure are useful in differentiating some genera and subfamilies.

On the head a distinct inverted Y-shaped epicranial suture exists among all species except Xiphydriidae. A vertical furrow occurs on each side of the head near the dorsal aspect of most sawfly larvae. It is wanting among some leaf miners and wood borers. The front is distinct, bounded by the arms of the epicranial suture and the clypeus and may bear setae. The coronal suture is usually distinct and in no case greatly reduced in length. The clypeus is usually a distinct transverse sclerite, much wider than long and never deeply pigmented. Two to ten setae may be present on the clypeus. Four is the usual number. The labrum, attached to the clypeus is a typical larval upper lip with a shallow or deep emargination on the distal margin near the meson. Two to several setae may be present. In the genus Dolerus a distinct assymmetry exists in that the sinistral half is much smaller than the dextral.

One distinct ocellus (ocellara) occurs on the lower half of each side of the head of most sawfly larvae. They are absent or vestigial among the Xiphydriidae or reduced to pigment spots among some Cephidae. Each ocellus is usually clear, globose, distinctly convex and usually surrounded by a deeply pigmented, conspicuous circular ring (ocularia). The single ocellus on each side is a very useful character for differentiating caterpillarlike sawfly larvae from most true caterpillars of the Lepidoptera.

Antennae (H1, B-E), are located on the lower half of the vertex dorsad of the mandibles. They may be cephalad or ventrad of the ocelli. About the base of each antenna a subcircular or subquadrate sclerotized ring, called the antennaria, exists. Within bounds of the antennaria a whitish, usually convex, membrane, called the antacoria, is present. The first antennal segments, crescentric remnants or small sclerotized subcircular areas of the antennae are surrounded by the antacoria. The number of segments in the antenna may be one (Siricidae) to seven (Pamphiliidae). In many cases the individual segments are somewhat or completely reduced to partial or vestigial, sclerotized rings or crescent-shaped pieces or bars located in the membranous antacoria. These pieces are considered to be remnants of segments and are counted in determining the number of segments in a given antenna. Their arrangement and structure also provide useful characters in the determination of species.

Formulae for segmented appendages showing the number and length of the segments apply among antennae. Segment number one is the proximal or basal segment. In the formula the numbers are arranged according to their length starting with the longest. If one or more segments are of the same size a parenthesis is placed about these in the formula. For example if the formula is (2,5) 3, 4, 1, then segments two and five are the longest and approximately the same length while segment number 1 is the shortest.

Distinct, strongly sclerotized, dentate, opposable and usually asymmetrical mandibles (H2-H5) are always present. They offer excellent characters for determination of various groups. In general the left mandible possesses more toothlike projections on its distal margin than the right mandible. Sharp points (dentes) on the mandibles are most prominent in newly moulted individuals, (H3, C and E.) Usage may reduce them to blunt rounded knobs. Maxillae and a distinct labium with palpi are present in most groups. On the labium a slitlike opening for the duct of the silk gland exists without a prominent protruding spinneret. In this respect they differ decidedly from larvae of Lepidoptera.

Thorax. The thorax consists of three segments bearing one or two pairs of spiracles. The first pair is usually distinct and located on the prothorax. The second pair may be absent. If present it is usually reduced in size, probably functionless in most species and located on the mesothorax or adjacent to the metathorax. Two or more annulets may occur on the dorsal aspect of each segment.

Three pairs of thoracic legs (H1, F-G) occur on thorax of most Symphyta. These may be conspicuous, distinctly segmented or reduced to mere lobes. Among Pamphiliidae typical straight five segmented legs occur, while among Heterarthrus fleshy clawless legs are present. Considerable variation in number, size, and shape of the segments and claws, presence of setae, spines, empodiumlike fleshy lobes and other features on the legs offer good characters for determining various groups.

Abdomen. The abdomen consists of ten segments with spiracles on the lateral aspects of the first eight. All segments of each species, but the last two, are more or less alike in structure except for prolegs (larvapods). Each may be subdivided into 2 to 7 annulets on the dorsal aspect. The tergum of the tenth segment (epiproct) is convex and usually bears setae or spinous processes which may be paired. Among the Cephidae, Siricidae and Xiphydriidae (H1 and H11) a distinct, median, sclerotized suranal process, called postcornu, is usually present at the caudal end. Among the Pamphiliidae the postcornu is a small hooklike structure which projects cephalad and is located on the dorsomeson of caudal segment, (H11, K). Segmented, paired, subanal processes or styli ventrad of the lateral ends of the anal slit are present among the Pamphiliidae (H11, K). Rudimentary, sclerotized, papilliform, subanal processes and setiferous knobs also occur among the Cephidae and Xyelidae respectively, (H11 and H5).

Spiracles are usually narrowly ovate, vertical in position, frequently rounded at both ends and located on segments 1 to 8. The last pair may be somewhat larger than the others. The peritreme of spiracles may be distinctly thickened and deeply pigmented. On the abdomen the spiracles are located about half way between the dorso-meson and the ventro-meson and on one of the first three annulets if several are present. Spiracles are called winged (Cimbicidae, H6, Q) if inverted, v-shaped pigmentation is present about the peritremes.

A typical proleg (larvapod) is a fleshy cone-shaped protuberance with a broad basal area and a distal smaller hookless portion. Among Xyelidae prolegs are present on all of the abdominal segments. Among Tenthredinidae six to eight pairs are present on segments 2 to 7 and 10, or 2 to 8 and 10, and less frequently on 2 to 6 and 10. Among Fenusini the tenth pair is obsolete or they may be fused (Metallus). Also among Argidae, Acorduleceridae, Heterarthrinae and other groups the prolegs are very small or rudimentary while among Heterarthrus they may be obsolete.

Pigmentation, armature and glands. Early instar sawfly larvae may differ decidedly from late instars especially the last instar frequently called the prepupal stage. Last instar larva or prepupa may be without distinct pigmented spots or areas even though these may be conspicuous in early instars. Also a complete change in color may take place. For example, red or brown early instar pamphilids may change to a distinct green in the prepupal, nonfeeding instar. Setae in the last instar also may be much smaller and in some cases less numerous. In this publication the author has figured for each species usually the next to the last instar or last feeding stage, especially among species where marked color or pigmentation changes occur.

Setae, spines or tubercles may be present on some annulets of the thorax and abdomen and also on the head and legs. Their distribution, number and size offer taxonomic differences of value in determining species. Wood boring larvae and leaf miners possess fewer or smaller setae than many leaf feeders, There appears to be no definite setal pattern which is so typical of lepidopterous larvae. Certain annulets, however, give rise to setae, spines or tubercles and these appear to be constant for various groups. Among species that possess distinct spines (or setae) a formula may be used to express their distribution, (Yuasa, 1922, page 33), In general they are numbered and their bifurcations expressed. For example the spinal formula of a mid abdominal segment indicates the arrangement of the spines on the first tubercle-bearing (usually the second) annulet, on the next small annulet if this is present, on the third tubercle-bearing (usually the fourth) annulet, on the subspiracular area, and on the postsubspiracular or surpedal areas, respectively.

There are various types of glands with exterior openings on larvae. Many larvae of the Nematinae and Cladiinae possess eversible ventral glands on the ventro-meson of abdominal segments 1 to 7. Among Xyelidae eversible cervical (c.g.) glands (H5, A) may be present. Cimbicidae possess crescent-shaped spiracular glands (H6, Q and R) immediately dorsad of each spiracle on abdominal segments 2 to 8. Minute wax glands are located on various parts of Tenthredinidae. Cutaneous glands provided with sclerotized external rings about their openings are called glandubae and may be stalked or sessile among various Tenthredinidae. Some larvae when alive are completely coated with flakes or strands of wax. Slimeglands of Caliroa are semi-sessile glandubae and few in number.

Suckerlike protuberances with a depressed, crescent-shaped center occur on the lateral projections of segments 2 to 4 or 5 and 8 among Acorduleceridae (H5, 0).

Yuasa, 1922 presents us with the most comprehensive study of the larvae of the Symphyta. The family subdivisions accepted by the author for this volume are the same as those recognized by Ross, 1937. The following subfamilies Diprioninae, Acordulecerinae, Cimbicinae of the Tenthredinidae by Yuasa are given family status namely, Acorduleceridae, Diprionidae and Cimbicidae, also the subfamilies Hylotominae and Schizocerinae comprise the Argidae.

KEY TO SOME OF THE FAMILIES OF HYMENOPTERA

Plant Infesting Species, - Chiefly Symphyta

Keys. Published keys to families of the Hymenoptera may be found in Brues and Melander 1932, "Classification of Insects." More complete and satisfactory keys to the suborder Symphyta are found in Yuasa'a 1922 publication on "Larvae of the Tenthredinoidea." The following family key is an adaptation of the key found in Yuasa to the family subdivisions of the Symphyta as presented by H. H. Ross, 1937.

1. ———— Thoracic legs present, usually segmented and with distinct claws 2

1a. Thoracic legs absent, if present, indistinctly four segmented and without claws or reduced to nonsegmented protuberances (mammalike) without claws 9

2. ———— No segmented subanal appendages on the tenth abdominal segment, if setiferous subanal knobs are present see 7a (Xyelidae); thoracic legs usually stout, short and irregular in shape; prolegs usually present . . . . , ... 3

2a. Paired, segmented, subanal appendages present on the sternum of the tenth abdominal segment; thoracic legs slender, elongated and straight; antennae seven segmented; prolegs absent . . . . (H11), Pamphiliidae

3. ———— Claws on thoracic legs usually small and without a pad (empodium) arising from the base of the tarsal (claw) segment. If pads occur they arise from the tibia 5

3a. Claws on thoracic legs usually conspicuous and with a distinct pad or divergent lobe arising from the base of each tarsal (claw) segment 4

4. ———— Suckerlike lateral protuberances on abdominal segments 2 to 4 or 5 and 8; mid-abdominal segments with three indistinct annulets; free leaf feeders and gregarious . . . . .
. . . . (H5), Acorduleceridae

4a. No suckerlike lateral protuberances on abdominal segments 2 to 4 or 5 and 8; spiracles usually inconspicuously winged . . . . (H6-7), Argidae

5. ———— Antennae possess more than one (or two) segment(s) 7

5a. Antennae possess one (or two) segment(s) 6

6. ———— Mid-abdominal segments with seven annulets; spiracles definitely winged; f.g.l. larger than 20 mm. . . . . (H6-7), Cimbicidae

6a. Mid-abdominal segments with one to four inconspicuous annulets; spiracles not definitely winged; body depressed; f.g.l. under 12 mm. chiefly leaf miners . . . .
. . . . (H11), Fenusinae-Y, Tenthredinidae

7. ———— Antennae never with more than five segments 8

7a. Antennae with six or seven segments; prolegs on all abdominal segments; setiferous knobs or protuberances on the subanal lobes areas of the caudal segment . . . .
. . . . (H5), Xyelidae

8. ———— Antennae possess three segments with the third peglike and the first and second incomplete crescent-shaped flattened areas; mid-abdominal segments with six annulets; prolegs present on abdominal segments 2 to 8 and 10 . . . .
. . . . (H8 and 10), (Diprioninae-Y) Diprionidae

8a. Antennae possess four or five segments; if only three appear all are complete or the third is short and not peglike, prolegs present on segments 2-6, 2-7, or 2-8 and 10; mid-abdominal segments with 2 to 7 annulets . . . . (H6, 9-10), Tenthredinidae

9, (1a).———— Thoracic legs mammalike or absent 10

9a. Thoracic legs indistinctly four segmented but without claws; prolegs vestigial on segments 2-8 and 10 with caudal pair united on meson forming a single protuberance . . .
. . . . (Phyllotominae-Y), Tenthredinidae

10. ———— Caudal segment with a median, sclerotized suranal process (postcornu) 11

10a. Caudal segment without a median sclerotized suranal process; mouth parts reduced to two sharp opposable mandibles; all species tiny, some produce galls or infest seeds. .
. . . . (Apocrita, H12), Chalcididae

11. ———— No subanal appendages present; eye-spot not pigmented 12

11a. Small and short, subanal appendages present; eye-spot pigmented; antennae with four or five segments; f.g.l. under 15 mm.; stem or twig borers . . . . Cephidae

240

12.   _____   Antennae appear to be one segmented; labial palpi 1 or 2 segmented; metathoracic spiracles conspicuous; f.g.l. 30+ mm.; wood borers. . . . . Siricidae

12a.   Antennae possess three or four segments; labial palpi 3 segmented; metathoracic spiracles vestigial; f.g.l. 10 to 20 mm.; wood borers . . . . Xiphydriidae

DESCRIPTIONS OF LARVAE OF MOST FAMILIES OF PLANT INFESTING HYMENOPTERA

The families are presented in alphabetical order. Except for the Chalcididae all belong to the Symphyta. The names accepted are those found in Ross, 1937. The approximate number of species recorded for North America after each family was provided by H. H. Ross, Ill. Nat. Hist. Survey, Urbana, Illinois.

The information on habits of the larvae of each family is very general. The descriptions present the most significant morphological characters of the last feeding instar with comments on the prepupal stage in some cases. For size characteristics see glossary under f.g.1. In most cases the morphological characters are presented in the following order size, head, thorax and abdomen.

ACORDULECERIDAE, H5

Acordulecerid sawflies, 20± species

Habits. The larvae are external leaf feeders and usually gregarious.

Description. Full grown larvae are very small, some species about 10 mm. in length. The body is subcylindrical with the ventral surface flattened, tapering from a distinctly swollen thorax toward a much smaller caudal end.

Head resembles usual sawfly type possessing an epicranial suture, cervical furrows, a pair of single ocelli each surrounded by a pigmented ring, and apparently one segmented antennae or antacoria possessing several sclerotized circular spots.

Thorax, especially mesothorax and metathorax, possess lateral areas covered with short setae or spines. A wingless spiracle is present on the prothorax. The five segmented legs project laterad, each increasing in length toward caudal pair. Each leg terminates in a claw with a membranous lobe (empodium) at the proximal end of each claw.

The distinctly ten segmented abdomen usually exhibits three inconspicuous annulets per segment, wingless spiracles, prolegs on segments 2 to 7 and 10 and crescentric, suckerlike, lateral protuberances on segments 2-4 or 5 and 8.

ARGIDAE, H1-2, H6-7

Argid sawflies, 50± species

Habits. The larvae feed on deciduous trees and shrubs.

Description. Full grown larvae are 10 to 20 mm. in length. Feeding larvae of most species are spotted with pigment areas, possessing one or more short setae or spines.

Head resembles the usual sawfly type possessing an epicranial suture, cervical furrows, a pair of single ocelli each located in the center of a pigmented ring, asymmetrical mandibles and antennae with three segments or each antacoria contains several sclerotized circular spots with no distinct segments.

The three segmented thorax, especially the mesothorax and the metathorax, possesses conspicuous, frequently pigmented, lateral areas of setae or short spines. Spiracles on the prothorax are winged. Each thoracic leg terminates in a claw and a distinct fleshy lobe (empodium) which arises from tarsus at base of claw.

Ten segmented abdomen posesses diagonal, fleshy, lateral projections bearing setae immediately ventrad of the spiracles and inconspicuous to fairly prominent prolegs on segments 2 to 8 and 10. Spiracles on abdominal segments 1 to 8 may or may not be distinctly winged.

242

HYMENOPTERA

CEPHIDAE, H2, H11

Stem sawflies, 16+ species

Habits. Larvae are stem or stalk borers in various species of Graminaceae, especially wheat, rye, barley, timothy, quack grass and other species. Species of Janus infest the tender shoots of shrubs and trees especially willows, poplar and currants.

Description. Full grown larvae of most species are small, seldom exceeding 12 mm. The body is usually cylindrical, somewhat S-shaped (reverse), enlarged in the thoracic region and uniformly tapering toward the caudal end; segmentation distinct; dorsal annulets (usually three), indistinct; cuticle usually smooth, sparsely setiferous and uniformly near white without distinct pigmented areas.

The head is semiglobose, moderately large, narrower than the thorax, sparsely setiferous and a pale brown or concolorous with the body. It possesses biting mouth parts that are directed ventrad, conical four or five segmented antennae, small ocelli or pigment spots located latero-caudad of the antennae, an epicranial suture and cervical furrows.

The three segmented thorax, which overlaps the head somewhat, possesses swollen dorsal and lateral areas on the mesothorax and to some extent on the metathorax. Enlarged functional spiracles are present on the prothorax and a rudimentary pair on the metathorax or between the mesothorax and metathorax. Vestigial, fleshy, mammalike, clawless legs are present on the three segments of the thorax.

The ten segments of the abdomen are legless and possess spiracles on segments 1 to 8, lateral lobes on each segment, a distinct, suranal, median process (postcornu) on the tergum of the last segment and a pair of inconspicuous, papilliform, subanal appendages ventrad of the cephalic end of the anal slit.

CHALCIDIDAE, H12

Chalcids, many species

Habits. Many species of chalcids belonging to the Apocrita are parasites on various stages of insects, however, members of the Eurytominae, Toryminae and Agaoninae infest plants, especially the stems of various grains and grasses and seeds of various fruits and legumes, namely, apple, grapes and clover.

Description. Full grown larvae of plant infesting species are tiny, seldom exceeding 5 mm. in length. In general the entire larva is near white to cream colored, spindle shaped, or somewhat c-shaped, pointed at both ends and swollen near the center.

Head usually distinct. Antennae and ocelli are absent or vestigial. Mouth parts are reduced to two sharp opposable mandibles.

Thorax and abdomen without legs. Segmentation indistinct and spiracles inconspicuous.

CIMBICIDAE, H1-2, H6-7

Cimbicid sawflies, 10± species

Habits. The larvae (at times gregarious) feed primarily on foliage of various trees, shrubs, and ground plants especially on apple, birch, beech, hawthorn, cherry, elm, linden, maple, poplar, willow, honeysuckle and strawberry.

Description. Full grown larva are 25 to 50 mm. They include the largest leaf feeding species of Symphyta in North America. The body is cylindrical, annulets usually seven per segment, glabrous with microscopic setae on annulets 2, 4, and 7. When alive the body is usually covered with a waxy bloom, and when disturbed ejects a yellow fluid from the spiracular glands.

Head large, pigmented and distinctly setiferous. It possesses one segmented, buttonlike antennae, a labrum (sometimes asymmetrical) divided into a median lobe and two lateral lobes by diverging depressions, slender maxillary and labial palpi, very thick galeae and a slitlike opening on the labium (sericos) for the duct of the silk gland which is large, pear-shaped, u or v-shaped.

The three segmented thorax possesses 5 segmented legs with the femur slightly longer than the tibia and two pairs of spiracles. The second pair apparently is vestigial.

The ten segmented abdomen possess prolegs on segments 2 to 8 and 10. Each proleg is divided into two unequal lobes on the distal surface with a few setae on the dorso-caudal aspect and none on the cephalic aspect. The spiracles on abdominal segments 1 to 8 are winged and possess conspicuous glands located dorsad of each spiracle on segments 2 to 8. The tenth abdominal tergum is without suranal protuberances.

DIPRIONIDAE H1-2, H8-9

Diprionid sawflies, 40± species

Habits. The larvae are somewhat gregarious and are external feeders on the needles of conifers especially, pines, spruces, hemlock, balsam and juniper.

Description. Full grown larvae are 18 to 25 mm. in length. The body is cylindrical, somewhat robust in the region of the thorax and tapers toward the caudal end. The general color is yellowish or greenish with grayish or brownish stripes or rows of black spots on the dorsal and lateral aspects. Conspicuous and elevated glandubae occur on the various segments.

The head, frequently black or brownish and spinous, is the usual sawfly type possessing an epicranial suture, cervical furrows, single ocelli surrounded by pigment and three segmented antennae. Each antenna consists of a distal peglike projection and two, frequently crescentric, flattened, sclerotized areas in the antacoria which are remanents of segments 1 and 2.

The three segmented thorax possesses a pair of spiracles on the prothorax and three pairs of five segmented and frequently deeply pigmented legs which may possess spines or setae especially on the coxae.

The ten segmented abdomen shows distinct segmentation, six annulets on most of the segments, prolegs, which are close together, along the meson, on segments 2 to 8 and 10 and spiracles on segments 1 to 8.

PAMPHILIIDAE H1-2, H11.

Webspinning and leaf rolling sawflies, 55+ species

Habits. The larvae attack foliage of deciduous trees and shrubs and to a limited extent conifers. Some form silken nests by pulling together leaves and are solitary or gregarious. Other species form tubelike nests by rolling the edges of leaves into tubes. These tubes may be portable cases for some species.

Description. Full grown larvae are small to medium size 15-25 mm. The body is slender to robust, subcylindrical, somewhat flattened on the ventral aspect, segmentation and annulets distinct, and with distinct sublateral lobes on the ventro-lateral margins. Color greenish, near white or distinct orange to reddish brown. A marked color change may occur in the last instar.

The head is semiglobose, distinct, as wide as the thorax, cream, brown or black, sparsely setiferous, and possesses biting mouth parts which project ventrad. It possesses an epicranial suture, long, setaceous, seven segmented antennae and ocelli located ventro-laterad of the antennae.

The thorax is three segmented bearing setiform, sharply pointed, cylindrical legs with elongated distal segments. The ten segments of the abdomen possess no prolegs but spiracles on segments 1 to 8. The tenth segment is usually rounded on the caudal margin, setiferous, somewhat depressed and often with colored patches, may also bear a median hooklike process (postcornu) near the caudal margin of the tergum. A pair of setiform, three segmented, subanal appendages are also present.

HYMENOPTERA

SIRICIDAE, H2, H11

Horn tails, wood wasps, 20+ species

Habits. The larvae are wood borers attacking conifers and deciduous trees especially maple, elm, apple, pear, beech, oak and sycamore. Some are of economic importance while others seem to confine their attack on subnormal trees.

Description. Full grown larvae are 30 to 40 mm. The body is cylindrical, orthosomatic, smooth, nonsetaceous and light in color.

The head is circular, one-half the dorsoventral diameter of the thorax and light colored. It possesses inconspicuous one segmented antennae, indistince vertical furrows but no ocelli or epicranial suture. The biting mouth parts are hypognathous, normal in form and with nearly symmetrical mandibles and one or two segmented labial palpi.

The three segmented thorax bears three pairs of subequal mammalike legs and two pairs of spiracles. The second pair of spiracles adjacent to the metathorax are not as conspicuous as those on the prothorax.

The ten segmented abdomen bears spiracles on segments 1 to 8, and a suranal sclerotized process (postcornu) on the tenth tergum. It also is without prolegs or subanal appendages but possesses distinct sublateral lobes and two inconspicuous dorsal annulets on each segment.

TENTHREDINIDAE, H1, H3-7, H9-11

Tenthredinid sawflies, 1500± species

Habits. The larvae of this large family have distinctly variable habits. Most species are open leaf feeders on many kinds of deciduous plants and to a limited extent on evergreens. They may be somewhat to decidedly gregarious especially in their early instars. Some species are leaf rollers, gall producers and leaf miners. Others bore into buds, fruits and petioles of leaves.

Description. Full grown larvae vary considerably in size, from less than 10 mm. to more than 30 mm. The body of leaf feeding species is cylindrical with the greatest diameter in the region of the thorax and usually tapering toward the smaller caudal end. Leaf miner species are small and distinctly depressed. The color varies decidedly. Many are greenish or yellowish, striped or spotted or more or less uniform in color. The body may be smooth, glabrous or covered with numerous short or long setae. Some species are covered with flakes or strands of wax, others are coated with a slimelike secretion.

The head of most species, except leaf miners, is a typical sawfly type each possessing a distinct epicranial suture, cervical furrows, a frons, clypeus and a labrum which may be asymmetrical (Dolerinae). A single ocellus surrounded by a pigmented ring (ocularium) is present on each side of the head. The antennae of most species are 4 or 5 segmented. In a few cases three segments occur while among leaf miners (Fenusa, etc.) they are one segmented. Mandibles of most forms are distinctly asymmetrical especially along the distal margin. The maxillary palpi are four segmented and the labial palpi three segmented.

The three segmented thorax possesses three pairs of legs that are five segmented. Other species have three, four or six segments with distinct claws, rarely indistinctly segmented and without claws (Phyllotominae). The functional spiracles on the prothorax are usually wingless while the metathoracic spiracles, if present, are vestigial.

The ten segmented abdomen possesses spiracles on segments 1 to 8 and prolegs on segments 2 to 7 or 2 to 8 and 10, occasionally the seventh and tenth pairs wanting. The abdominal segments may show 6, 7, 5, 4, 3 or 2 annulets named in the order of their frequency. The caudal segment is without a prominent suranal process or subanal protuberances. Some species, however, possess setae or spines. Ventral glands (Nematinae) and glandubae, stalked or sessil, may be present.

XIPHYDRIIDAE H1

Xiphydriid sawflies, 6+ species

Habits. The larvae are wood borers in dead and dying deciduous trees, especially birch and maples.

Description. Full grown larvae are small, 12-15 mm. The body is subcylindrical, ?-shaped, distinctly segmented, annulation obsolete, color near-white and without pigmented areas, glabrous and without setae but the venter is microscopically spinulate.

The head differs from the usual sawfly type in that the ocelli or eye spots and vertical furrows are absent, however, it possessed three to four segmented antennae, two segmented maxillary palpi and three segmented labial palpi.

The thorax is somewhat enlarged and possesses three pairs of rudimentary, fleshy, mammalike, clawless legs, one pair of fairly conspicuous functional spiracles on the prothorax and a vestigial metathoracic pair.

The abdomen is legless and possesses spiracles on segments 1 to 8. The tenth or caudal segment terminates in a suranal sclerotized process (postcornu) and possesses on its tergum a deep meso-dorsal depression.

XYELIDAE, H5

Xyelid sawflies - 25+ species

Habits. The larvae are single-brooded, solitary and feed externally on the deciduous foliage of forest trees and shrubs especially hickory, butternut, pecan, elm and on pines particularly the staminate flowers.

Description. Full grown larvae are 13 to 18 mm. The body is caterpillarlike, subcylindrical, flattened on the ventral aspect, uniform in diameter except the last two constricted and stout segments; segmentation and annulation usually distinct; ectoskeleton smooth, tuberculate and setiferous but never shiny; color shades of green, yellow, brown or near black.

Head circular, sparsely setiferous, lateral diameter, usually more than one-half that of the thorax; mouth parts directed ventrad; antennae long with six or seven segments; ocelli very small and located caudo-dorsad of the antennae.

Thorax three segmented with prothorax overlapping head slightly; prothorax sometimes with a pair of lateral, eversible cervical glands, also possessing a large, colored, shieldlike area on the dorsum and lateral aspects; thoracic legs small, subequal in size and normal in form.

Abdomen possesses ten segments with prolegs on each, however, those on the first and ninth are reduced in size; four annulets on abdominal segments 1 to 8 with spiracles on the second annulet; ninth abdominal tergum with three annulets; tenth abdominal tergum constricted distinctly and transversely on its cephalic fourth and with a distinct humplike protuberance on the meson caudad of the cephalic constriction, concolorous with the head and setiferous tubercles; anal prolegs and ventral or subanal lobes distinctly large, contiguous, forming a trilobate prominence on the meson of the tenth sternum; subanal lobe with a pair of setiferous protuberances (knobs) dorsad of the anal prolegs.

HYMENOPTERA

SOME COMMON, IMPORTANT OR UNUSUAL PLANT INFESTING SPECIES

Note: The species marked with an asterisk (*) are figured. The author has not seen the unmarked (no asterisk) species or the material on hand is unsatisfactory. In a future revision it is hoped that most of these and others may be incorporated. The scientific and common names, with a few exceptions, are taken from the list approved by the American Association of Economic Entomologists, C. F. W. Muesebeck, 1946. Jour. Econ. Ent. 39:427 or H. H. Ross 1937. In this list parentheses are places about the describers name when the genus differs from the original description. Elsewhere in his publication all parentheses about describers names are omitted. Also the scientific names are underscored in this list.

ACORDULECERIDAE

*Acordulecera sp. H5
  on oak.

ARGIDAE

*Arge (Hylotoma) macleayi Leach, H2, H7
  hazelnut sawfly
*Sterictiphora krugii Cress, H1.
  from Puerto Rico
*Sofus zabriskiei W. and M., H2, H6
  portulaca sawfly

CEPHIDAE

Cephus cinctus Nort.
  wheat stem sawfly
*Cephus pygmaeus (L.), H11
  European wheat stem sawfly
*Cephus tabidus (F.), H2, H11
  black grain stem sawfly
*Janus abbreviatus (Say), H11
  willow shoot sawfly
Janus interger (Nort.)
  currant stem girdler

CHALCIDIDAE

Bruchophagus gibbus (Boh.)
  clover seed chalcid
Evoxysoma vitis (Saund.)
  grape seed chalcid
Harmolita grandis (Riley)
  wheat straw-worm
*Harmolita tritici (Fitch), H12
  wheat jointworm
*Torymus druparum Boh., H12
  apple seed chalcid

CIMBICIDAE

*Cimbex americana Leach, H1, H2, H7
  elm sawfly
*Zaraea inflata Nort., H2, H6
  honeysuckle sawfly

DIPRIONIDAE

Diprion frutetorum (Fab.)
  on red and Scotch pines
*Diprion hercyniae (Htg.), H1, H2, H8
  European spruce sawfly
*Diprion simile (Htg.), H2, H8
  introduced pine sawfly
*Neodiprion abietis (Harr.), H8
  balsam-fir sawfly
*Neodiprion americanum Leach, H8
  on Loblolly and short leaf pines.
Neodiprion banksianae Roh.
  jack-pin sawfly
Neodiprion burkei Midd.
  lodge pole sawfly
*Neodiprion dyari, Roh, H8
  on jack and pitch pines
Neodiprion flemingi Peck,
  on red pine
Neodiprion lanielensis Peck,
  on red and jack pines
*Neodiprion lecontei (Fitch), H1, H2, H8
  red-headed pine sawfly
Neodiprion nanulus Schedl.
  on jack and red pine
*Neodiprion pinetum (Nort.), H8
  white-pine sawfly
Neodiprion rugifrons Midd.
  on jack pine
*Neodiprion sertifer, (Geoff.) H8
  on red, Scotch and other pines
Neodiprion tsugae Midd.
  hemlock sawfly

PAMPHILIIDAE

Acantholyda erythrocephala (l.)
pine false webworm
Neurotoma inconspicua (Nort.)
plum web-spinning sawfly
*Neurotoma fasciata Nort., H1, H2, H11
wild cherry web-spinning sawfly

SIRICIDAE

Sirex juvencus L.
blue horntail
*Tremex columba (L.), H2, H11
pigeon tremex

TENTHREDINIDAE

*Allantus cinctus (L.), H4, H6.
curled rose sawfly
*Ametastegia glabrata (Fall), H5, H7
dock sawfly
Ametastegia pallipes (Spin.),
violet sawfly
*Caliroa cerasi (L.), H5, H10
pear-slug
Caulocampus acericaulis (MacG.)
maple petiole borer
*Cladius isomerus Nort., H3, H6
bristly rose-slug
Croesus latitarsus Nort.
dusky birch sawfly
*Dolerus similis Nort., H1, H3, H6
horsetail sawfly
*Endelomyia aethiops (F.), H3, H10
rose slug
*Erythraspides pygmaea (Say), H3, H10
grape sawfly
*Euura salicis-nodus Walsh., H5, H9
willow-gall sawfly
Fenusa dohrnii (Tisch.)
European alder leaf miner
*Fenusa pusilla (Klug.). H11
birch leaf miner
Fenusa ulmi Sund.
elm leaf miner

Hemichroa crocea (Fourc.)
striped alder sawfly
Hoplocampa cookei (Clarke)
cherry fruit sawfly
*Hoplocampa testudinea (Klug), H4, H6
European apple sawfly
*Macremphytus varians (Nort.), H5, H7
on dogwood (Cornus)
*Macremphytus tarsatus (Say), H4, H7
on dogwood (Cornus)
Monophadnoides rubi (Harr.), H3, H10
raspberry sawfly
Nematus (Pontania) bozemani (Cooley)
poplar leaf-folding sawfly
*Nematus ribesii (Scop.), H4, H9
imported currantworm
*Nematus ventralis Say, H1, H4, H9
willow sawfly
*Pikonema alaskensis (Roh.), H4, H7
yellow-headed spruce sawfly
Pikonema dimmocki (Cress.)
Green-headed spruce sawfly
*Priophorus rubivorus Roh., H3, H9
on St. Regis raspberry
*Pristiphora erichsonii (Htg.), H4, H9
larch sawfly
*Pristiphora geniculata (Htg.), H4, H9
mountain ash sawfly
*Profenusa canadensis (Marl.), H5, H11
hawthorn leaf miner
Strongylongaster sp., H1
on a fern
Tethida cordigera (Beauv.)
black-headed ash sawfly
*Tomostethus multicinctus (Roh.), H2, H10
brown-headed ash sawfly

XIPHYDRIIDAE

*Xiphydria maculata Harris, H1
in dead maple wood

XYELIDAE

*Megaxyela sp. H5
on hickory and pecan

HYMENOPTERA

EXPLANATION OF FIGURES H1, A-P

LARVAE OF SAWFLIES AND PARTS

Figure A. Lateral view of a typical sawfly larva. Diprionidae, Neodiprion lecontei Fitch, red-headed pine sawfly. See H8, D-F

Figures B to E. Types of antennae among larvae of sawflies.

Figure B. A seven segmented antenna, Pamphiliidae, Neurotoma sp. See H11.

Figure C. A five segmented antenna, Tenthredinidae, Strongylogaster sp.

Figure D. A three segmented antenna. Segments one and two are incomplete sclerites located in the membranous area (antacoria) from which the antennae arise. Diprionidae, Diprion hercyniae Htg., European spruce sawfly. See H10, N-P.

Figure E. One segmented antenna, Cimbicidae, Cimbex americana Leach, elm sawfly. See H7, P-R.

Figure F. Metathoracic leg. Tenthredinidae, Dolerus sp. on timothy.

Figure G. Metathoracic leg. Pamphiliidae, Neurotoma sp. See H11.

Figure H. Ventral view of the sixth abdominal segment and a portion of the fifth showing an everted and an inverted gland, Tenthredinidae, Nematus ventralis Say, willow sawfly. See H9, J-L

Figure I. Lateral view of a typical sawfly abdominal segment (A3 of Neodiprion sertifer Geof. with pigment omitted, see H8, J-L, showing names of areas. A, B, C^1, C^2, C^3 and D designate the dorsal annulets, PSA-postspiracular area, SA-spiracular area, Prep-preepipleurite, Psep-postepipleurite, Hypop-hypopleurite and uropod). For more details see Middleton 1921 or Atwood and Peck, 1943.

Figure J. Ventral view of the tenth caudal segment showing two subanal segmented appendages, Pamphiliidae, Neurotoma sp. See H11, K.

Figure K. Cephalic view of a typical head capsule showing prominent ocelli surrounded by pigmented areas (ocularia), antennae arising from the epicranium, an epicranial suture surrounding a frons (front), also a clypeus, labrum, mandibles, maxillae and labium. Tenthredinidae, Strongylogaster sp.

Figure L. Cephalic view of a typical sawfly head capsule with an asymmetrical labrum characteristic of all Dolerinae, so far as known. Tenthredinidae, Dolerus similis Nort., horsetail sawfly. See H6, A-C.

Figure M. Xiphydriidae, Xiphydria maculata Harris. F.g.l. 12-14 mm. Lateral view of a ?-shaped larva which is cream colored to near white including the head; ventral margin of the head, mandibles and sclerotized postcornu at caudal end brown to black; mammalike, clawless legs on the thorax; caudal segment with a deep depression on the meson which terminates in a prominent, sclerotized projection (postcornu). Found in dead or dying wood of deciduous trees.

Figures N to P. Argidae, Sterictiphora krugii Cress. F.g.l. 25± mm. Preserved specimens are light colored with numerous small brown pigment spots on all segments; living late instars are pinkish with a light green line along the dorsomeson; numerous small black spots scattered over all segments; head reddish with a conspicuous black stripe on the meson and a dark ocellar area; thoracic legs pinkish with dark spots and each terminates in a single claw and a fleshy empodium. Food, seagrape, Coccolobis uvifera common in lowlands. According to L. F. Martorell this species is the only sawfly in Puerto Rico. Martorell, 1941.

Figure N. Lateral view of head and thorax.

Figure O. Lateral view of fourth abdominal segment.

Figure P. Lateral view of caudal segments.

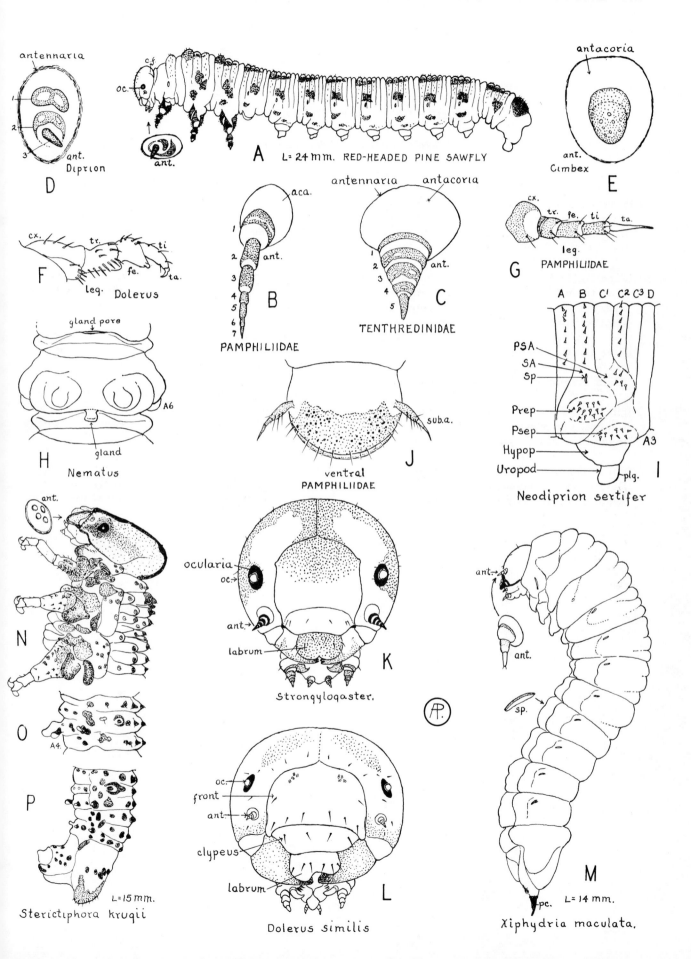

antennaria

1
2
3   ant.
Diprion
D

c.f.
oc.
ant.
A   L=24mm. RED-HEADED PINE SAWFLY

antacoria
ant.
Cimbex
E

aca.
1
2   ant.
3
4
5
6
7
PAMPHILIIDAE
B

antennaria   antacoria
1
2   ant.
3
4
5
TENTHREDINIDAE
C

cx.   tr. fe. ti   ta.
leg.
PAMPHILIIDAE
G

cx.   tr.   ti
fe.
F   leg. Dolerus
ta.

gland pore
A6
H   gland
Nematus

sub.a.
ventral
J   PAMPHILIIDAE

A B C¹ C² C³ D
PSA
SA
Sp
Prep
Psep
Hypop
Uropod   plg.
A3
I
Neodiprion sertifer

ant.
N

A4
O

P
L=15mm.
Sterictiphora krugii

ocularia
oc.
ant.
labrum
Stronqyloqaster.
K

P.

oc.
front
ant.
clypeus
labrum
Dolerus similis
L

ant.
ant.
sp.
pc.   L=14mm.
Xiphydria maculata.
M

HYMENOPTERA

EXPLANATION OF FIGURES H2, A-P

MANDIBLES OF SAWFLY LARVAE

Mesocaudal (oral) views

Figure A. Pamphiliidae, Neurotoma fasciata Nort., wild cherry web-spinning sawfly. See H11, K. Right mandible symmetrical with left.

Figure B. Siricidae, Tremex columba L., pigeon tremex. See H11, F. Left mandible with rounded edge more conspicuous than similar portion on the right mandible.

Figure C. Cephidae, Cephus tabidus Fab., black grain stem sawfly. See H11, H-I. Right mandible nearly symmetrical with left.

Figure D. Cimbicidae, Cimbex americana L Leach., elm sawfly. See H7, P-R. Right mandible nearly symmetrical with left.

Figures E and F. Cimbicidae, Zaraea prob. inflata Nort., honeysuckle sawfly. See H6, P-R. Right and left asymmetrical mandibles.

Figures G and H. Argidae, Sofus zabriskiei W. and M., Portulaca sawfly. See H6, M-O. Right and left asymmetrical mandibles.

Figures I and J. Argidae, Arge (Hylotoma) macleayi Leach, hazelnut sawfly. See H7, D-F. Right and left asymmetrical mandibles.

Figures K and L. Diprionidae, Diprion simile Htg., introduced pine sawfly. See H8, S-U. Right and left asymmetrical mandibles.

Figures M and N. Diprionidae, Neodiprion lecontei Fitch., red-headed pine sawfly. See H8, D-F. Right and left somewhat asymmetrical mandibles.

Figures O and P. Diprionidae, Diprion hercyniae Htg. European spruce sawfly. See H10, N-P. Right and left asymmetrical mandibles.

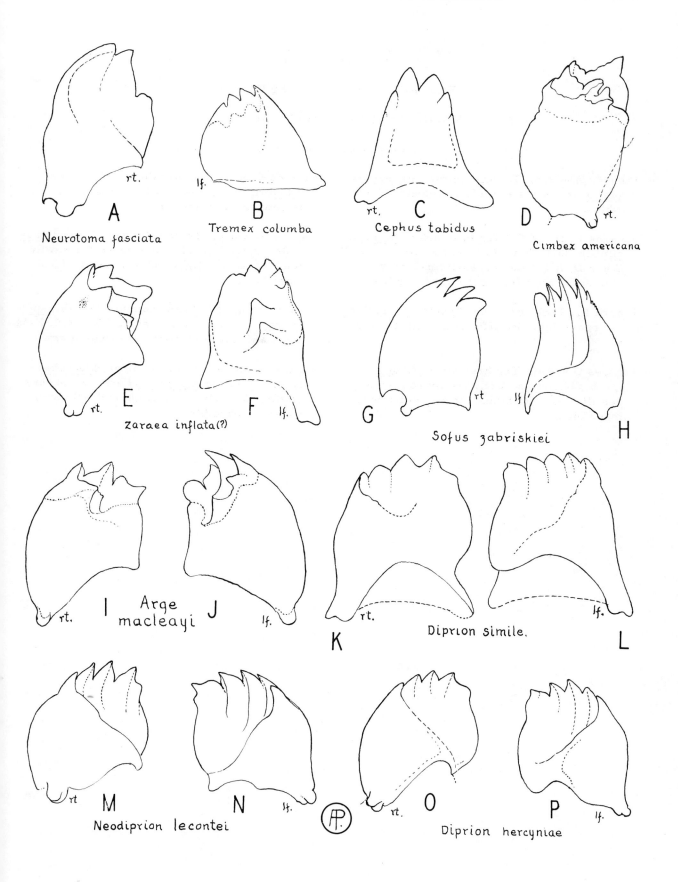

A Neurotoma fasciata

B Tremex columba

C Cephus tabidus

D Cimbex americana

E F Zaraea inflata(?)

G H Sofus zabriskiei

I J Arge macleayi

K L Diprion simile.

M N Neodiprion lecontei

O P Diprion hercyniae

HYMENOPTERA

EXPLANATION OF FIGURES H3, A-P

MANDIBLES OF SAWFLY LARVAE

Mesocaudal (oral) views

Figures A and B. Tenthredinidae, Strongylogaster sp. Right and left asymmetrical mandibles.

Figures C, D and E. Tenthredinidae, Dolerus similis Nort., horsetail sawfly. See H6, A-C. C and D, Right and left asymmetrical mandibles; E. Worn (eroded) right mandible.

Figure F. Tenthredinidae, Endelomyia aethiops F., rose-slug. See H10, B-D. Right mandible.

Figures G and H. Tenthredinidae, Cladius (prob.) isomerus Nort., bristly rose-slug. See H6, J-L. Right and left asymmetrical mandibles.

Figures I and J. Tenthredinidae, Priophorus rubivorus Roh. See H9, G-I. Right and left asymmetrical mandibles.

Figures K and L. Tenthredinidae, Tomostethus multicinctus Roh., brown-headed ash sawfly. See H10, E-G. Right and left assymetrical mandibles.

Figures M and N. Tenthredinidae, Erythraspides pygmaea Say, grape sawfly. See H10, K-M. Right and left asymmetrical mandibles.

Figures O and P. Tenthredinidae, Monophadnoides (Blennocampa) rubi Harr., raspberry sawfly. See H10, H-I. Right and left asymmetrical mandibles.

HYMENOPTERA, SAWFLY LARVAE—MANDIBLES. FIGURE H3

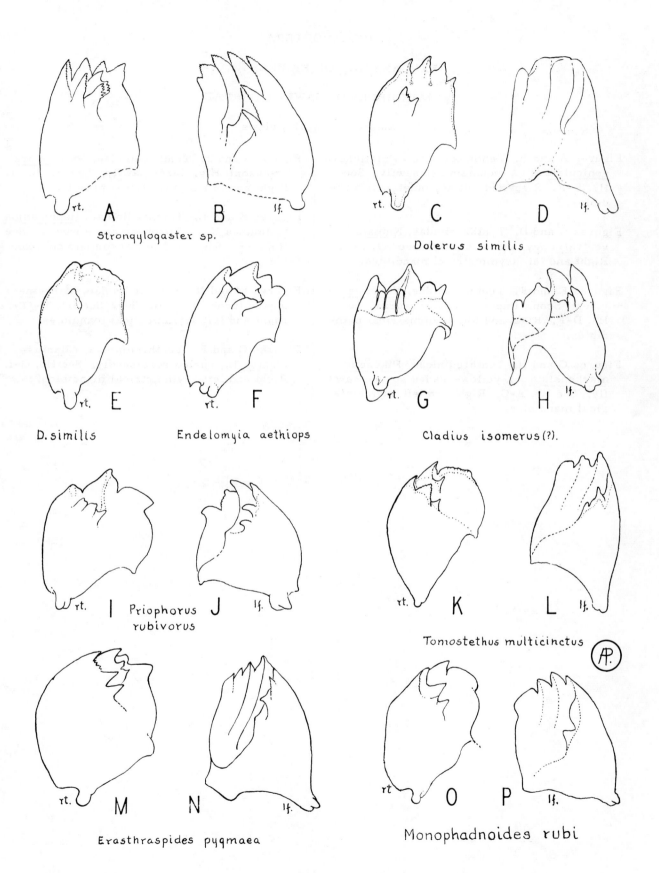

Stronqyloqaster sp.

Dolerus similis

D. similis

Endelomyia aethiops

Cladius isomerus (?).

Priophorus rubivorus

Tomostethus multicinctus

Erasthraspides pyqmaea

Monophadnoides rubi

HYMENOPTERA

EXPLANATION OF FIGURES H4, A-P

MANDIBLES OF SAWFLY LARVAE

Mesocaudal (oral) views

Figures A and B. Tenthredinidae, _Pristiphora geniculata_ Htg., mountain ash sawfly. See H9, P-R. Right and left asymmetrical mandibles.

Figures C and D. Tenthredinidae, _Nematus ventralis_ Say, willow sawfly. See H9, J-L. Right and left asymmetrical mandibles.

Figures E and F. Tenthredinidae, _Nematus ribesii_ Scop., imported currantworm. See H9, D-F. Right and left asymmetrical mandibles.

Figures G and H. Tenthredinidae, _Pikonema alaskensis_ Roh., yellow-headed spruce sawfly. See H7, A-C. Right and left asymmetrical mandibles.

Figures I and J. Tenthredinidae, _Pristiphora erichsonii_ Htg., larch sawfly. See H9, M-O. Right and left asymmetrical mandibles.

Figures K and L. Tenthredinidae, _Hoplocampa testudinea_ Klug, European apple sawfly. See H6, D-F. Right and left asymmetrical manbles.

Figures M and N. Tenthredinidae, _Macremphytus_ (prob.) _tarsatus_ Say. See H7, M-O. Right and left asymmetrical mandibles.

Figures O and P. Tenthredinidae, _Allantus cinctus_ L., curled rose sawfly. See H6, G-I. Right and left asymmetrical mandibles.

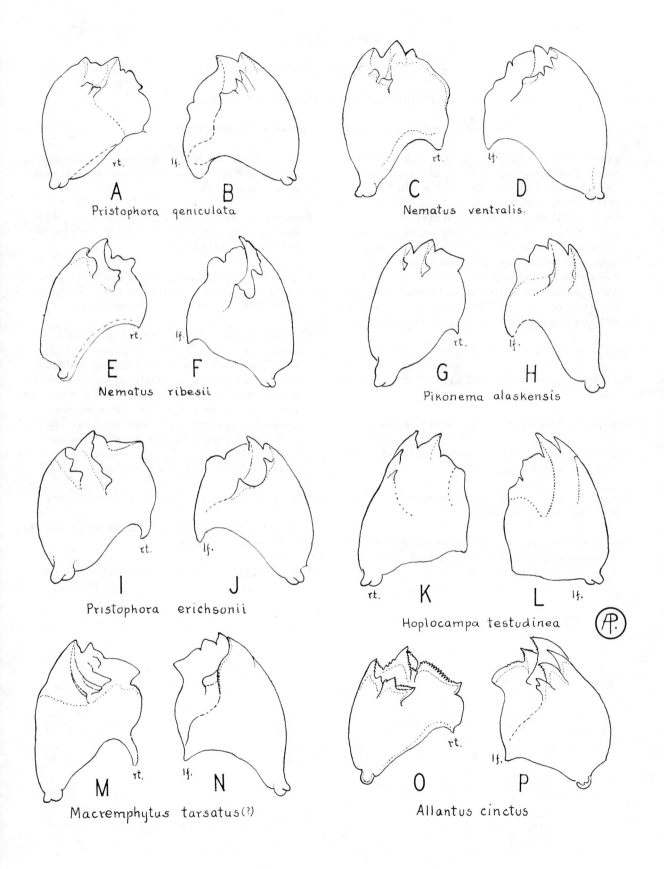

rt. | lf.

A   B

Pristophora geniculata

rt. | lf.

C   D

Nematus ventralis.

rt. | lf.

E   F

Nematus ribesii

rt. | lf.

G   H

Pikonema alaskensis

rt. | lf.

I   J

Pristophora erichsonii

rt. | lf.

K   L

Hoplocampa testudinea

rt. | lf.

M   N

Macremphytus tarsatus(?)

rt. | lf.

O   P

Allantus cinctus

HYMENOPTERA

EXPLANATION OF FIGURES H5, A-P

SAWFLY LARVAE AND MANDIBLES

Acorduleceridae N-P, Tenthredinidae F-M, Xyelidae A-E

Figures A to E. Megaxyela sp. F.g.l. 18-20 mm. Preserved specimens show a light to deep brown dorsal areas on the ninth and tenth abdominal segments; light colored prolegs on all abdominal segments; rounded wartlike protuberances varying in size on dorsum of most segments; a pair of small subanal, setiferous, rounded projections on the caudal segment; spiracles on the prothorax, metathorax and abdominal segments 1 to 8. Food plants, chiefly foliage of various nut bearing trees, hickory, pecan and others.

Figure A. Lateral view of head and thorax.

Figure B. Lateral view of third abdominal segment.

Figure C. Lateral view of caudal segments.

Figures D and E. Mesal (oral) views of right and left mandibles.

Figure F. Caliroa cerasi L., pear-slug. See H10, A. Right mandible.

Figures G and H. Euura salicis-nodus Walsh., willow gall. See H9, A-C. Right and left asymmetrical mandible.

Figures I and J. Macremphytus prob. varians Nort., See H7, J-L. Right and left asymmetrical mandibles

Figures K and L. Ametastegia glabrata Fall., dock sawfly. See H7, G to I. Right and left asymmetrical mandibles.

Figure M. Profenusa canadensis Marl., hawthorn leaf miner. See A11, A-C. Right mandible (left somewhat asymmetrical).

Figures N to P. Acordulecera sp. F.g.l. 9± mm., somewhat depressed greenish body and a yellow head with nonsegmented antennae; prominent lateral projections on abdominal segments 2 to 8 with lateral suckers on 2 to 4 and 8; lateral projections also present on thoracic segments; thoracic legs far apart and each terminates in a single claw and a fleshy empodium. Gregarious feeders on foliage of deciduous plants including oaks.

Figure N. Lateral view of head and thorax.

Figure O. Lateral and dorsal views of second abdominal segment.

Figure P. Lateral view of caudal segments.

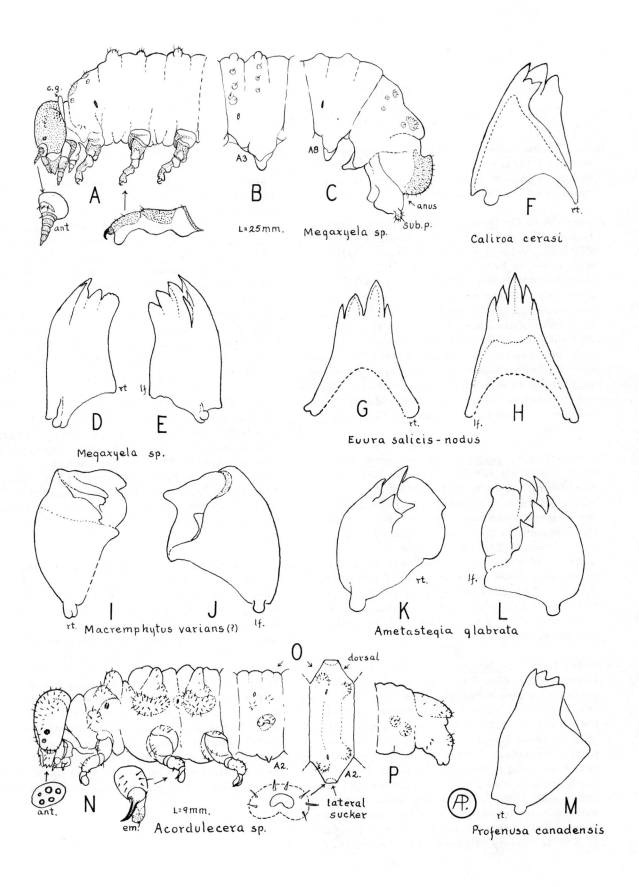

A

c.g.

ant

B

A3

L=25mm.

C

A8

anus

sub.p.

Megaxyela sp.

F

rt.

Caliroa cerasi

D

E

rt lf.

Megaxyela sp.

G

rt.

H

lf.

Euura salicis-nodus

I

J

rt. Macremphytus varians (?) lf.

K

rt.

L

lf.

Ametastegia glabrata

N

ant.

em.

L=9mm.

Acordulecera sp.

O

dorsal

A2.

A2.

lateral sucker

P

M

rt.

Profenusa canadensis

HEMENOPTERA

EXPLANATION OF FIGURES H6, A-R

ARGIDAE M-O, CIMBICIDAE P-R, TENTHREDINIDAE A-L

Note: Three parts are figured for each species, namely lateral views of the head and thorax, the third (A3) or fourth (A4) abdominal segment and the caudal segments.

Figures A to C. Dolerus similis Nort., horsetail sawfly. Also H1, L; H3, C-E. F.g.l. 25± mm., yellowish-green to brown striped with a yellow head and a black ring about each ocellus; a broad light colored stripe occurs on the dorsomeson; broad, near brown, subdorsal stripes extend to lines immediately dorsad of the spiracles; broad spiracular and subspiracular light areas occur on each side bordered on the ventral aspect by a narrow irregular brown line particularly noticeable at the base of each light colored proleg; the distinctive mandibles are decidedly asymmetrical. Food plant, horsetail, Equisetum arvense.

Figures D to F. Hoplocampa testudinea Klug., European apple sawfly. Also H4, K-L. F.g.l. 10-14 mm. In early instars they are near white with a dark colored head especially on the vertex. Also deeply pigmented sclerotized plates occur on the dorsum of abdominal segments 8 to 10. The last instar is near white with a yellow head and no deeply pigmented areas on the dorsum of segments 8 to 10. The larva enters very small to partially grown fruit and tunnels within. Each larva may enter 2 to 6 apples. Food apple and pear. Miles, 1932.

Figures G to I. Allantus cinctus L., curled rose sawfly. Also H4, O-P. F.g.l. 15± mm., yellowish green larva which assumes a coiled position when it feeds on the foliage; the structure of the mandibles separate this species from Endelomyia aethiops. Without prominent setae. Tiny conelike projections occur on some of the crenulations. In its early instars it skeletonizes patches on the under side of the leaf. During later instars it eats holes in leaves and may consume an entire leaflet except the largest veins. Feeds on a wide variety of roses. Middleton, 1922.

Figures J to L. Cladius isomerus Nort. (prob.), bristly rose-slug. Also see H3, G-H. Fig. 1. 10-12 mm., sluglike, greenish, bearing fairly long stout dark setae which give it a bristly appearance; these setae are scattered in transverse rows over the dorsum; below and adjacent to the spiracles they are in the form of verrucae; head lightly pigmented yellowish to brown with darkened areas about ocelli and a brown spot on front; mandibles of this species are distinctive, see figure H3, G-H. The first instar skeletonizes the foliage. Later instars eat holes in the foliage and may consume the entire leaflet except the largest veins. Feeds on a wide variety of roses. Middleton, 1922.

Figures M to O. Sofus zabriskiei W. & M. Portulaca (purslane) sawfly. Also H2, G-H. F.g.l. 11± mm. Body creamy white to greenish; head light yellow with brown areas on the lateral aspects; thorax and abdominal segments possess rows or groups of tiny, lightly pigmented, wartlike elevations; spiracles somewhat winged especially on the prothorax; thoracic legs yellow. Food plant Portulaca (purslane).

Figures P to R. Zarea inflata Nort. (prob.) honeysuckle sawfly. Also H2, E-F. F.g.l. 18-20 mm. A preserved specimen shows a plump body with a broad light band on the dorsum possessing a row of black dots irregular in size along the meson; between this light stripe and the spiracles grayish bands exist each possessing 3 to 4 black spots per segment; below each spiracle one black spot is present; the spiracles are winged and those on abdominal segments 2 to 8 have a small, sclerotized, half-ring, gland opening immediately dorsad of each spiracle. Living specimens are recorded to be greenish with a near-white waxy coating over the body. Food plant foliage of Lonicera species (honeysuckle).

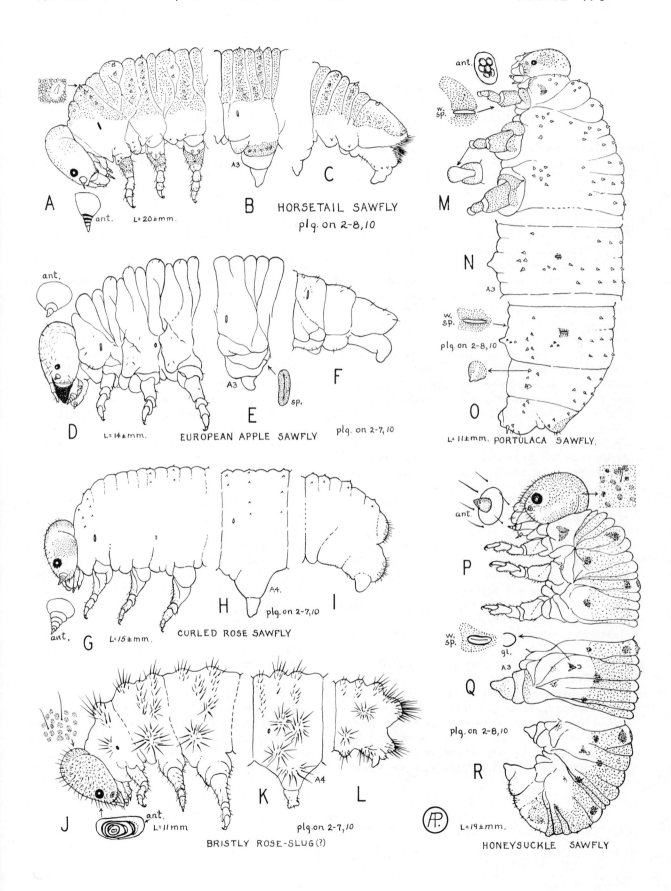

A
ant.
L=20±mm.

B

C

HORSETAIL SAWFLY
plg. on 2-8,10

A3

ant.

D
L=14±mm.

A3

E
sp.

F

plg. on 2-7,10

EUROPEAN APPLE SAWFLY

ant.

G
L=15±mm.

H
A4
plg. on 2-7,10

I

CURLED ROSE SAWFLY

J
ant.
L=11mm.

K

L
A4

plg. on 2-7,10

BRISTLY ROSE-SLUG(?)

ant.
w.
sp.

M

N
A3

w.
sp.
plg. on 2-8,10

O
L=11±mm. PORTULACA SAWFLY.

ant.

P

w.
sp.
gl.
A3

Q

plg. on 2-8,10

R

(P.)   L=19±mm.

HONEYSUCKLE   SAWFLY

EXPLANATION OF FIGURES H7, A-R

ARGIDAE D-F, CIMBICIDAE P-R, TENTHREDINIDAE A-C, G-O

Note: Three parts are figured for each species namely a lateral view of the head and thorax, third (A3) or fourth (A4) abdominal segments (plus a dorsal view) and caudal segments.

Figures A to C. *Pikonema alaskensis* Roh., yellow-headed spruce sawfly. Also H4, G-H. F.g.l. 20± mm. Body dark yellowish green marked with longitudinal gray-green stripes; a narrow light line on the dorso meson bordered by narrow darker stripes; laterad a broader light stripe and then a dark stripe adjacent to a light supraspiracular stripe; immediately below the spiracles an irregular dark stripe; venter light in color; head yellow. Food plants white, red, black, Norway, Colorado and Englemann spruces. Young larvae prefer new growth. Last feeding instar prefers old needles. Most abundant on young trees.

Figures D to F. *Arge* (*Hylotoma*) *macleayi* Leach, hazelnut sawfly. Also H2, I-J. F.g.l. 15-18.mm. Head reddish brown to near black; body pale yellowish-green with four distinct rows of brown spots on the dorsum and an irregular row above and adjacent to the spiracles; prominent diagonal projections ventrad of the spiracles on the abdomen are pigmented and bear numerous setae; base of thoracic legs deeply pigmented, each terminates in a claw and a distinct fleshy lobe (empodium); spiracles usually winged. Food plants chokecherry and hazelnut. Felt, 1905.

Figures G to I. *Ametastegia glabrata* Fall., dock sawfly. Also H5, K-L. F.g.l. 14-17 mm., slender, almost without setae, finely wrinkled (crenulations), olive green to blue-green dorsad of the spiracles with rows of setigerous usually whitish tubercles on some of the crenulations; dorsal vessel yellowish along the dorsomeson; venter light yellow; anal region bears numerous setae and a pigment spot dorsad of the anus; head light brown, minutely punctured and has transverse, darker bands extending between the ocelli and the caudal margin of the head. Food plants are numerous docks and sorrels (Rumex), knotweeds, bindweeds, wild buckwheat and others including rhubarb (in Russia). It skeletonizes and also may consume large portions of leaves. In its northern nearctic range it may enter apples for hibernation in the early fall. Newcomer, 1916.

Figures J to L. *Macremphytus* prob. *varians* Nort. Also H5. I-J. F.g.l. 30± mm., uniformly light colored, probably greenish yellow, covered with a waxy white coat; head dark brown; a near black pigment spot at the tip end of the dorsum of the tenth segment; setae numerous above and below the anus, also present on the thoracic legs and the head, very few elsewhere. Food plant dogwood shrub (Cornus).

Figures M to O. *Macremphytus* prob. *tarsatus* Say. Also H4, M-N. F.g.l. 22± mm., grayish green to lighter color with a waxy coat over the body especially during the late feeding instars; under the waxy coat the pigment distribution may be as indicated or less producing rows of spots; head light brown to near black with many distinct round dark marks some of which are shallow pits; thoracic legs and prolegs light colored; body parts without setae or spines. Food is foliage of dogwood shrubs (Cornus).

Figures P to R. *Cimbex americana* Leach, elm sawfly. Also A1, E; H2, D. F.g.l. 45-50 mm., pale yellowish green with a conspicuous black stripe along the dorsomeson; head light colored with black ring (ocularia) about each single ocellus; antennae one segmented; spiracles winged; eight pairs of prolegs. Food plants chiefly foliage of elm and willow, also recorded from linden, maple and poplar.

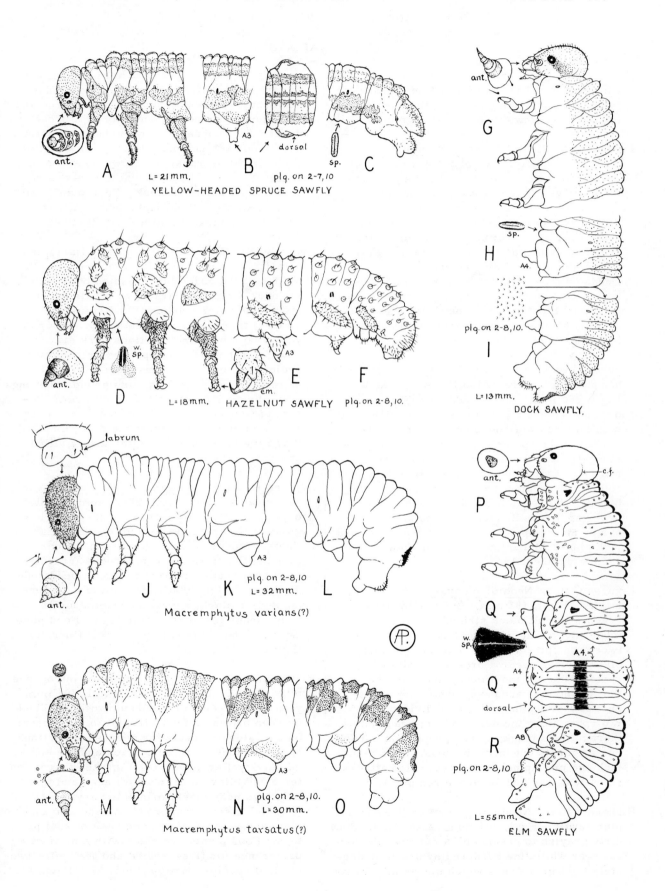

YELLOW-HEADED SPRUCE SAWFLY

L=21mm.

A3

dorsal

sp.

plq. on 2-7,10

HAZELNUT SAWFLY

L=18mm.

plq. on 2-8,10.

w. sp.

ant.

em.

A3

DOCK SAWFLY.

sp.

A4

plq. on 2-8,10.

L=13mm.

labrum

Macremphytus varians(?)

plq. on 2-8,10
L=32mm.

ant.

A3

Macremphytus tarsatus(?)

plq. on 2-8,10.
L=30mm.

A3

ELM SAWFLY

ant.

c.f.

w. sp.(?)

A4

A4

dorsal

A8

plq. on 2-8,10

L=55mm.

EXPLANATION OF FIGURES H8, A-U

DIPRIONIDAE A-U

Note: Three parts are figured for each species namely, lateral views of head and thorax, third (A3) or fourth (A4) abdominal segments (plus dorsal views) and caudal segments.

Figures A to C. Neodiprion pinetum Nort., white pine sawfly. (Abbott's sawfly.) F.g.l. 23-25 mm., with a jet black head and yellowish body with four longitudinal rows of dark spots dorsad of the spiracles; the subdorsal spots are elongated and the supraspiracular spots nearly square; no spots occur on the abdomen below the spiracles; suranal area with a black patch divided on the meson. Feeds on pine needles; destructive on young trees; distinctly gregarious. White pine preferred food yet recorded on pitch, short leaf, red and Mugho pines. Atwood and Peck, 1943; Schaffner, 1943.

Figures D to F. Neodiprion lecontei Fitch, redheaded pine sawfly. Also H1, A; H2, M-N. F.g.l. 25± mm., with a reddish orange to brown head and a pale to deep yellowish body with four rows of conspicuous black spots dorsad of the spiracles; subdorsal spots are elongated and angular and the supraspiracular spots are more square but irregular; on each abdominal segment two smaller spots occur between the spiracles and the base of the prolegs. Feeds in groups on the old needles of a number of pines especially red, white and jack pines. Middleton, 1921; Atwood and Peck, 1943; Schaffner, 1943.

Figures G to I. Neodiprion dyari Roh., a pine sawfly. F.g.l. 18± mm. Body yellowish-green with dull black stripes bordering a moderately wide, light mid-dorsal line. Between the spiracles and the continuous dull black stripes occur a broken line of dark spots which are most conspicuous on the thorax and the caudal segments; dorsal aspect of last segment black subdivided into two spots along the dorsomeson; head and thoracic legs black; spines present on various segments but inconspicuous. Food plants jack and pitch pines preferred. Also attacks short leaf, red and Japanese red pines.

Figures J to L. Neodiprion sertifer (Geor.), a pine sawfly. F.g.l. 22± mm. Also H1, I. Body dirty grayish to green with a narrow mid dorsal near white line bordered by broad moderately light gray areas which merge into a dis-

tinct dark green supraspiracular stripe that is darker in spots especially on the caudal segments; spiracular stripe light colored and conspicuous bordered ventrally by a broad darker area possessing two groups of distinct spines on each segment (H1,I); similar spines occur in three transverse rows on abdominal segments 1 to 9; head, thoracic legs and dorsum of anal segment black. Food plants red, Scotch, Japanese red, jack, Swiss mountain and Mugho pines. Schaffner, 1939, 1943.

Figures M to O. Neodiprion abietis Harr., balsam-fir sawfly. F.g.l. 15± mm. with a yellow to black head and a dull greenish body with six dark stripes separated by a pale dorsal stripe and paler subdorsal and spiracular stripes; thoracic legs black and prolegs pale yellow with proximal portions dark green; rows of minute, pointed prongs or spinelike projections occur on three dorsal crenulations on most of the segments, also groups of prongs occur below the spiracles. Food plants balsam and spruce. Also recorded from cedar and pitch pine, however, these determinations may have been confused with closely allied species. Schaffner, 1943.

Figures P to R. Neodiprion americanum Leach, American sawfly. F.g.l. 20-25 mm. Body pale green with two dark-grayish-green longitudinal lines on the dorsum bordering a lighter middorsal stripe; between the dark line and the spiracles conspicuous irregular dark spot occurs on each segment; head reddish-brown; legs black, dorsum of anal segment near black; spines inconspicuous on body, prominent on thoracic legs. Food plants Loblolly and shortleaf pines. Schaffner, 1943; Hetrick, 1941.

Figures S to U. Diprion simile Htg., introduced pine sawfly. Also H2, K-L. F.g.l. 30± mm., yellowish green on the dorsum with two black or deep brown stripes adjacent to the meson; on the lateral aspects the depressed portions of the segments are near black and the elevated parts yellow producing a spotted larva; venter pale yellow to near white; head and thoracic legs near black; mandibles asymmetrical (H2, K-L); setae numerous on head, suranal plate and ventrad of anus on base of anal prolegs. Food plants are pines with a distinct preference for five-needled and the softer two-needled species. Britton, 1915; Middleton, 1923.

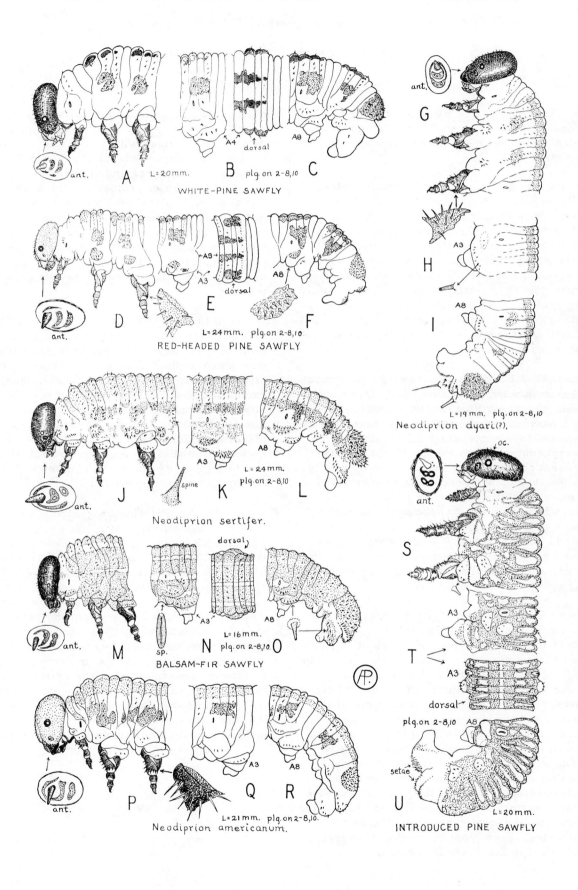

WHITE-PINE SAWFLY

L=20mm.   plg.on 2-8,10

A   B   C

RED-HEADED PINE SAWFLY

L=24mm. plg.on 2-8,10.

D   E   F

Neodiprion sertifer.

L=24mm.
plg.on 2-8,10

J   K   L

BALSAM-FIR SAWFLY

L=16mm.
plg.on 2-8,10.

M   N   O

Neodiprion americanum.

L=21mm. plg.on 2-8,10.

P   Q   R

Neodiprion dyari(?).

L=19mm. plg.on 2-8,10

G   H   I

INTRODUCED PINE SAWFLY

L=20mm.

S   T   U

EXPLANATION OF FIGURES H9, A-R

TENTHREDINIDAE A-R

Note: Three parts are figured for each species namely, lateral views of the head and thorax, third abdominal segment and caudal segments except (F).

Figures A to C. Euura salicis-nodus Walsh, willow-gall sawfly. Also H5, G-H. F.g.l. 9± mm. Body cylindrical and near white to cream colored without setae on most parts of the body; head lightly (yellow) pigmented possessing a few setae, nonsegmented antennae ventrad of black oculariae; mandibles somewhat asymmetrical; suranal area faintly pigmented. Produces galls one-half to one and one-half inches long on small branches of willows especially low growing species adjacent to water.

Figures D to F. Nematus ribesii Scop., imported currantworm. Also H4, E-F. F.g.l. 20± mm. Head near black; body yellowish green with numerous dark spots on all segments except the last instar which is uniformly green except the yellowish ends. When spots are present on the abdominal proleg bearing segments there are on each side of every segment 9 to 10 distinct brown to black pinacula (each bearing one seta) above the spiracles and 4 pinacula below the spiracles bearing one to several setae; the anal plate has two short points on its caudal margin. Feeds on currant and gooseberry foliage frequently stripping the plant of all leaves.

Figures G to I. Priophorus rubivorus Roh., on St. Regis raspberry. Also H3, I-J. F.g.l. 12-14 mm. Preserved specimens of this hairy larva possess a broad, dark, longitudinal band on the dorsum with a lighter area along the meson. Ventrad of the dorsal pigmented area, starting at a point somewhat dorsad of the spiracles, the general color is very light; head yellowish with numerous brown specks and deeply pigmented areas caudad of the ocelli and on the mid-dorsal portion of the epicranium. The numerous well developed setae on the body for the most part are bunched in lots of 6 to 12 resembling verrucae and located above and below the spiracles. Food plant St. Regis raspberry. Collected in San Jose, California.

Figures J to L. Nematus ventralis Say, willow sawfly. Also H1, H and H4, C-D. F.g.l. 20-24 mm., near black with 11 conspicuous yellowish spots on the lateral aspects of the mesothorax, metathorax and abdominal segments 1 to 9; six pairs of prolegs greenish-yellow and two small protuberances on distal margin of the anal area dorsad of the anus. The larva rests or may feed in a J position with the caudal end bent forward. It consumes foliage of various kinds of low growing willows especially basket willows and young new growth of poplars.

Figures M to O. Pristiphora erichsonii Htg., larch sawfly. Also H4, I and J. F.g.l. 20-22 mm. Entire larva glaucous greenish yellow, with a pearly bloom; no lateral stripes or pigmented spots; two dorsal crenulations on each abdominal segment possess rows of slightly elevated pinacula bearing minute setae; head and distal ends of thoracic legs near black; eversible glands present on the ventromeson (caudad of the legs) on abdominal segments 1 to 7. Feeds on the needles of tamarack or larches. Hewitt, 1912.

Figures P to R. Pristiphora geniculata Htg., mountain ash sawfly, Also H4, A-B. F.g.l. 17± mm. Preserved specimens are pink or light reddish and living specimens greenish white with numerous deep brown to near black spots; adjacent to the dorso meson four small spots occur on all the segments except on abdominal segments 2 to 5 where they are very inconspicuous or absent. In addition to these spots, on each spiracle bearing abdominal segment, five larger spots, in groups of two and three, occur dorsad of the spiracles and two still larger spots ventrad of each abdominal spiracle; head entirely yellowish except the black ocularia; thoracic legs yellow to orange. Food plant mountain ash, (Sorbus).

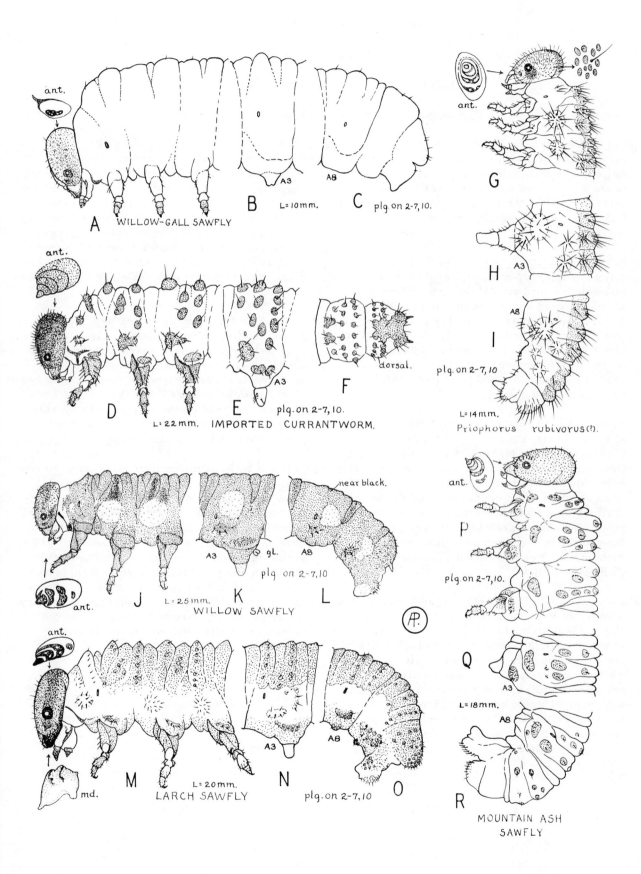

A   WILLOW-GALL SAWFLY

ant.

B   A3   L=10mm.

C   plg. on 2-7,10.

ant.

D   E   plg. on 2-7,10.   A3

L=22mm.   IMPORTED CURRANTWORM.

F   dorsal.

G   ant.

H   A3

I   A8   plg. on 2-7,10   L=14mm.   Priophorus rubivorus(?).

J   ant.   K   A3   gl.   L   A8   near black.   plg. on 2-7,10   L=25mm.

WILLOW SAWFLY

ant.   M   md.   N   A3   O   A8   L=20mm.   LARCH SAWFLY   plg. on 2-7,10

P   ant.   plg. on 2-7,10.

Q   A3   L=18mm.

R   A8   MOUNTAIN ASH SAWFLY

EXPLANATION OF FIGURES H10, A-P

DIPRIONIDAE N-P, TENTHREDINIDAE A to M

Note; Except for the lateral view of an entire larvae (L10,A) and a dorsal view of the caudal segments (L10,M) of one species three parts are figured for each species, namely, lateral views of the head and thorax, the third (A3) abdominal segment and the caudal segments.

Figure A. Caliroa cerasi L., pear-slug. Also H5, F. F.g.l. 10± mm. Lateral view of a late feeding instar. All feeding instars are slime covered and resemble slugs. The pre-pupal or nonfeeding last instar is orange-yellow without a slime covering. Setae present about anus. Spiracles winged. Larvae feed on the upper surface of foliage and leave a skeleton of veins. Food plants are chiefly pear, plum and cherry.

Figures B to D. Endelomyia aethiops F., rose-slug. Also H3, F. F.g.l. 8-10 mm., yellowish-green with a darker, olive green line on the meson due to food in the alimentary tract; mandibles distinctive; a few, short, distinct, conical projections occur on some of the crenulations on all segments including the anal plate. The larva skeletonizes the upper surface of the foliage leaving a yellowish-brown membrane. Feeds on most varieties of roses. Chittenden, 1908.

Figures E to G. Tomostethus multicinctus Roh., brown-headed ash sawfly. Also H3, K-L. F.g.l. 17-20 mm. Early instars are yellowish-green with light lateral lines on both sides of the darker dorsum and covered with a fine white powder. After the fifth moult the larva assumes a bluish smoky color on the dorsum with ventral areas and prolegs yellow. Distinct dorsal crenulations without setae or spines. Foliage of white ash may be completely consumed. Sasscer 1911, Lanford and McConnell, 1935.

Figures H to J. Monophadnoides (Blennocampa) rubi Harr., raspberry sawfly. Also H3, O-P. F.g.l. 20± mm. Light green in color with all segments except the head possessing a number of prominent spine-bearing scoli many of which are bifurcate or multifurcate prongs. Feeds upon foliage, leaving only the larger veins. Also may consume flower buds, young fruit and tender bark of growing shoots. Food plants are raspberry, blackberry and dewberry.

Figures K to M. Erythraspides pygmaea Say., grape sawfly. Also H3, M-N. F.g.l. 13± mm., greenish-yellow with a near black head and caudal end. Dorsal half of most segments bear two transverse rows of conspicuous near black, pointed prongs. The larvae are gregarious and feed on the foliage side by side in rows consuming the entire leaf. Food plants wild and cultivated grapes.

Figures N to P. Diprion hercyniae Htg., European spruce sawfly. Also H2, O-P. F.g.l. 15-20 mm. Body dark green with five longitudinal white lines on the dorsum and lateral aspects in the fourth and fifth instars and none in the last instar; the spiracular light stripe is broad extending ventrad to darker areas on the prolegs; head yellowish-brown flecked with brown spots as indicated, thoracic legs yellowish; spines on segments very inconspicuous. Larvae feed singly on old needles of white, red, black and Norway spruces.

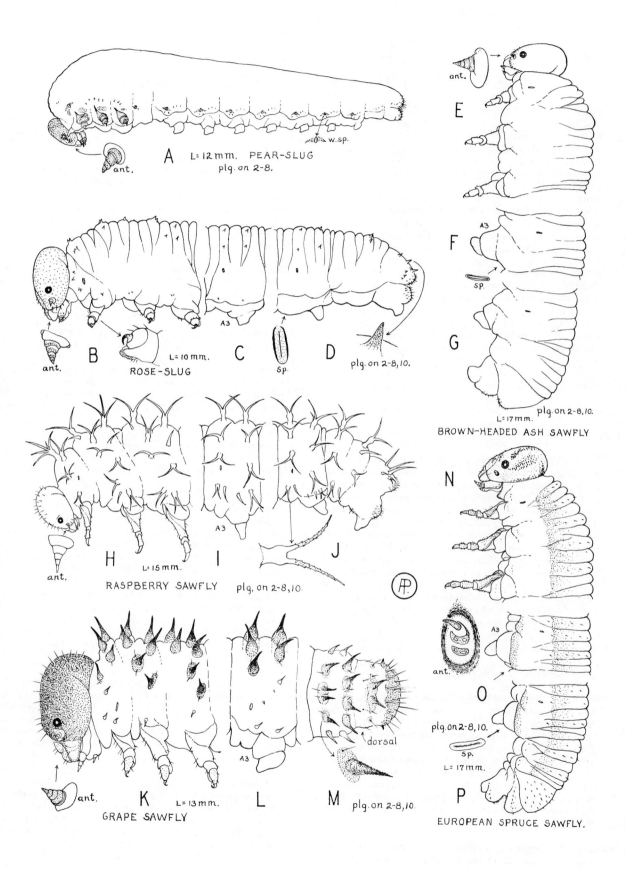

ant.

E

A

L=12mm. PEAR-SLUG
plg. on 2-8.

w. sp.

F

A3

sp.

B

ant.

ROSE-SLUG

L=10mm.

C

A3

D

sp.

plg. on 2-8,10.

G

L=17mm.

plg. on 2-8,10.

BROWN-HEADED ASH SAWFLY

H

ant.

L=15mm.

I

A3

J

RASPBERRY SAWFLY   plg. on 2-8,10.

N

P.P.

ant.

A3

K

ant.

GRAPE SAWFLY

L=13mm.

L

A3

M

dorsal

plg. on 2-8,10.

O

plg. on 2-8,10.

sp.

L=17mm.

P

EUROPEAN SPRUCE SAWFLY.

EXPLANATION OF FIGURES H11, A-K

CEPHIDAE G-J, PAMPHILIIDAE K, SIRICIDAE F, TENTHREDINIDAE A-C

Figures A to C. Profenusa canadensis Marl., hawthorn leaf miner. Also H5, M. F.g.l. 7± mm. entirely near white or cream colored with an internal mid-abdominal green food line; late feeding instars possess crescent-shaped pigment areas about prolegs on abdominal segments 2-8 and pigment spots immediately above each proleg, also pigment spots on the venter of abdominal segments 1 and 9 and a nearly complete pigment circle about the single anal proleg; head somewhat depressed possessing a single pair of ocelli located dorsad of the antennae; antennae short and indistinctly three segmented; thorax slightly wider than abdomen with three pairs of widely separated segmented legs; short, rounded, paired prolegs on abdominal segments two to eight and vestigial, lightly sclerotized remnants of prolegs on the first and ninth abdominal segments and one median proleg on the tenth segment. Food plant hawthorn (Crataegus) and cherry. Produces blotch mines along the margins of the foliage early in the growing season. Parrot and Fulton, 1915.

Figure A. Lateral view of larva.

Figure B. Ventral view of head and thorax.

Figure C. Antenna.

Figures D and E. Fenusa pusilla Klug. birch leaf miner. F.g.l. 6± mm. Body translucently whitish, slightly depressed and abdominal segments divided dorsally into annulets; conspicuous black areas occur on the venter of each thoracic segment and the first abdominal segment during the second to fourth instars, absent in the first and fifth instars; head prognathous in all instars except the fifth, nonfeeding instar; fifth instar more cylindrical and yellowish; setae almost absent except on the head; thoracic legs small and far apart; tiny vestigial prolegs occur on abdominal segments 2 to 8 especially noticeable on the fifth instar. A leaf miner of several species of Betula, birches. Friend, 1933.

Figure D. Ventral view of a fourth instar larva.

Figure E. Ventral view of a head.

Figure F. Tremex columba L., pigeon tremex. Also H2, B. F.g.l. 45± mm. Lateral view of cylindrical, orthosomatic near white borer with a brown sclerotized caudal prong (postcornu) on the last segment dorsad of the anus; head near white except mandibles and area adjacent to mouth parts and ventrocaudal margin; three pairs of non-segmented, near white, clawless thoracic legs; two pairs of spiracles on thorax and eight pairs on abdominal segments 1 to 8. Borers in dead and dying wood of elm, hickory and maple.

Figure G. Cephus pygmaeus L., European wheat stem sawfly. F.g.l. 10-14 mm. Lateral view of a cylin-drical, slightly S-shaped (reversed), near white borer; thoracic segments slightly swollen and bear mamma-like legs without claws and two pairs of spiracles; head rounded, hypognathous, light yellow with pigmented mouth parts and a dark pair of ocelli adjacent to and laterad of the antennae; antennae four segmented; caudal segment terminates in a caudodorsal nonsclerotized projection except the sclerotized ring at the tip end (not tubelike as in C. cinctus Nort.); bears two, small, subanal, sclerotized, blunt spines; setae present on the head and caudal segments, otherwise naked; lateral view of dorsal area of caudal segment triangular sloping toward caudal end; dorsum of eighth and ninth segments without setae; food plants wheat, barley, rye and a species of Chess. Bores in stems and hibernates in stubble near ground level. Ries, 1926, Gahan, 1920.

Figures H and I. Cephus tabidus F., black grain stem sawfly. Also H2, C. F.g.l. 10± mm. This larva resembles C. pygmaeus closely; lateral view of dorsal area of caudal segment not triangular but rounded with caudal portion as wide as cephalic portion; a few setae present on dorsum of eighth and ninth segments. Food chiefly wheat, rarely rye. Injury similar to that of C. pygaemus. Gahan, 1920.

Figure H. Mesal view of mandible.

Figure I. Lateral view of caudal end.

Figure J. Janus abbreviatus Say, willow-shoot sawfly. F.g.l. 12± mm. Lateral view of cylindrical, slightly S-shaped (reversed), near white borer with a small head and a somewhat enlarged thorax; head pale yellow possessing pigmented mandibles and one dark ocellus adjacent to each five segmented antenna; thoracic legs mammalike without claws; two pairs of spiracles on thorax and eight on abdominal segments; terminal prong (postcornu) above anus single and deeply sclerotized at caudal end; subanal palpiform appendages apparently two segmented and without pigmentation; setae present on head and portions of anal segment. Food plants willows, especially pussywillow. Bores in the small shoots to larger branches of living trees.

Figure K. Neurotoma fasciata Nort., wild cherry web-spinning sawfly. Also H1, B, G and J; H2, A. F.g.l. 20± mm. Lateral view of a reddish-brown larva with a near black head; during last instar the body color changes to a bright green; antennae seven segmented; one pair of dark ocelli located lateroventrad of antennae; thoracic legs, near black, straight, segmented and sharp pointed; sclerotized areas on the prothorax; caudal segment possesses sclerotized areas above and below the anus; a pair of three segmented palpiform structures ventrad of. anus; a sclerotized hook (postcornu) pointing cephalad on the meson of the suranal area. Food plant, foliage of wild cherry, gregarious and web-spinning. Yuasa, 1920.

HYMENOPTERA, SAWFLY LARVAE.

FIGURE HII

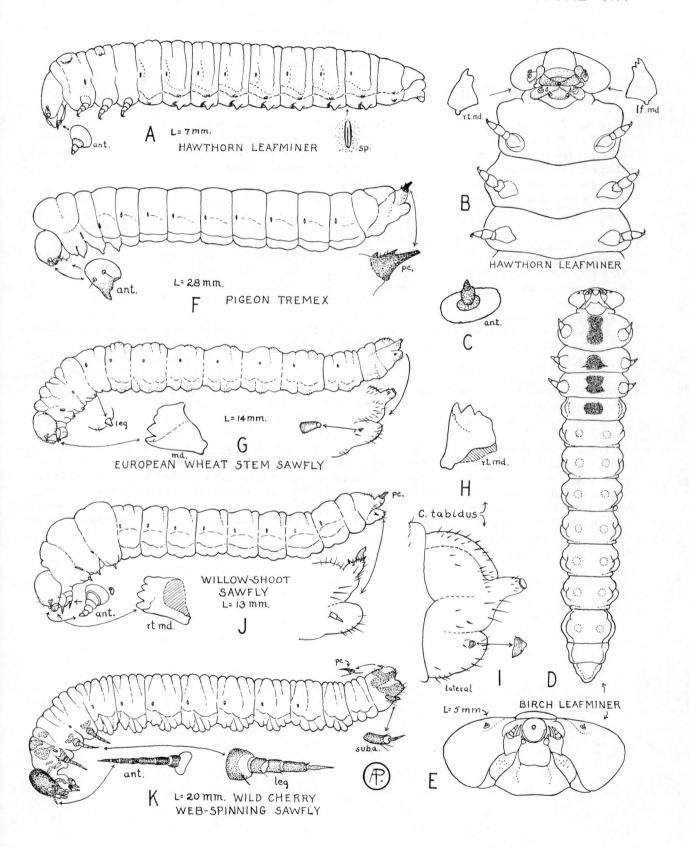

A
L= 7mm.
HAWTHORN LEAFMINER
ant.
sp.

B
HAWTHORN LEAFMINER
rt.md.
lf.md

C
ant.

F
L= 28mm.
PIGEON TREMEX
ant.
pc.

G
L= 14mm.
EUROPEAN WHEAT STEM SAWFLY
leg
md.

H
rt.md.

J
WILLOW-SHOOT
SAWFLY
L= 13 mm.
ant.
rt md.
pc.

I
C. tabidus
lateral
L= 5mm.

D
BIRCH LEAFMINER

K
L= 20mm. WILD CHERRY
WEB-SPINNING SAWFLY
ant.
leg
pc.
sub.a.

E

EXPLANATION OF FIGURES, H12, A-G

APIDAE G, BRACONIDAE C-D, CHALCIDIDAE A-B, FORMICIDAE F, VESPIDAE E

Figure A. Torymus druparum Boh., apple seed chalcid. F.g.l. 3.5± mm. Lateral view of an entirely near white, somewhat crescent-shaped, cyphosomatic larva; mouth parts reduced to two sharp pointed, nearly opposable mandibles. Infests seeds of various fruits, especially apple. Crosby, 1909; Cushman, 1916.

Figure B. Harmolita tritici Fitch., wheat jointworm. F.g.l. 4.5 mm. Lateral view of an entirely near-white cylindrical, somewhat spindle-shaped larva; mouth parts are reduced to two sharp pointed nearly opposable mandibles as indicated. Infests stems of wheat and grasses producing slight gall-like swellings in the straws usually just above a joint. Phillips, 1920.

Figures C and D. Macrocentrus ancylivorus Roh., a primary parasite of the oriental fruit moth larva. F.g.l. 5± mm.

Figure C. Lateral view of a first instar larva which is entirely near white or translucent except the deep yellow, dorsal and lateral aspects of a depressed head; mandibles long, sharp pointed, yellow and opposable; caudal end hook-shaped. Found in larvae of several hosts especially the oriental fruit moth and the strawberry leaf roller.

Figure D. Lateral view of a full grown, near white to cream colored, opaque larva which emerges from its host and spins a cocoon; sclerotized mouth parts absent in this stage.

Figure E. Vespa sp. wasp larva. F.g.l. 14± mm. Lateral view of a larva which has been removed from its cell; cream colored with a light yellowish head possessing a distinct labrum, paired, tridentate, opposable mandibles vestigial maxillae and a labium; inconspicuous circular spiracles are present, two on the thorax and eight on the abdomen.

Figure F. Aphaenogaster (prob.) tennesseensis Mayr. red ant. F.g.l. 3,5 mm. Lateral view of a dirty white somewhat pear-shaped larva with a very small, well developed head; most of the setae on the head and body appear to be bifurcate. Found under bark of a log near Columbus, Ohio.

Figure G. Apis mellifera L., honey bee. F.g.l. 12 mm. Lateral view of a full grown, near white larva of a worker bee removed from its cell; C-shaped; pointed at the head end; head nonsclerotized possessing nonsclerotized lobes about mouth opening; two pairs of spiracles on the thorax and eight pairs on the abdomen.

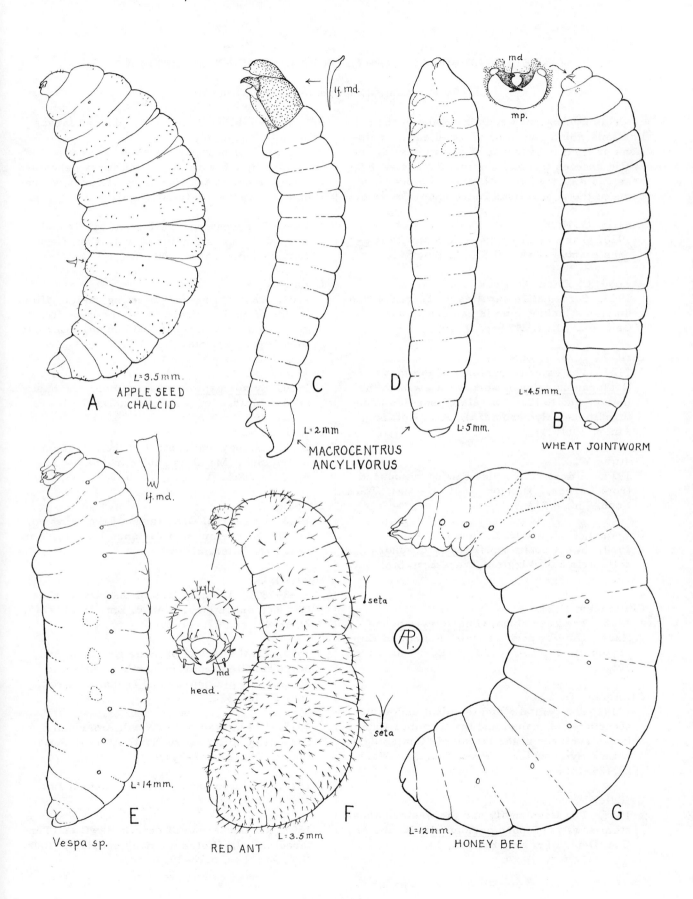

L=3.5 mm.

A   APPLE SEED CHALCID

lf. md.

C

L=2 mm

MACROCENTRUS ANCYLIVORUS

D

L=5 mm.

md

mp.

L=4.5 mm.

B   WHEAT JOINTWORM

lf. md.

E   L=14 mm.

Vespa sp.

head.

md

seta

seta

F   L=3.5 mm

RED ANT

L=12 mm.

G   HONEY BEE

A.P.

A SELECTED BIBLIOGRAPHY FOR LARVAE OF HYMENOPTERA

Chiefly Plant Infesting Species of the Symphyta

This bibliography contains many of the publications which give good to excellent descriptions or figures of larvae of plant infesting, nearctic species that are common or pests. Figures and descriptions of larvae also occur in some of the publications listed under "A select-ed general bibliography on nymphs and larvae of insects," page 56.

In this bibliography the scientific name (that used by the author) of each larva described has been added to the title in most cases where it does not appear in the original.

Ainslie, C. N.
1920. The western grass-stem sawfly (Cephus cinctus Nort.) U.S.D.A. Bul. 841.

Atwood, C. E. and O. Peck.
1943. Some native sawflies of the genus Neodiprion attacking pine in eastern Canada. Can. Jour. Res. 21, Sec. D, 109.

Bird, R. D.
1927. The external anatomy of the larva of Hoplocampa halcyon Nort. with a key to the instars and to those of related species (Tenthredinidae, Hymenoptera). Ann. Ent. Soc. Amer. 20:481.

Britton, W. E.
1915. A destructive pine sawfly introduced from Europe. (Diprion simile Hartig). Jour. Econ. Ent. 8:379.

Chapman, P. J. and G. E. Gould.
1929. Sweet potato sawfly (Stericitiphora cellularis Say). Virginia Truck Exp. Sta. Bul. 68.

Chittenden, F. H.
1908. The rose slugs, (Endelomyia rosae Harr., Cladius pectinicornis Four. and Emphytus cinctus L.). U.S.D.A. Bur. Ent. Circ. 105.

Crampton, G. C.
1919. The genitalia and terminal abdominal structures of males, and the terminal abdominal structures of the larvae of "Chalastogastrous" Hymenoptera. Proc. Ent. Soc. Wash. 21:129-155.

Criddle, N.
1915. The Hessian-fly and the western wheat-stem sawfly, (Cephus occidentalis R. and M.) Can. Dept. Agr. Ent. Br. Bul. 11.

1924. The western wheat-stem sawfly and its control, (Cephus cinctus Nort.). Can. Dept. Agr. Ent. Br. Pamph. No. 6.

Crosby, C. R.
1909. On certain seed-infecting chalcis-flies. (seeds of apple, sorbus, rose, Douglas fir, grape, Virginia creeper and sumac). Cornell Univ. Agr. Exp. Sta. Bul. 265.

Cushman, R. A.
1916. Syntomaspis druparum Boh., the apple seed chalcid. Jour. Agr. Res. 7:487.

Daniel, D. M.
1928. Biology and control of the blackberry leaf-miner, (Metallus rubi Forbes). N.Y. Agr. Exp. Sta. (Geneva) Tech, Bul. 133.

Dusham, E. H.
1928. The larval wax glands of the dogwood sawfly (Macremphytus varianus Norton). Ann. Ent. Soc. Amer. 21:92.

Dyar, H. G.
1893-1895. Descriptions of the larvae of certain Tenthredinidae. Canad. Ent. 25:244-248, 26:42-45, and 27:191-196.

1895. On the larvae of some Nematoid and other sawflies from the northern Atlantic states. (24 plus species) Trans. Am. Ent. Soc. 22:301-312.

1895. The larvae of the North American sawflies. (Key to larvae of North Atlantic States.) Canad. Ent. 27:337-344.

1896. Notes on sawfly larvae. Canad. Ent. 28:235-239.

1897. On the larvae of certain sawflies (Tenthredinidae). (Notes on many species.) Jour. N.Y. Ent. Soc. 5:18-30.

1897. New sawflies (Tenthredinidae) with descriptions of larvae. (14 species.) Jour. N. Y. Ent. Soc. 5:190-201.

1897. Some structural points in sawfly larvae. Proc. Ent. Soc. Wash. 4:218-220.

1897. A new sawfly (Lophyrus pratti n. sp.) Proc. Ent. Soc. Wash. 4:262.

1898. On the larvae of certain Nematinae and Blennocampinae with descriptions of new species. (Key to North American larvae of Blennocampinae.) Jour. N. Y. Ent. Soc. 6:121.

1898. Notes on some sawfly larvae, especially the Xyelidae. Canad. Ent. 30:173-176.

1899. Larvae of Xyelidae. Canad. Ent. 31:127.

1900. On the larvae of Atomacera and some other sawflies (8 species). Jour. N. Y. Ent. Soc. 8:26-31.

Essig, E. O.
1914. The cherry fruit sawfly (Holocampa cookei Clarke). Month. Bul. Cal. State Comm. Hort. 1914, 31-35.

Felt, E. P. 1908. Injurious and other insects. Poplar sawfly (Trichiocampus viminalis Fall.) 24th Rept. State Ent. N. Y. Mus. Bul. 134, page 13.

Fernald, H. T.
1903. The plum webbing sawfly (Neurotoma sp.). Ent. News 14:298-302.

Foster, S. W.
1913. The cherry fruit sawfly (Hoplocampa cookei Clarke). Bul. U.S.D.A. Bur. Ent. Bul. 116, pt. 3.

Friend, R. B.
1933. The birch leaf-mining sawfly, (Fenusa pumila Klug.) Conn. A. E. S. Bul. 348.

Frost, S. W.
1925. The leaf mining habit in the Hymenoptera (list of species and their food plants). Ann. Ent. Soc. Amer. 18:399.

Gahan, A. B.
1920. Black grain-stem sawfly of Europe in the United States. (Key for larvae of Trachelus tabidus, Fab., Cephus pygmaeus, Linn. and Cephus cinctus, Nort.) U.S.D.A. Bul. 834.

Hall, W. B.
1917. Notes on the immature stages of Hemitaxonus multicinctus Roh. Proc. Ent. Soc. Wash. 19:28.

Hetrick, L. A.
1941. Life history studies of Neodiprion americanum (Leach). Jour. Econ. Ent. 34;373-377.

Hewitt, C. G.
1912. The large larch sawfly (Nematus erichsonii) with an account of the parasites, other natural enemies and means of control. Can. Expt. Farms Bul. Vol. 10, Second series (Ent. Bul. 5), 1-42.

Hopping, G. R. and H. B. Leach.
1936-1937. Sawfly biologies. I Neodiprion tsugae Midd. II Hemichroa crocea Geof. Canad. Ent. (I) 68:71-79 and (II) 69:243-249.

Horsfall, W. R.
1929. The grapevine sawfly (Hym.), (Erythraspides pygmaeus Say). Ent. News 40:174.

Houghton, C. O.
1908. The blackberry leaf-miner (Scolioneura capitalis Nort.) Ent. News 19:212-216, also see Del. Agr. Exp. Sta. Bul. 87.

Langford, G. S. and H. S. McConnell.
1935. Biology of Tomostethus multicinctus (Roh.), a sawfly attacking white ash. Jour. Econ. Ent. 28:208-10.

Lowe, V. H.
1898. The raspberry sawfly, (Monophadnus rubi Harr.). N. Y. Agr. Exp. Sta. (Geneva) Bul. 150.

Marlatt, C. L.
1890. The final moulting of tenthredinid larvae. Proc. Ent. Wash. 2:115-117.

Martorell, L. F.
1941. Biological notes on the sea-grape sawfly, Schizocera krugii Cresson, in Puerto Rico. Caribbean Forester, 2:141.

Middleton, W.
1915. Notes on some sawfly larvae belonging to the genus Dimorphopteryx. Proc. U. S. Nat. Mus. 48:497-501.

1917. Notes on the larvae of some Cephidae (key to larvae). Proc. Ent. Soc. Wash. 19:174-179.

1921. LeConte's sawfly, an enemy of young pines. Jour. Agr. Res. 20:741-760.

1921. Some notes on the terminal abdominal structures of sawflies. Proc. Ent. Soc. Wash. 23:139-144.

1921. Some suggested homologies between larvae and adults in sawflies. Proc. Ent. Soc. Wash. 23:173-192.

1922. Sawflies injurious to rose foliage (Cladius isomerus Nort. Caliroa aethiops Fab. and Emphythes cinctipes Nort.) U.S.D.A. Farmers' Bul. 1252.

1923. The imported pine sawfly (Diprion simile Hartig). U.S.D.A. Bul. 1182.

Miles, H. W.
1932. On the biology of the apple sawfly, Hoplocampa testudinea Klug. Ann. App. Biol. 19:420-43.

1936. On the biology of Emphytus cinctus L. and Blennocampa waldheimi Gimm. (Hym. Symphata). Bul. Ent. Res. 27:467-473.

1936. On the biology of certain species of Holcocneme Kon. (Hym. Symph.) Ann. Appl. Biol. 23:781-802.

Mitchener, A. V.
1931. The brown headed spruce sawfly, (Pachynematus ocreatus Marl.). Ont. Ent. Soc. Ann. Rept. 62:57-60.

Nash, R. W.
1939. The yellow headed spruce sawfly in Maine (Pikonema alaskensis Roh.). Jour. Econ. Ent. 32:330-334.

Nelson, J. A.
1924. Morphology of the honey bee larva. Jour. Agr. Res. 28:1167-1214.

Newcomer, E. J.
1916. The dock false-worm; an apple pest (Ametastegia glabrata Fallen) U.S.D.A. Bul. 265.

Nougaret, R. L., W. H. Davidson and E. J. Newcomer.
1916. The pear leaf-worm (Gymnomychus californicus Marl.) U.S.D.A. Bul. 438.

Parrott, P. J. and B. B. Fulton.
1915. The cherry and hawthorn sawfly leaf-miner (Profenusa collaris MacGil.) New York Agr. Exp. Sta. (Geneva) Bul. 411.

1915. Cherry and hawthorn sawfly leaf miner. Jour. Agr. Res. 5:519.

Pearsall, R. F.
1902. The life history of Lyda fasciata (Norton), Fam. Tenthredinidae, (on wild cherry). Canad. Ent. 34:214-16.

Phillips, W. J.
1920. Studies on the life history and habits of the jointworm flies of the genus Harmolita (Isosoma) with recommendation for control. U.S.D.A. Bul. 808.

Ries, D. T.
1926. A biological study of Cephus pygmaeus Linn., the wheat-stem sawfly. Jour. Agr. Res. 32:277-295.

Riley, C. V. and C. L. Marlatt.
1891. Wheat and grass sawflies (species of Cephus, Dolerus and Nematus). Insect Life 4:168-181.

Riley, C. V.
1888. The habits of Thalessa and Tremex (Tremex columba). Insect life 1:168-179.

Rohwer, S. A. and R. A. Cushman.
1917. Idiogastra, a new suborder of Hymenoptera with notes on the immature stages of Oryssus. Proc. Ent. Soc. Wash. 19:89-98.

Rohwer, S. A. and W. Middleton.
1922. North American sawflies of the subfamily Cladiinae with notes on habits and descriptions of larvae. Proc. U. S. Nat. Mus. 60:1-46.

Ross, H. A.
1937. A generic classification of the nearctic sawflies (Hymenoptera, Symphata). Illinois Biol. Monographs 15:2; 1-173.

1938. The nearctic species of Pikonema, a genus of spruce sawflies (Hymenoptera-Tenthredinidae) (Pikonema dimmockii Cress and Pikonema alaskensis Roh.). Proc. Ent. Soc. Wash. 40:17-20.

Sasscer, E. R.
1911. Notes on a sawfly injurious to ash (Tomostethus multicinctus Roh.). Proc. Ent. Soc. Wash. 13:107-110.

Schaffner, J. V. Jr.
1939. Neodiprion sertifer (Geoff), a pine sawfly accidentally introduced into New Jersey from Europe. Jour. Econ. Ent. 32:887-88.

1943. Sawflies injurious to conifers in the northeastern states. Jour. Forestry 41:580.

Schwarz, E. A.
1909. Illustrations of the life history of a sawfly (Hylotoma pectoralis Leach) injurious to willows. Proc. Ent. Soc. Wash. 11:106-108.

Severin, H. C. 1920. The webspinning sawfly of plums and sandcherries (Neurotoma inconspicua Nort.). S. Dak. Agr. Expr. Sta. Bul. 190.

Slingerland, M. N.
1905. Two new shade-tree pests. I. European elm sawfly leaf-miner, Kaliosysphinga ulmi Sundeval, and II. European alder sawfly leaf-miner, K. dohrnii Tisch., Cornell Agr. Exp. Sta. Bul. 233.

Sorenson, C. J.
1930. The alfalfa-seed Chalcis fly in Utah in 1926-29 inclusive, (Bruchophagus funebris How.). Utah Agr. Exp. Sta. Bul. 218.

Swenk, M. H.
1910. A new sawfly enemy of the bull pine in Nebraska (closely related to Diprion townsendi), 24th Rept. Nebr. Agr. Exp. Sta. for 1910, pp. 333.

Taylor, R. L.
1931. On "Dyar's Rule" and its application to sawfly larvae. (Phyllotoma nemorata Fallen.) Ann. Ent. Soc. Amer. 24:451.

Thomas, I.
1936. On the occurrence of the pear fruit sawfly, (Hoplocampa brevis Klug.) Ann. Appl. Biol. 23:633-639. 2 good figs.

Townsend, H. T.
1894. Notes on the Tenthredinid gall of Euura orbitalis on Salix and its occupants. Jour. N. Y. Ent. Soc. 2:102-104.

Urbahns, T. D.
1920. The clover and alfalfa seed chalcis-fly (Bruchophagus funebris, How.) U.S.D.A. Bul. 812.

Walden, B. H.
1912. A new sawfly pest of the blackberry, (Pamphilus dentatus MacG.). Rept. Conn. Agr. Exp. Sta. 1912, pp. 236-240.

Webster, F. M. and G. I. Reeves.
1909. The wheat strawworm, (Isosoma grande Riley) U.S.D.A. Bur. Ent. Circ. 106.

Webster, R. L.
1915. Two strawberry slugs, (Empria fragaria Roh. and Empria maculata Nort.). Iowa Agr. Expt. Sta. Ext. Sect. Bul. 162.

Young, C.
1899. Descriptions of sawfly larvae (Macroxyela ferruginea on Ulmus americana; Pteronus fulvricus on Salix sericea; Phymetocera fumipennis on Smilacina racemosa.) Canad. Ent. 31:41-3.

Yuasa, H.
1922. A classification of the larvae of the Tenthredinoidea. Ill. Biol. Mono. 7:1-172.

KEY TO ABBREVIATIONS USED ON FIGURES IN PART I

Note: For abbreviations to names of setae, setal punctures and armature on all parts of larvae of Lepidoptera see figures L1 to L8 and Table 2, page 65.

a.c. = anal comb
aca. = antacoria
a.h. = anal horn
a.p. = anal plate
ant. = antenna
asp. = asperites
bw. = brown
b.t. = breathing tube
cer. = cerci
cerv. = cervical shield
c.f. = cervical furrow
c.g. = cervical gland
con. = condyle
cor. = cornicle
cr. = crochets
cre. = cremaster
cx. = coxa
em. = empodium
fe. = femur
f.g.l. = full grown larva or length
fl. = fleshy filament
gi. = gills
gib. = gibbose area
gl. = gland
hypo = hypopleurite
l. = length
la. = labium
lb. pl. = labial palpus
lc. = lacinia
lf. = left
lp. = larvapod
lr. = labrum
md. = mandible
meso. = mesothorax

meta. = metathorax
m.h. = mouth hooks
mp. = mouthparts
ms. = microspines
mx. pl. = maxillary palpus
oc. = ocellus
os. = osmeteria
pc. = postcornu
pd. = paddlelike setae
plg. = proleg
pn. = penicillus
prep = preepipleurite
pro. = prothorax
psa. = postspiracular area
psep. = postepipleurite
psp. = prothoracic spiracle or prothoracic
        Kappa group.
ret. = retinaculum
rt. = right
sa. = spiracular area
sp. = spiracle
spn. = spinneret
sp. p. = spiracular prong
sub. = subventral
sub. a. = subanal appendage
sub. p. = subanal setiferous protuberance
ta. = tarsus (plus claw)
ti. = tibia
tr. = trochanter
tr. gi. = gills
wh. = white
w.p. = wing pads
w. sp. = winged spiracles
yel. = yellow

The following terms, chiefly morphological, are found in the published literature on immature stages of insects. In this volume all general terms and those that apply specifically to the Lepidoptera and Hymenoptera are included. Many adjectives, adverbs and descriptive terms used commonly in describing adults, which apply equally well to immature stages, have been omitted. These may be found in "A Glossary of Entomology" by J. R. de la Torre-Bueno, 1937. A few terms have two or more meanings. So far as immature stages are concerned, especially those relating to larvae, the first definition presented is the one most widely accepted or used. The letters and numbers in parentheses refer to figures in this volume. (T-B) refers to glossary by Torre-Bueno.

Acariform: Shaped like a mite (Acarina).

Accessory ventral condyle: An additional condyle or articulating process on the ventral side of the mandible and located mesad of the regular ventral condyle.

Acetabulum (a): The articulating cavity in which an appendage or condyle of an appendage operates; a cuplike cavity within the sucking mouth of a maggot.

Addorsal line: Among caterpillars, a longitudinal line a little to one side of the dorsal and between it and the subdorsal line (T-B)

Adfrontals, adfrontal areas, sclerites or pieces: Among larvae of Lepidoptera a pair of long oblique sclerites on the front of the head laterad of the frons extending from the base of the antennae to the epicranial (coronal) suture where they meet, (L4,A-B).

Adfrontal seta(ae): Setae borne on the adfrontal areas and usually numbered according to their proximity to the vertex, the closest being termed the first adfrontal seta, (Adf 1 and 2).

Adfrontal suture: The sutures separating the adfrontal sclerites or areas from the epicranium.

Adventral line: Among caterpillars a line along the venter between the meson and the base of the legs.

Adventral tubercle: A tubercle on each of the abdominal segments of caterpillars on the inner base of the leg, seta sigma (8).

Ambulatory, ambulatorial: Fitted or formed for walking or locomotion.

Ambulatorial warts: See ampulla.

Amphipneustic respiratory system: A type of larva in which only the first (thoracic) and the last or two last (abdominal) pairs of spiracles are open.

Ampulla(ae): Blister or wartlike protuberances used as organs of locomotion usually confined to the abdominal segments, ventral or dorsal, rarely lateral, in position; sometimes called ambulatorial or scansorial warts.

Anal comb: Among lepidopterous larvae the sclerotized prong or fork ventrad of the anal plate, located on the meson and adjacent to the anal opening (L2,H); used to eject faeces; urogomphi of coleopterous larvae.

Anal fork: See anal comb.

Anal horn: A spinelike horn located on the meson of the eighth abdominal segment of most sphingid larvae, (L55, G).

Anal plate: Among caterpillars and other larvae the dorsal shieldlike covering of the last abdominal segment; suranal plate; epiproct.

Anal prolegs: The prolegs on the last abdominal segment.

Anal segment: The most caudal segment of the abdomen.

Anal slit: Anal opening which may be transverse or parallel with meson.

Annular spiracle: A simple, ringlike spiracle, having a single opening with no accessory chambers, (L2, I).

Annulet: One of the small rings into which a segment is divided by complete transverse constrictions, crenulations, plicae, (H1, I).

Annuliform: In the form of rings or ringlike segments (T-B).

Antacoria: The coria or basal segmental membrane of each antennal segment; the basal articulating narrow ring of membrane connecting an antenna with the head (MacGillivray), (L1, D).

Antenna(ae): Among larvae, paired segmented sensory organs on each side of head, usually located near base of mandibles.

Antennaria: Annular sclerite forming the periphery of each antacoria (MacGillivray).

Antepenultimate: Second segment from the last; if nine segments occur the antepenultimate would be segment seven.

Anterior: Equals cephalic.

Anterior stigmatal tubercle: Prominence on the thoracic and abdominal segments of caterpillars (T-B).

Antlered larvae: Newly hatched larvae of certain <u>Heterocampa</u> among Lepidoptera, which have on the first thoracic segment a pair of large antlerlike horns (scoli) and other horns on the abdominal segments (Comstock).

Anus: The posterior opening of the alimentary canal; located at the end of the body in the tenth or last abdominal segment.

Apistognathous: A hypognathous type where the mouth parts arise from the caudo-ventral portion of the head capsule and project caudo-ventrad; common among Homoptera and cockroach heads; see opistognathous.

Apneustic respiratory system: Without functional spiracles; respiration through the skin or trachael gills; tracheal system usually absent or rudimentary.

Apoid: Resembling larvae of honey bee

Armature: Setae, spines or sclerotized processes on the body, head or appendages of insects.

Asperities: Usually small spinelike structures frequently arranged in rows or confined to specific areas; also surface roughenings, sculpturings, or dotlike elevations; see microspines.

B

Basal articulating membrane of antenna: Equals antacoria.

Beta Group: The beta group consists of setae, alpha (Ia or 1) and beta (Ib or 2).

Bigibbous: Possessing paired, large, rounded, dorsal swelling(s).

Birodinal: Said of crochets when they are arranged in a single series (or row) but of two alternating lengths.

Biserial: Said of crochets when their proximal ends are arranged in two rows, usually concentric.

Bisetose: Consisting of or bearing two setae.

Biting mouth parts: Mouth parts with mandibles opposable and fitted for chewing.

C

Campodeiform: Applied to larval forms which in their early active stages resemble Campodea (Thysanura) with well-developed legs; leptiform.

Cardo(dines): The proximal sclerite of the maxilla by means of which it is joined to the head, usually bipartite, a subcardo and a precardo.

Caterpillar: Most larvae of Lepidoptera and many saw-flies among the Hymenoptera; eruciform type.

Cauda: Tail

Caudal (adj.), caudad (adv.): Pertaining to the cauda (tail) or anal end, directed toward the tail end.

Cephalic (adj.), cephalad (adv.): Belonging to or attached to the head, directed toward the head; anterior; frontal.

Cephalon: The head; the vertical or frontal surface of the head end of the insect body, especially among hypognathous heads.

Ceratheca: That portion of the pupal shell that envelops the antenna (T-B).

Cercus(ci); An appendage (generally paired) of the tenth (or ninth) abdominal segment, usually slender, filamentous and segmented; urogomphi among Coleoptera, (06, A, C and E).

Cervical glands: Dorso-lateral glands located between the head and thorax, Xyelidae, (H5, A).

Cervical triangle: See vertical triangle.

Chaetotaxy: The arrangement of the setae of a particular insect head or segment; see setal maps, (L4 to L8).

Chalaza(ae): A simple sclerotized projection of cuticle bearing one seta or two to four setae on separate elevated prominences (H5, B); between papilla and cornicula in size (Fraker); among coccinillids it is a distinct but slight pimplelike projection of the body wall. It may be considerably wider than long and bears on its distal end a stout seta (Gage).

Chrysalis, chrysalid(es): Pupal stage of butterflies, (010, D-F).

Claw(s): Usually one or two sharp, hooklike, heavily sclerotized structures located at the distal end of the tarsus or tarsungulus.

Clypealia(ae): The small subtriangular or quadrangular area at each lateral end of the postclypeus; antecoxal piece of the mandible; e.g., corydalis larva.

Clypeus; A sclerotized area located between the frons (front) and the labrum.

Coarctate: Among Diptera a form of pupa in which all the parts of the future adult are concealed by a thickened, usually cylindrical case or covering which is often the last larval skin contracted, (012, A-C).

Cocoon: A protective covering for a hibernating larva or the pupa constructed (spun or secreted) by the full grown larva previous to the prepupal stage. It consists of silk or viscid material which hardens upon exposure to air.

Cocoon breaker or cutter: A structure or elevated ridge of the pupa of certain Lepidoptera, often located on the meson of the head, used when the pupa forces its way out of the cocoon.

Collophore: Among Collembola a ventral tube or pouch projecting ventrad from the first abdominal segment.

Compressed: Flattened laterally.

Condyle: Specifically a process or knoblike structure on the base of a mandible which fits into an acetabulum and serves as a movable point; in general any process of an appendage which fits into a cavity and serves as a point of articulation, (L1, O-P).

Corniculum(a): A small hornlike process of cuticula, not associated with primary setae (Fracker); similar to a chalaza in shape but does not bear a seta; often present on the suranal plate, (L12, C).

Coronal suture or branch: The stem of the Y-shaped epicranial suture; metopic suture, (L4).

Coxa(ae): The proximal segment of the leg articulating with the pleuron, also with the sternum.

Cranium: The sclerotized skull-like part of the head capsule.

Cremaster: The terminal segment of the abdomen of a pupa which may be spinelike among subterranean pupae or anal hooks for suspending chrysalids, Lepidoptera, (010).

Crenulations: Small, evenly rounded, rather deeply curved scallops; transverse ridges or plicae, also see annulets and plicae.

Cribriform: Sievelike openings, common among spiracles.

Crochet(s),(crotchet): One of the series of sclerotized hooklike, cuticular structures, usually arranged in rows or circles on the prolegs of lepidopterous and other larvae; also on cremaster of chrysalides; frequently called hooks, (L3).

C-shaped: Semi-circular or crescent shaped; equals U-shaped.

Culmen: The longitudinal carina of a caterpillar.

Cyatotheca: The cover of the thorax in the pupa.

D

Dentes, dentate: Teeth, toothed, provided with toothlike projections.

Denticulate: Set with little teeth or notches.

Depressed: Flattened dorsoventrally; lateral diameter much greater than dorsoventral diameter.

Diaton rake: In mayfly nymphs, a structure of the galea composed of bristles and pectinated spines or of hairs or spines on the maxillae, used in scraping food from stones, etc.

Distal (adj.), distad (adv.): That part of appendage farthest from the point of attachment to the body; toward the distal end.

Dististipes: The distal portion of the maxillary stipes.

Dorsal line: A longitudinal line along the dorsomeson of caterpillars.

Dorso-meson: The intersection of the meson with the dorsal surface of the body.

Dorsum, (adjective dorsal, adverb dorsad): The entire back or upper region or surface above the pleural regions; specifically the back region of a segment.

Dyar's law: An observational rule which shows that among lepidopterous larvae the increase in the width of the head shows a regular geometrical progression in successive instars.

E

Ecdysis: Moulting; the process of casting the cuticle.

Eclosion: Emergence of the adult from the pupa; the act or process of hatching from the egg.

Ectal (adj.), ectad (adv.): Outward or without; the outer surface of the body or parts; from the center toward the outer surface of the insect body.

Ectognathous: With mouth parts exposed and free; ectotrophous.

Egg-burster: A projecting point or ridge on the head of an embryo used in breaking the shell when hatching.

Egg-case: Covering or case secreted by the adult to hold or enclose an egg mass; see ootheca.

Empodium: A pad located between the claws or arising from the base of a single claw; (H5, M).

Ental (adj.), entad (adv.): Inner; from without toward the center of a body or part; structures within or the inner surface

Entognathous: With mouth parts buried in the head; retracted; entotrophous.

Epicranial suture: The suture which usually separates the two epicranial plates on the dorsal surface of the head. Anteriorly (or ventrally) it is frequently forked into two branches, the frontal branches of the epicranial suture or epicranial arms, on either side of the frons. The basal, sagittal portion on the meson is sometimes referred to as the metopic suture (Berlese) or coronal suture (Snodgrass) or epicranial stem.

Epicranium: Refers to the entire sclerotized cranium, or to the cranium exclusive of the frons, or preferable to the upper part of the head-capsule.

Epignathous: Having mouth parts directed cephalad; prognathous.

Epiproct: See suranal plate.

Epistoma: The area immediately dorsad (or caudad) of the labrum which may be the clypeus or an intermediate area.

Epistomal suture: The frontoclypeal suture.

Eruciform: Caterpillarlike in form or appearance, usually with prolegs.

Eucoiliform larva: In Hymenoptera with hypermetamorphosis, a primary larva with three pairs of long thoracic appendages and without the cephalic process and girdle of setae of the teleaform larva; a stage in which a fairly advanced protopod larva emerges from the egg.

Exarata pupa: A type of pupa in which the legs and wings are free from the body, characteristic of the many Endopterygota, especially Coleoptera.

Ex larva: From or out of larva; applied to specimens reared from larvae.

Ex ovum: From or out of egg; applies to specimens reared from the egg state.

Exserted: Protruded; projecting beyond the body or over a given point.

Exuvium: The cast skin of a larva or nymph at metamorphosis.

Exuviation: The act of moulting; the cast-off skin or exuvium; ecdysis.

F

Femur (Femora): The thigh and usually the third and largest segment of an insect leg.

Filament: A flexible attenuate fleshy process of the body wall, found on some butterfly larvae, (L33, I).

Filator: The silk spinning apparatus of caterpillars.

F.g.l.: Full grown larva or length; tiny = under 5 mm.; very small = under 10 mm.; small = 10 to 25 mm.; medium = 25 to 50 mm.; large = 50 to 75 mm.; very large = over 75 mm.

Fleshy filament: A flexible, attenuate process of the body wall, found on some butterfly larvae.

Free pupa: A pupa in which the appendages are not fused to the outer covering; exarate.

Frons, front: The area of the cranium bounded by the frontal and epistomal (fronto-clypeal) sutures;

Frontal puncture: Small cavities or punctures (two) located centrally in the basal or ventral portion of the frons or front.

Frontal seta(ae): Setae (two) borne on the frons or front among caterpillars.

Frontal suture: The arms of the epicranial suture diverging ventrally (or cephalad) from the coronal suture toward the anterior articulations of the mandibles and bounding the frons laterally.

Full grown larva or length: See F.g.l.

G

Gasterotheca: The abdominal case; that part of the theca or pupal-case which encloses the abdomen (T-B).

Geometrid: A larva of the Geometridae, which when walking, alternately elevates and straightens the middle of the body; loopers; opposite to rectigrade (T-B), (L18).

Gibbose: A large, rounded, dorsal hump; a surface presenting one or more large elevations, swellings or protuberances, (L25, H).

Glandubae: Cutaneous glands, sessil or stalked, provided with sclerotized rings about their external openings; on sawfly larvae (Yuasa).

Glandular bristles (or hairs); Stout and rigid glandular setae; the urticating hairs of certain Lepidoptera.

Grub: An insect larva; more specifically certain U- or C-shaped larvae especially among Coleoptera and Hymenoptera.

Gula, gular area or plate: The mesal throat sclerite on the head located on the ventral or caudal aspect between the mesal margins of the epicranium (genae) and extending from the submentum to the caudal margin.

Gular suture: The division line between the gula and the right or left gena or cheek of the epicranium.

H

Hatching membrane: A membranous sheath covering the young insect at time of hatching; pronymph.

Head capsule: Fixed parts of the head exclusive of appendages, chiefly epicranium.

Heel: A padlike prolongation of the base of the tarsungulus, opposing the claw.

Hemipneustic respiration: A type of insect respiration in which one or more spiracles are closed, prevalent among larvae; hypopneustic (T-B).

Hemimetabola: A division of the Heteromotabola containing Odonata, Plecoptera and Ephemeroptera, in which the young, which live in water, differ from the adults in the presence of provisional organs (Imms).

Heteroideus: A mesoseries of crochets possessing a median well developed series of hooks flanked on each end by smaller or rudimentary crochets, most Arctiidae, (L1, Y).

Heterometabola: Insects with an incomplete or direct metamorphosis, applied to members of the more generalized orders which pass through a simple metamorphosis; immature stages called nymphs.

Hibernaculum: A protective cover made out of a leaf or other material, in which a larva hides or hibernates; any place of hibernation; a winter cocoon.

Holometabolous: Having a complete transformation; egg, larval, pupal and adult stages distinct.

Holopneustic respiratory system: All the spiracles (usually 10 pairs) open and functional; the primitive type of insect respiratory system.

Homoideus: A mesoseries of crochets possessing well developed hooks throughout the entire series; homogeneous; not heteroideus, most Phalaenidae.

Homorpha: Insects in which the larvae resemble the adults.

Hooks: See crochets, sclerotized prongs with decurved ends.

Horn: A stiff, pointed, unbranched cuticular process.

Hypermetamorphosis: A larva which passes through two or more markedly different instars in the course of its development is said to undergo hypermetamorphosis.

Hypognathous: A vertical head with the mouth parts directed ventrad, most caterpillars.

Hypopharynx: The upper sensory surface of the labium that serves as an organ of taste or true tongue.

Hypopleurite: An enlarged area of a proleg immediately ventrad of the postepipleurite (H1, I).

- I - J - K -

Imago(ines): Adult or sexually developed insect.

Instar: The period or stage between molts in the larva, numbered to designate the various periods; e.g., the first instar is the stage between the egg and first molt, etc; see stadium.

Jointed: Equals segmented by most workers.

Kappa group: The Kappa group consists of setae theta (III), kappa (IV) and eta (V); theta frequently absent; on the prothorax it is called the prespiracular wart or group and is usually a distinct sclerotized area; if no sclerotized area exists all setae cephalad of the spiracle belong to the Kappa group.

L

Labial palpus(i): A pair of segmented feelers on the distal portion of the labium.

Labial palpiger: That sclerite (or lobe) of the labium to which the labial palpus is attached; corresponds to the palpifer of the maxilla and has been used in the same general sense.

Labial stipes: That part of the labium, distad to the mentum, which bears the labial palpigers, palpi and the ligula, but which is termed the prementum when fused with the labial palpigers.

Labium: The lower lip or second maxillae; a complex structure which forms the floor of the mouth in the mandibulate insects; consisting of submentum, mentum, prementum, ligula and labial palpi in larvae of Coleoptera.

Labrum: The upper lip, a simple flap attached to the clypeus which forms the roof of the mouth.

Lacinia: The inner or mesal lobe of the maxilla mesad of and adjacent to the galea.

Lambda seta; See figure L8,A and D.

Large larvae or lengths: 50 to 75 mm.

Larva: An insect which hatches from the egg in an early stage of development and differs fundamentally in the form from the adult; feeding and growing stage of holometabolous insects that undergo complete metamorphosis.

Larvapod: Larval prolegs (Yuasa).

Lateral (adj.), laterad (adv.): Relating, pertaining or attached to or toward the sides.

Laterodorsal: Toward the side and dorsum.

Lateroventral: Toward the side and venter.

Lateral line: In case-bearing trichopterous larvae, a delicate longitudinal cuticular fold beset by fine hairs on each side of the abdomen (Imms); in caterpillars a line at the margin of the dorsum between the subdorsal and suprastigmatal lines (Smith).

Lateral penellipse: An almost complete circle of crochets open or incomplete toward the meson (Psychidae).

Lateral ridge; In slug caterpillars, a raised line along the lateral series of abdominal tubercles (T-B).

Lateral space: In slug caterpillars the area on each side of the body between the subdorsal and lateral ridges (T-B).

Lateral tubercle: A tubercle on the thoracic and abdominal segments of caterpillars (T-B).

Lepismoid: Habing the shape or appearance of a silver-fish or bristle tail of the family Lepismidae, order Thysanura, possessing filamentous caudal cerci, slender many-jointed antennae, and subcylindrical or depressed body sometimes covered with shiny scales.

Ligula: The terminal lobes of the labium collectively (labial palpi, glossae and hypopharynx).

Linear: A straight line or structure.

Looper: Geometrid or other groups of caterpillars usually with two or more of the cephalic ventral prolegs wanting; crawls in a looping manner.

Lyre: The upper wall or border of the spinning tube of caterpillars (T-B).

M

Macula: A pigmented mark larger than a tiny spot and of indefinite shape.

Maculate: Spotted or marked with pigmented figures of varying shape.

Mandible: The first pair of opposable appendages below the labrum in the head of mandibulate insects; the parallel mouth hooks among larvae of the Cyclorrhapha are called mandibles by some investigators.

Mammiform: Having the form of a breast or nipple.

Mask: In dragon fly nymphs the protrusible labium which at rest covers the mouth parts.

Maxilla(ae): The second pair of mouth appendages caudad or ventrad of the mandibles; each usually possessing two cardines, stipes, palpifer, maxillary palpus, galea and lacinia.

Maxillary palpus(i): A segmented feeler arising from the latero-distal portion of the stipes of a maxilla.

Meconium: The substance excreted by certain holometabolous insects soon after their emergence from the chrysalis or pupa.

Medium larvae or lengths: 25 to 50 mm.

Mentum: The distal sclerite of the labrum bearing the movable parts, attached to and sometimes fused with the submentum; corresponds to the united stipes of the maxillae; in larvae of Coleoptera the labial area is limited anteriorly by the posterior margin of the premental area and posteriorly by a transverse suture running approximately between the front margins of the maxillary cardines (B and C).

Mesal penellipse: An almost complete circle (at least two-thirds) of crochets open or incomplete on the lateral margin (Pyralidae).

Meson, mesal (adj.), mesad (adv.): An imaginary longitudinal middle plane dividing the insect body vertically into right and left parts; same as saggital plane; a mesal line; toward the meson.

Mesoseries: A band of crochets or hooks extending longitudinally on the mesal side of a proleg; when curved, varying from a quadrant to slightly more than a semicircle in extent, seldom exceeding two-thirds of a circle.

Mesothorax; The second segment of the thorax bearing, when present, the second pair of thoracic legs and in some families the only thoracic spiracles.

Metatarsus: The proximal segment of the tarsus adjacent to the tibia.

Metathorax: The third segment of the thorax bearing, when present, the third pair of legs.

Metathoracotheca: The pupal covering of the metathorax.

Metopic suture: See coronal suture.

Microspines: Minute microscopic spines on the exterior of the body wall only visible under a high power microscope; e.g., Phalaenidae, Heliothis sp. (L36).

Moult: To cast off the out grown skin or cuticula in the process of nymphal or larval growth; the cast skin itself; exuvium; ecdysis.

Multiarticulate: Many segmented.

Multiordinal: Said of crochets or hooks when they arise from a single row but of many alternating lengths.

Multiserial: Said of crochets or hooks arranged in several rows, as the crochets of Hepialus, Acrolophus, etc. (L3, M-N).

Multiserial circle: In the caterpillar proleg, the arrangement of the crochets in several, three or more, concentric circles (T-B).

Multisetiferous: Bearing many setae.

Mumia: The pupa.

Mummylike: A body with all appendages in a fixed position and adjacent to the body.

N

Naiad: The aquatic nymphs of the Hemimetabola, namely Odonata, Plecoptera and Ephemeroptera.

Naupliform: The form or shape of the nauplius stage in Crustacea; first instar of Platygasteridae-Hymenoptera.

Nymph: A young insect which hatches from the egg in a relatively advanced stage of morphological development and resembles the adult; compound eyes usually present; ocelli; complete wings and genitalia absent; a young stage of insects with incomplete metamorphosis.

O

Obtect pupa: One in which the appendages and body covering are compactly united by a hardening of the outer skin, termed the theca in older literature; most species of Lepidoptera and many Nemocera: (L10, L11).

Occipital sinus: Among caterpillars a distinct depression in the epicranium at the dorsomeson (see Whelan, 1935); vertical triangle.

Ocellar group: As applied to certain lepidopterous larvae; the six ocelli on the lateral aspect of the larval head, the dorsal four of which usually form the quadrant of a circle, with the remaining two ventral and farther apart. Beginning at the caudal ocellus of the dorsal group these may be termed the first to the fourth in regular order. The fifth is caudoventrad of the fourth and in some cases farther ventrad than the sixth which is the one most cephalic in position (Fracker designation). Many investigators reverse numbers five and six.

Ocellara(ae): Equals ocellus(i).

Ocellus(i): Simple eyes of larvae on the sides of the head; among caterpillars referred to as stemma (stemmata) by some workers.

Ocularium(a): Area about ocellus(i), a pigmented ring among sawflies, (H1, K).

Oligopod larva: An active larva with well-developed functional limbs; the thysanuriform or campodeiform larvae of older literature.

Onisciform: Depressed and broadly spindle-shaped, like an oniscid or woodlouse, e.g., lycaenid or psephenid larvae.

Ootheca: The covering or case over an egg mass as in certain Orthoptera (T-B).

Opposable mandibles: Mandibles which move from side to side and meet on the meson; typical of most chewing insects.

Opisthognathous: Head and mouth parts projecting caudad as in cockroaches; see apisthognathous.

Ordinal: When describing crochets it refers to the length or arrangement of the tip ends.

Orthosomatic: A straight body; ventral and dorsal surfaces straight, flat and usually subparallel; lateral aspects also usually subparallel.

Osmeterium(ia): Fleshy, tubular, eversible processes frequently v or y-shaped producing a penetrating odor, capable of being projected through a slit in the prothoracic segment of certain papilionid caterpillars, and from openings elsewhere in the bodies of other forms (T-B), (L2, K).

- P - Q -

Palpifer: A small sclerite bearing the maxillary palpus and itself articulated to the stipes.

Palpiform: Resembling a palpus.

Palpiger: A small sclerite bearing the labial palpus and itself attached to the mentum.

Palpus(i): A mouth feeler; tactile, usually segmented (fingerlike) structures borne by the maxillae (maxillary palpi) and labium (labial palpi).

Papilla(ae), papillose: A soft minute elevation or projection; a raised dot or pimple; a minute, soft projection; sense organs are frequently associated with papillae.

Paraclypeus: Among caterpillars the small sclerited adjacent to the lateral margins of the clypeus, also see Raphidia or Corydalis of the Neuroptera.

Paurometabola: A division of the Heterometabola characterized by a gradual development in which the young resemble the adults in general form and mode of life; changes in metamorphosis gradual and inconspicuous.

Penellipse: A series of crochets usually much more than a semicircle in extent and less than a complete circle. It may be either lateral, covering at least the lateral half of the planta, as in Psychidae, or mesal, covering at least the mesal half of the proleg and interrupted laterally, as in Pyraustinae (Fracker), (L3, G-H).

Penultimate: Next to last.

Peripneustic respiratory system: Where one pair of thoracic and all (usually eight) abdominal spiracles are functional, typical of many insect larvae.

Peritreme: Any sclerite about a body opening, especially spiracles, (L2, I-J).

Pi group of setae: The thoracic Pi groups of Fracker consists of setae pi and nu which Heinrich numbers VI. On the abdominal segments Fracker adds seta tau with this group and Heinrich designates the three by number VII. For names by Forbes see table 2.

Piercing mouth parts: Mouth parts with mandibles or maxillae or both (needle or bladelike) fitted for piercing plant or animal tissue.

Pilifer, Piliger: Lateral projection of the labrum in lepidopterous pupa and imago.

Pinaculum(a): A small, flat or very slightly elevated chitinized area bearing from one to four setae (L2, A). In caterpillars an enlarged seta-bearing papilla forming a flat plate (Tillyard).

Planta: Distal portion of a proleg on which the crochets are borne.

Plate: An extended sclerotized area of the body wall; e.g., prothoracic shield, anal or suranal plate.

Plica(ae): Folds, wrinkles, crenulations or scallops, usually in a transverse position, also see annulet.

Polymorphic: Having various and many forms or shapes.

Polypod: Possessing many feet; in general larvae with legs or feet on nearly all segments.

Polypod larvae: One characterized by the presence of abdominal limbs and a peripneustic tracheal system (Folson and Wardle).

Porrect head: Projecting forward horizontally (cephalad); prognathous.

Postcornu: A single, suranal, sclerotized caudal projection on wood, stem and grass boring sawflies (H1, M; H11, F.).

Postclypeus: When the clypeus is subdivided transversely across the meson into a caudal (dorsal) and cephalic (ventral) part the caudal (dorsal) portion is designated a postclypeus.

Postembryonic: In general the stages of development between hatching and the appearance of the adult.

Postepipleurite: An area on sawfly larvae caudo-ventrad of spiracles and dorsad of prolegs; equals surpedal area (H1, J).

Posterior: Equals caudal.

Posterior stigmatal tubercle: On the thoracic and abdominal segments of caterpillars, a tubercle which varies in position (T-B).

Posterior trapezoidal tubercle: A tubercle on the thoracic and abdominal segments of caterpillars, subdorsal, posterior, always present (T-B).

Poststigmatal primary tubercle: A tubercle on the thoracic segment of caterpillars; subprimary, stigmatal, posterior (T-B).

Postspiracular area: Area caudad of spiracles (H1, I).

Precardo: Distal part of bipartite cardo.

Pre-eruciform: Before the caterpillar stage; specifically applied to the early larvae of some Proctotrupidae (T-B).

Preimago: The last phase of a pupal stage when the structures of the apparently completed adult can be seen within the pupal covering.

Prepupa: A full grown fully fed larva; that part of the last larval instar immediately preceding the pupal stage which is usually shorter and thicker than the active, feeding, full grown larva.

Prespiracular wart: See Kappa group, fig. L5, B.

Primary seta(ae): Those setae with a definite arrangement found on generalized caterpillars of Lepidoptera in all instars.

Preepipleurite: A subspiracular area immediately ventrad of spiracles (H1, I).

Prognathous: Mouth parts directed cephalad from a horizontal head; equals epignathous.

Proleg: A fleshy abdominal leg with or without crochets; said to be present when crochets are present even when there is no fleshy swelling. Any process or appendage that serves the purpose of a leg, common on caterpillars of Lepidoptera and Hymenoptera; larvapod, uropod, false legs, spurious legs.

Pronymph: A newly hatched nymph surrounded by an embryonic sheath or hatching membrane which is shed before the nymph is able to move about; present among aphids, Odonata, some Orthoptera, etc.

Propneustic respiratory system: Larvae with only the first pair of spiracles open and functional.

Propupa: A stage in the nymphal development of Aspidiotus (scale insects) in which wing pads are present and the legs are short and thick, preceding the true pupa; the first stage in some Thysanoptera showing external wing pads and small short thick antennae.

Prothorax: The first segment of the thorax bearing, when present, the first pair of legs and in many families the only thoracic spiracles.

Protopod larva or phase: A stage in which there is a lack of differentiation in the internal and external organs; segmentation incomplete, abdomen incomplete and appendages more or less rudimentary.

Protracted head: A head not retracted or withdrawn into the prothorax.

Protrusile: Capable of being extended or protruded.

Protuberance: A general term including most any projection, usually fleshy and with or without setae, found on the body of a larva.

Proximal (Adj.), proximad (Adv.): That part of an appendage nearest to the point of attachment; toward the point of attachment.

Proxistipes: The proximal portion of the maxillary stipes.

Pseudocercus(ci): The median cercus, see mesal, segmented, terminal filament in Thysanura and Ephemeroptera.

Pseudocircle of crochets: An arrangement of crochets consisting of a well developed mesoseries and a row of small hooks (a lateroseries) on the lateral aspect of the proleg (Fracker).

Pulvillus(li): Lateral lobe or lobes of the protarsus or tarsungulus arising beneath the bases of the claws. Same as paronychial appendix.

Pupa: The resting inactive instar in all holometabolous insects; the intermediate stage between the larva and the adult; chrysalis; incorrectly applied to the active last nymphal instar of insects (Thysanoptera etc.) having incomplete metamorphosis (T-B).

Pupa adheranena: An adherent pupa; one which hangs perpendicularly, head down (T-B).

Pupa angularis: A pupa with a pyramidal process or nose on the back (T-B).

Pupa-chromogenic phase: Among Diptera-Trypetidae, etc., the last pupal phase preceding the emergence of the adult, in which the pigmentation of the body and its appendages occur (Dean).

Pupa-chromoptic phase: Among Diptera-Trypetidae, etc., the pupal phase following the telemorphic in which pigmentation of the compound eyes commences. This may be considered a subphase of chromogenic (Dean).

Pupa coarctate: A puparium or last larval skin surrounding an exarate pupa; many Diptera.

Pupa conica: A conical pupa, as opposed to an angular pupa (T-B).

Pupa contigua: A bound pupa; one which remains upright against a vertical object and is supported by a silk thread across the thorax (T-B).

Pupa-cryptocephalic substage: Among Diptera-Trypetidae etc., the earliest form of the pupa in which the legs and wing buds are everted but the head is still inverted within the thorax. The form of the abdomen resembles that of the fourth larval instar (Snodgrass, Wahl).

Pupa custodiata: A guarded pupa; one in a partly open cocoon (T-B).

Pupa dermata: A pupa which retains the larval skin and no trace of the position of the future limbs is apparent (T-B).

Pupa exarata: A sculptured pupa; a pupa in which the limbs of the encased adult lie free but adjacent to the body (T-B).

Pupa folliculata: An incased pupa; a pupa in a case or cocoon (T-B).

Pupa incompleta: In the Lepidoptera, a pupa in which the appendages are often partly free and more than three of the abdominal segments are movable (Imms).

Pupa larvata: A masked pupa; one in which the different parts of the forming adult are traceable as lines on the surface (T-B).

Pupa libera: In the Lepidoptera, a pupa with a large number of free segments (Imms).

Pupa-macrocephalic phase: Among Diptera-Trypetidae etc., the phanerocephalic pupa when the head is of normal size and before the adult structures begin to appear (Dean).

Pupa-microcephalic phase: Among Diptera-Trypetidae etc., the earliest phase of the phanerocephalic substage in which the head is very small. There is some question as to the existence of this phase (Dean).

Pupa nuda: A naked pupa free of any attachment (T-B).

Pupa obtecta: One in which the appendages and body are fused; among Lepidoptera the fourth, fifth and sixth abdominal segments may be free; obtect pupa.

Pupa-phanerocephalic substage: Among Diptera-Trypetidae etc., any phase of the pupa after the eversion of the head; literally visible headed (Snodgrass and Wahl).

Pupa subterranea: Underground pupa; one which is buried during the transformation (T-B).

Pupa-teleomorphoric phase: Among Diptera-Trypetidae etc., literally the perfect or complete form. The pupal phase in which the adult form of the external structures become visible through the pupal integument as the pupal body wall is replaced by the adult body wall, the pupal integument still enclosing the insect which is unpigmented. This change in form first becomes apparent in the legs, wings and proboscis (Dean).

Pupal respiratory horns: Among syrphid larvae hornlike processes which grow up from the pupa and pierce the upper portions of the operculum in saprophytic forms; they possess numerous respiratory openings (Heiss).

Puparium(ia): Among Cyclorrhapha-Diptera, the thickened, hardened, barrellike last larval skin within which the pupa is formed (012).

Puparium respiratory prong. Sclerotized inconspicuous prongs apparently located on the dorsolateral aspects of the first abdominal segments of puparia of some Metopiidae; (L12, B-C).

Quiescent stage: Inactive stage; hibernating larvae, prepupae or pupae of insects with complete metamorphosis.

R

Rectal (tracheal) gills: Lamelliform structures in the rectum of the nymphs of some Odonata (Anisoptera) nymphs, supplied with trachea and tracheoles and serving as a respiratory organ (T-B).

Rectigrade: Straight walking as in larvae with sixteen legs; no pronounced looping.

Respiratory prong: See puparium respiratory prong.

Retinaculum: Accessory projection(s) or toothlike structure(s) on the oral or mesal surface of a mandible among Lepidoptera, (L1, P); among Coleoptera a fixed tooth, usually pointed, situated along the middle or the mesal or oral edge below the distal dentes.

Retracted head: Among larvae of some families of several orders the entire head and mouth parts are retracted into the prothorax.

Rho group: The Rho group in Lepidoptera consists of setae epsilon (IIIa) and rho (III).

S

Sagittal plane: The longitudinal vertical plane or meson which divides an animal into right and left halves.

Scansorial: Tarsi and claws fitted for climbing on or clinging to hairs; see Anoplura.

Scansorial warts: See ampulla.

Scape: The basal segment or stalk of an insect antenna.

Scarabaeiform: U or C-shaped, resembling a white grub of the Scarabaeidae.

Sclerite: Any sclerotized (hardened) portion of a body wall frequently in part bounded by sutures.

Scleroma(ata): The sclerotic annulus of a body segment in distinction to the membranous conjunctiva; areas called sclerites by others.

Sclerotized: Hardened by the deposit of sclerotin or hardening substances; same as chitinized in older literature.

Scolus(i): A spinose projection of the body wall, as in saturnian larvae (Fracker); among coccinellids a branched projection of the body wall, usually more than five times as long as wide (Gage).

Secondary seta(ae) or hair: Among Lepidoptera numerous setae having a general indefinite distribution; also not limited to verrucae or other forms of tubercles; frequently confined to the venter; if present always more than four on the prolegs.

Semilooper: A caterpillar with one or two pairs of the ventral prolegs wanting; in crawling only small loops are formed; see looper.

Semipupa: That stage of the larva just preceding pupation; more specifically the interpolated stage between the active larva and the true larva, in hypermetamorphosis (T-B); prepupa.

Serial: Refers to the distribution of the bases or points of attachments of the crochets.

Sericose: Slitlike opening for the duct of the silkglands among Hymenoptera.

Seta(ae): A sclerotized hairlike projection of cuticula arising from a single trichogen cell and surrounded at the base by a small cuticular ring.

Setal map: A diagrammatic drawing showing the chaetotaxy or arrangement of the setae on one-half of a bilaterally symmetrical thoracic or abdominal segment; the top edge is the dorso-meson and the lower edge the ventro-meson, (L5).

Setiferous: Bearing one to many setae.

Setaceous, setose: Bristly or set with many bristles, setae or stiff hairs.

Shagreened: A surface roughened with minute toothlike or rounded projections; numerous bumps; a mosaic pattern may be produced.

Simple eyes: Ocelli.

Single band of crochets: Said of crochets arranged in a mesoseries.

Skippers: Larvae of Piophilidae-Diptera found in cheese, ham and other provisions; also larvae of Hesperidae-Lepidoptera.

Small larvae or lengths: 10 to 25 mm.

Sphingiform: Similar to a sphingid caterpillar, possessing a cylindrical body, with setae very short or wanting and no other armature except a mediodorsal horn or button on the eighth abdominal segment, (L55, G).

Spindlelike or shaped: Pointed at both ends and swollen in the middle; fusiform.

Spine: A thornlike continuous process arising from the cuticula, without a cuticular ring about its base, typical of most setae, consequently it usually maintains a fixed position.

Spiniform: Shaped like a spine.

Spinneret: The external apparatus or nozzle from which silk exudes and is spun; sericose; usually located on the labium of a larva, (L1, G-N).

Spinose: Set with acute processes or spines.

Spinule: One of the short lateral branches of a scolus.

Spinulae: A small spine.

Spinulose: Set with little spines or spinules; same as spinulate, also see microspines.

Spiracle: A breathing pore or an external opening of the tracheal system.

Spiracular cleft: Spiracles located within a deep, closed or open, cavity; if closed one or two movable liplike structures may be present.

Spiracular line: Among caterpillars the color or pigmented line adjacent to or coinciding with the line of spiracles; same as stigmatal.

Spurious legs: False legs, see prolegs.

Stadium(ia): The interval between the ecdyses or moults of the larva; instar.

Stage: Stadium, any definite period in the development of an insect, egg stage, caterpillar stage, etc.

Stemapoda: Elongated anal prolegs in certain notodontid larvae, (L1, X).

Stemma(mata): A name sometimes given to simple eyes of the often circular, lateral eye groups in Holometabolous larvae; a lateral ocellus; a simple eye; also small tubercles borne by antennae (T-B).

Stigma(mata): A spiracle or breathing pore.

Stigmatal field: Among larvae it refers to the spiracular field or area; also termed spiracular disk, respiratory disc, etc.

Stigmatal line: In caterpillars, same as spiracular line.

Stilt prolegs: Unusually long prolegs which raise the larva off the surface on which it may be walking.

Stipes(pites): The basic sclerite of the maxilla, immediately distad to the cardo and bearing the movable parts; articulating partly to the head, partly to the cardo.

Stipple, stippled, stippling: Numerous points or dots; shading effects produced by dots, points or small marks.

Strainer: In certain may-fly nymphs, a row of stiff hairs used in straining out plankton organisms; in some on fore-tibiae, in others on mouth parts.

Stria: An impressed line or scratch.

Sub-: As a prefix means that the main term is not entirely applicable; slightly greater or less than; almost or not quite; position below or under.

Subanal: Ventrad of the anus.

Subanal appendages, lobes or protuberances: Structures of the caudal segment located below the anus.

Subcardo: Proximal part of bipartite cardo.

Subequal: Nearly equal in size and structure.

Submentum: The basal sclerite of the labium by means of which it is attached to the head; among larvae of Coleoptera an unpaired median area lying approximately between the maxillary cardines on the underside of the head (B and C).

Subdorsal line: A longitudinal line in caterpillars to the side of the dorsal and between it and the lateral; or, if there is one addorsal line, between that and the lateral line (T-B), (L2, M-N).

Subdorsal ridge: In slug caterpillars, a raised longitudinal line along the subdorsal row of abdominal tubercles (T-B).

Subparallel; Nearly parallel.

Subprimary seta(ae): A seta having a definite position in certain larvae but not present in the first instar or generalized groups; no distinction is made in primary and subprimary setae in keys and description; see primary seta (Fracker).

Subspiracular line: In caterpillars, a stripe or line below the spiracles (T-B).

Subspiracular lobe or area: Lobe or area immediately below spiracle, among sawflies preepipleurite (H1, I).

Subventral line: In caterpillars, a stripe or line along the side just above the bases of the feet at the edge between the lateral and ventral lines (Smith).

Subventral ridge: In slug caterpillars a longitudinal raised line along the subventral series of abdominal tubercles (T-B).

Subventral space: In slug caterpillars, the area on each side, between the lateral ridge and the lower edge of the body, in which are the spiracles (T-B).

Succincti: Chrysalides of butterflies which are held in place by a silken cord, passing around the body (T-B), (O10, F).

Supraspiracular or suprastigmatal line: In caterpillars a line or stripe above the spiracles (T-B).

Suranal: Above the anus.

Suranal plate: Usually a rather heavily sclerotized area on the dorsum of the last abdominal segment; plate or lobe dorsad of the anus; anal plate; epiproct.

Suranal process: A sclerotized process on the meson of the suranal lobe; postcornu.

Surpedal lobe: Lobe or area at base of prolegs; among sawfly larvae called postepipleurite (H1, I).

Suspensi; Chrysalides of butterflies suspended by the tail only, (O10, D).

Sustenters; The two posterior projections of a butterfly chrysalis (T-B).

Suture: A seam or line separating two adjacent sclerities of the body wall or appendages.

T

Tarsus(si): The fifth segment of the leg which may be one to five segmented and bears one or two claws. If tarsal segments are present among larvae most species possess only one segment.

Tau group of setae: The Tau group is an indefinite group of setae between pi (VII) and sigma (VIII); it may consist of setae pi (VII), tau (VII), omega (IX) and other setae.

Termitiform; Resembling a termite.

Theca: A case or covering; cases of Trichopterous larvae; outer covering of the pupa, etc.

Thysanuriform: Resembling a thysanuran, same as campodeiform.

Tibia(iae): The fourth segment of the leg.

Tiny larvae or lengths: Less than 5 mm.

Tracheal gills: Flattened, digitate or hairlike cuticular processes, abundantly supplied with tracheae and tracheoles.

Transverse band of crochets: Said of crochets arranged transversely or across the longitudinal axis of the body in a single uniserial or multiserial band, or in two such bands, (L9).

Triordinal: Said of crochets when their proximal ends are in a single row but their distal ends of three alternating lengths, (L3, G).

Trisetose: Consisting of or bearing three setae.

Trochanter: The usual second segment of the insect leg, probably composed of two united trochanteral segments; in some cases (Odonata) showing a division between its component parts.

Tubercle, tubercule: A small abrupt elevation of varying form; a little solid pimple or small button; in caterpillars, tubercles (verrucae) sometimes bearing setae.

Tuberculate: Shaped like a tubercle; a surface covered with tubercles.

Tuft, tufted setae: A group of more or less parallel setae arising from a given area, verrucca etc.

- U - V - W - X - Y - Z -

Uniordinal: Said of crochets when they are arranged in a single row and are of a single length throughout or somewhat shorter towards the ends of the row; opposed to biordinal (Fracker), (L3, A).

Uniserial: Said of crochets when they are arranged in a single row or series with their bases in a continuous line (Fracker), (L3, A).

Unisetose: Consisting of or bearing one seta.

Uropod: See proleg.

Urticating hairs: In certain caterpillars and adults, hairs or chaetae are connected with cutaneous poison glands and may cause irritation; barbed hairs also may cause irritation without poison.

U-shaped: Semi-circular; equals C-shaped.

Venter (adjective ventral, adverb ventrad): The entire under surface or belly side of an animal or any part thereof; pertaining to the under surface of the body; toward the venter.

Ventral glands: Eversible glands located on the venter of larvae, (L2, L and L1, H), (Lepidoptera and Tenthredinidae).

Ventral prolegs: All prolegs on ventral aspect of any abdominal segments except the last; those on last segment are called anal prolegs.

Ventrodorsal: Extending from the belly to back, ventral to dorsal surface.

Ventromeson: The intersection of the meson with the ventral surface of the body.

Vermiform: Wormlike; shape resembling an an earthworm.

Verricule, verriculus: A dense tuft of upright setae, modified from a verruca or scolus, (L2, F or L24 K).

Verruca: A definitely bounded, somewhat elevated portion of the cuticle, bearing several to many setae pointing many directions (Fracker); wart, (L2, E).

Vertical triangle: The thinly sclerotized dorsal area bounded laterad by the caudal projections of the head capsule and caudad by the prothorax (Fracker); cervical triangle, (L4, A).

Very large larvae or lengths: Over 75 mm.

Very small larvae or lengths: Less than 10 mm.

Vestigial: Under developed or degenerate; only a trace or remnant of a previously functional organ.

Vitta(tae): A broad longitudinal pigmented stripe.

Wart: See verruca and tubercle.

Wing pads (buds): External pouchlike structures in which wings are developing located on the cardo-lateral portions of the mesothorax and metathorax of late instar nymphs of most Heterometabola (Hemimetabola and Paurometabola).

Winged spiracle: When a spiracle is located in the center of an inverted V-shaped pigment area, Cimicidae, (H7, P-R).

HOST INDEX FOR PLANT INFESTING HYMENOPTERA, CHIEFLY SYMPHYTA

This index cites the more important and common hosts of the species figured in Part I. The letters and numbers refer to the figures of the species on each host.

- A, B -

Apple; H6D, H7 G, H12 A
Ash; H10 E

Balsam-fir; H8 M
Barley; H11 G
Bindweed; H7 G
Birch; H11 D
Blackberry; H10 H
Buckwheat; H7 G

- C, D -

Cedar; H8 M
Cherry; H10 A, H11 A, H11 K
Chess; H11 G
Chokecherry; H7 D
Cornus; H7 J; H7 M
Crataegus; H11 A
Currant; H9 D

Dead or dying wood; H1 M, H11 F
Dewberry; H10 H
Dock, H7 G
Dogwood shrub; H7 J, H7 M

- E, F -

Elm; H7 P, H11 F
Equisetum; H6 A

Fruit seeds; H12 A

- G, H, I, J -

Gooseberry; H9 D
Grape; H10 K
Grasses; H12 B

Hawthorn; H11 A
Hazelnut; H7 D
Hickory; H5 A, H11 F
Honeysuckle; H6 P
Horsetail; H6 A

- K, L -

Knotweeds; H7 G

Larch; H9 M
Linden; H7 P
Lonicera; H6 P

- M, N, O -

Maple; H7 P, H11 F
Mountain Ash; H9 P

Nuts; H5 A

Oaks; H5 N

- P, Q -

Pear; H5, D; H10, A.
Pecan; H5 A
Pines:
   Jack; H8 D; H8 G; H8 J
   Japanese red; H8 G; H8 J
   Loblolly; H8 P
   Mugho; H8 A, H8 J
   Pitch; H8 A, H8 D, H8 M
   Red; H7 A, H8 D, H8 G, H8 J
   Scotch; H8 J
   Short leaf; H8 A, H8 G, H8 P
   Swiss mountain; H8 J
   White; H8 A, H8 D, H8 S
Plum; H10 A
Poplar; H7 P, H9 J
Portulaca (purslane); H6 M

- R, S -

Raspberry; H9 G, H10 H
Roses; H6 G, H6 J, H10 B
Rhubarb; H7 G
Rye; H11 G, H11 H

Sea-grape; H1 N
Sorrels; H7 G
Spruces; H7 A, H8 M, H10 N.
   Black; H7 A, H10 N
   Colorado; H7 A
   Englemann; H7 A
   Norway; H7 A, H10 N
   Red; H7 A; H10 N
   White; H7 A, H10 N

- T, U, V, W, X, Y, Z -

Tamarack; H9 M

Wheat; H11 G, H11 H, H12 B
Wild buckwheat; H7 G
Wild Cherry; H11 K
Willow; H7 P, H9 A, H9 J, H11 J.

HOST INDEX FOR LARVAE OF LEPIDOPTERA

This index cites the more important and common hosts of the species figured in Part I. The letters and numbers refer to the figures of the species feeding on each host. For general feeders that commonly attack more than five kinds of hosts it only lists some of the more common plants or products.

- A -

Acorns; L30 N
Ailanthus; L42 G
Alder; L25 G, L26 I, L38 K, L54 D
Alfalfa; L37 E, L41 H, L50 G, L50 J
Almond; L15 O; L49 note
Animal meat (meals); L57 A, L57 F
Apple; L11 A, L11 F, L13 F, L13 K, L14 A, L18 A, L18 C, L21 A, L21 G, L24 I, L25 C, L25 G, L25 H, L26 C, L26 G, L29 A, L29 G, L31 K, L32 K, L37 O, L47 O, L48 P, L49 P, L54 A,
Apricot; L9 P, L15 O, L29 G, L32 K, L49 N.
Artichoke; L43 D
Ash; L9 D, L11 F, L12 I, L21 D, L21 G, L22 A, L26 G, L26 I, L54 A, L54 B, L54 D, L55 K.
Asparagus; L37 A, L39 D.
Aspen; L21 D, L25 E, L25 H, L27 E
Asters; L 11 K, L23 I, L40 A, L47 I, L52 A.
Avacado; L30 J, L34 F

- B -

Bald cypress; L15 A
Balm of Gilead; L27 E
Balsam; L32 O
Barberry; L18 H, L21 A, L54 B
Barley; L37 E, L40 A, L50 J
Basswood; L21 D, L23,A, L25 C, L27 F, L50 D.
Bayberry; L26 I
Beans; L34 F, L36 K, L37 A, L38 A, L39 K, L40 A, L47 A, L48 G, L48 J, L52 A.
Beech; L21 A, L25 B, L25 F, L26 C, L26 G, L54 C, L54 D, L55 K, L55 L, L57 K.
Beehives; L45 D, L45 I
Beets; L37 A, L37 E, L50 A, L51 A, L51 M, L52 A
Beggar-ticks; L52 J
Birch; L12 A, L21 A, L21 D, L25 C, L25 J, L26 C, L37 O, L54 B, L54 C, L54 D, L55 K
Blackberry; L25 H, L25 J, L26 I, L30 A, L31 K, L40 A
Bloodroot; L34 F
Blueberry; L56 G
Boxelder; L54 A
Bran; L49 E, L49 P
Brussel sprouts; L41 A, L42 B
Buckeye; L32 H
Buckhorn; L47 I

Burdock; L40 A
Butternut; L12 I, L26 G, L54 C

- C -

Cabbage; L37 E, L39 D, L39 N, L41 A, L42 A, L42 B, L50 K, L50 O, L51 M
Candytuft; L42 B
Canna; L20,B
Cantelope; L51 G, L51 J
Calendula; L51 A
Carnation; L30 J, L39 D, L51 A
Carrots; L28 A, L47 I
Casein; L57 A, L57 F
Castor beans; L34 F, L40 A
Catalpa; L55 N
Cattails; L46 E, L52 J
Cauliflower; L39 D, L41 A, L42 B, L50 O, L51 M
Celery; L28 A, L33 H, L37 E, L51 A, L52 A
Century Plant; L20 A
Cereals; L49 A, L49 E
Cherry; L9 K, L9 P, L10 J, L13 F, L13 K, L21 A, L22 C, L23 A, L25 E, L25 G, L25 H, L26 C, L31 K, L32 E, L32 K, L47 D, L49 N, L54 B, L54 D, L54 F.
Chestnut; L11 F, L22 C, L23 A, L25 B, L26 C.
Chocolate; L49 J
Chrysanthemum; L36 K, L37 A, L40 A, L51 A, L52 A
Chokecherry; L32 E
Cineraria; L51 A
Citrus; L23 D, L33 G, L34 F
Clover; L34 F, L39 K, L41 H, L50 J
Cocklebur; L52 J
Collards; L42 A, L50 O
Columbine; L40 A
Conifers; L12 J, L21 D, L24 C, L42 A
Corn; L13 Q, L17 G, L23 A, L34 K, L34 O, L35 I, L36 K, L37 E, L38 A, L40 A, L44 A, L44 E, L44 I, L47 A, L47 I, L49 E, L49 P, L50 J, L52 A, L52 J, L52 N, L53 I, L56 J.
Cornus; L42 J
Cotton; L13 Q, L16 F, L30 J, L34 A, L34 F, L35 A, L36 A, L36 K, L38 G, L52 J.
Cottonwood; L27 E, L54 A
Cowpeas; L36 K, L47 A
Crab; See L29 A
Crabgrass; L35 F, L47 A

Cranberry; L48 A, L48 M
Crataegus; L13 F, L14 A, L19 H, L23 I, L25 C,
   L25 G, L25 H, L26 G, L29 A, L31 K, L56 F
Cruciferous plants; L39 H, L41 A, L41 D.
Cucumbers; L9 A, L51 G, L51 J
Cucurbs; L9 A
Currant; L32 K, L40 A, L48 D, L56 F, L56 G
Cypress; L15 A

- D -

Dahlia; L40 A
Daisies; L47 I
Dandelion; L39 D
Dates; L49 N
Decayed wood; see wood
Dead insects; L45 D, L49 A, L57 A, L57 F
Dewberry; L30 A
Dock; L39 D
Dogwood, flowering; L9 I, L25 G
Dogwood, shrub; L42 J
Dried food products; L49 J
Dried fruit; L13 Q, L45 D, L49 A, L49 N
Dried roots; L49 A
Dutchman's pipevine; L33 A

- E -

Egg Plant; L16 A, L16 K, L40 A, L53 A, L55 D,
   L55 G
Elder; L53 E
Elm; L10 J, L11 A, L11 F, L18 A, L18 C, L21
   D, L23 D, L25 A, L25 G, L27 F, L27 K, L37
   O, L54 D, L55 K, L55 L.
English Walnut; L29 A
Evergreens; See Conifers
Excrement; L49 A

- F -

Feathers; L57 A, L57 F.
Figs ; L27 D, L49 N
Filberts; L30 N
Fishmeal; L57 A, L57 F
Flax; L37 I
Flour; L49 A, L49 E
Flowering elderberry; L53 E
Flowers; L10**, L34 O, L39 N, L40 A, L52 A
Forest trees; L10 F, L10**
Fruit trees; L10 F, L11 A, L18 I, L24 C, L24 F,
   L24 I, L25 C, L33 F

- G -

Garden Crops; L10 E
Geranium; L51 A
Gladioli; L52 A
Goldenglow; L40 A
Goldenrod; L52 J

Gooseberry; L32 K, L40 A, L48 D, L56 G
Grapefruit; L30 J
Grains; L17 G, L34 A, L34 K, L34 O, L35 E,
   L35 I, L37 E, L49 P.
Grapes; L28 J, L30 G, L43 H, L49 N, L51 D,
   L53 E, L55 C, L56 B, L58 A, L58 C.
Grasses; L10**, L14 D, L20 D, L20 F, L34 K,
   L35 A, L37 E, L44 A, L44 E, L44 I, L47 I,
   L49 A, L56 J.
Ground cherry; L36 A, L36 G.
Gourds; L9 A

- H -

Hackberry; L23 C, L23 D, L27 A, L27 F, L27 K
Haw; See Crataegus
Hawthorn; See Crataegus
Hazelnut; L12 G, L25 G, L26 C, L26 I, L30 N,
   L54 F
Herbs; L49 A
Hickory; L12 I, L26 G, L37 O, L47 P, L54 C
Hollyhock; L40 A
Honey locust; See locust
Hops; L23 I
Hornbean; L26 C
Horseradish; L37 E, L41 A, L42 B, L50 O
Huckleberry; L25 H, L54 G

- I, J, K -

Indian hemp; L51 P
Iris; L38 D
Ironwood; L26 I, L54 C

Japanese quince; L31 K
Japanese walnut; L47 P
Junipers; L15 J

Kale; L39 D, L41 A, L42 B
Kohlrabi; L40 A

- L -

Lamb's quarter; L50 G, L52 J
Larch; L13 A
Legumes; L20 I, L35 A, L39 K, L41 H, L48 G,
   L48 J
Lespedeza; L23 I
Lettuce; L37 A, L39 D, L41 A
Lilac; L9 D, L54 B
Lillies; L39 N, L40 A
Lima beans; See beans
Linden; L26 C, L55 K, L55 L
Locust ; L11 F, L14 L, L19 A, L20 I, L25 G,
   L25 J, L26 C, L26 G, L38 A, L54 D
Lotus; L52 N

- M -

Maple; L11 A, L12 E, L21 D, L25 B, L25 J, L54 A, L54 B, L54 D, L56 F, L57 K
Mangels; L50 A
Meal; L49 A, L49 E
Mignonette; L39 D, L41 A
Milk chocolate; L49 A
Milk, powdered; L49 A
Milkweed; L33 A
Morning Glory; L56**
Mountain ash; L9 D, L47 D
Mulberries; L49 N, L58 H
Museum animals; L57 A, L57 F
Muskmelon; L9 A
Mustard; L41 A, L42 B, L50 O

- N -

Nasturtium; L41 A, L50 K
Nectarine; L9 P, L29 G, L49 N
Nettles; L27**
Nightshades; L53 A
Nuts; L49 A, L49 J, L49 N

- O -

Oaks; L11 F, L12 A, L12 G, L18 F, L19 B and C, L19 K, L21 A, L21 D, L22 C, L23 A, L23 D, L25 B, L25 C, L25 F, L25 G, L25 J, L26 C, L31 K, L31 O, L54 C, L54 D, L54 F, L56 F
Oats; L37 E
Oleander; L10 A, L34 F
Onions; L37 A, L37 E
Oranges; L30 J
Osage orange; L58 H

- P, Q -

Pansy; L27 H
Parsley; L33 H, L39 D
Parsnip; L28 A
Passion Flower; L27 H
Peach; L9 K, L9 P, L11 F, L15 O, L21 A, L29 G, L31 K, L34 A, L47 D, L49 N
Pea hay; L40 L
Peanuts; L35 A, L47 A
Pear; L13 F, L19 H, L22 C, L24 I, L26 C, L29 A, L31 K, L32 K, L47 D, L49 N.
Peas; L37 A, L39 D, L39 K, L47 A, L48 G, L50 G.
Pecan; L47 L, L47 P
Peppers; L30 J, L37 A, L40 A, L53 A, L55 D, L55 G.
Persimmon; L12 I, L25 C, L47 D.
Petunia; L34 A
Peony; L40 A
Pigweed; L50 G

Pines; L12 I, L12 J, L12 K, L14 P, L15 E, L31 A, L31 G, L45 A, L55 A.
Plantain; L47 I
Plum; L9 K, L9 P, L13 F, L13 K, L15 O, L21 A, L23 A, L23 D, L24 I, L25 H, L29 G, L31 K, L32 K, L47 D, L48 P, L49 N, L54 A, L54 C
Pollen in beehives; L49 A, L49 E
Poplar; L11 F, L21 A, L21 D, L21 G, L24 A, L26 A, L27 E, L27 K, L38 K, L54 D
Potato; L16 A, L37 A, L37 E, L39 D, L40 A, L52 A, L53 A, L55 D, L55 G.
Prepared food products; L49 A, L49 E
Prune; L9 P, L49 N
Pumpkin; L9 A, L51 G.
Purslane; L50 O

Quince; L13 F, L19 H, L24 I, L26 C, L29 A, L29 G, L32 K, L48 P.

- R -

Radish; L41 A, L42 B, L50 O
Ragweed; L31 N, L40 A, L50 G, L52 J.
Raisin; L49 N
Rape; L42 B
Raspberry; L21 A, L30 A, L31 K, L32 K, L40 A
Redbud; L51 D
Rhubarb; L37 E, L40 A, L52 N
Rice; L44 A, L53 M
Roses; L21 A, L23 D, L25 H, L30 J, L32 K, L54 F.
Rye; L40 A

- S -

Sassafrass; L12 I, L26 I, L33 B, L54 B, L54 D.
Seeds; L49 P
Shade Trees; L10 F, L10**, L11 A, L12 J, L18 A, L18 I, L22,A, L22 E, L24 C, L24 F, L24 I, L25 C, L33 F, L39 Q, L42 A, L54 A, L54 B, L54 C, L54 D, L54 G
Shepherds Purse; L50
Silphium; L31 I
Smartweed; L52 J, L39 N, L52 N
Snapdragon; L43 F, L51 A
Solanaceae; L53 A
Sorghum; L44 A, L44 E, L44 I, L47 A
Sour gum; L19 F.
Soybeans; L38 A, L39 K
Spice bush; L33 B
Spinach; L50 A, L51 A
Spirea; L18 F
Spruce; L31 E, L32 O
Squash; L51 G, L51 J
Stock; L42 B
Stored food products; L17 G, L49 A, L49E, L53 I
Strawberry; L30 A, L32 A, L34 K, L37 E, L39 K, L56 F

Strawberry tomatoes; L36 G
Sugar beets; L37 A, L50 A
Sugar cane; L44 A, L44 E, L44 I, L47 A, L56 J
Sunflower; L40 A
Sweet alyssum; L41 A, L42 B
Sweet clover; L37 I, L40 O
Sweet gum; L12 I, L54 C
Sweet peas; L39 N
Sweet potato; L34 F, L56**
Swiss chard; L50 A
Sycamore; L10 B, L23 D
Syringa; L21 G

- T -

Thistle; L43 D
Timothy; L40 A
Tobacco; L16 A, L34 A, L34 F, L34 K, L35 A, L36 A, L36 K, L47 I, L49 J, L53 A, L55 D, L55 G
Tomato; L16 A, L16 P, L30 J, L36 K, L37 A, L37 E, L39 D, L40 A, L55 D, L55 G
Tree of Heaven; L42 G
Tulip; L54 B
Tupelo; L19 F
Turnip; L37 E, L39 D, L41 A, L42 B, L47 A

- U, V -

Vegetables; L10 E, L10**, L34 A, L34 F, L34 K, L34 O, L35 A, L37 E, L39 N, L40 A

Vetch, L36 K, L39 K
Viburnum; L25 B
Violets; L27 H, L34 A, L51 A
Virginna creeper; L28 J, L51 D, L55 C, L56 B, L58 A, L58 C.

- W -

Wall flower; L42 B
Walnut; L12 I, L25 C, L26 C, L26 G, L30 J
Water cress; L42 B, L46 E
Watermelon; L34 A, L34 F, L51 J
Wax bees; L45 I
Weeds; L10**
Wheat; L17 G, L37 E, L47 A, L49 E
Wild cherry; See cherry
Wild plum; See plum
Willows; L11 F, L21 A, L22 C, L24 A, L25 E, L25 H, L26 A, L26 G, L26 I, L27 E, L27 K, L34 F, L38 K, L54 A, L54 C, L54 F.
Wisteria; L20 I
Witch hazel; L21 A
Wood; See Aegeriidae and Cossidae
Wood decayed; L39 A
Woodland trees; See shade trees
Wool; L57 A, L57 F.

- X, Y, Z -

Yucca; L58 E, L58 F.

The general index cites chiefly the location of the common and scientific names and terms used in this volume. For host plant citations see Host Index for Hymenoptera and Lepidoptera, pages 291 and 292. The glossary also locates some of the more important parts, page 279.